PEARSON

Pre-calculus 12

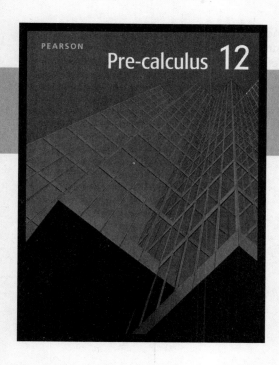

Garry Davis

Jack Hope

Linda Rajotte

Delcy Rolheiser

Alan Sarna

David Sufrin

David Zimmer

PEARSON

www.pearsoncanada.ca

Feedback on this publication can be sent to editorialfeedback@pearsoned.com

Pearson Canada Inc.
26 Prince Andrew Place
Don Mills, ON M3C 2T8
Customer Service: 1-800-361-6128

ISBN-13   978-0-321-74266-7

Publisher: Mike Czukar
Research and Communications Manager: Craig Featherstone
Publishing Team:
Claire Burnett
Lesley Haynes
Alison Rieger
Stephanie Boragina
Bronwyn Enright
Ioana Gagea
Lynne Gulliver
Cheri Westra
Carolyn Sebestyen
Karen Bradley
Judy Wilson
Design and Art Direction: David Cheung
Composition: MPS Limited, a Macmillan Company
Vice-President, Publishing: Mark Cobham

13   18

Printed and bound in the United States of America

Advisers and Reviewers

Pearson would like to thank its advisers and reviewers who have helped shape the vision for *Pre-calculus 12* through discussions and reviews of prototype materials and manuscript.

Advisers

Bernadette Abrioux
Saint Michael's University School
Victoria, BC

Enid Haley
Publishing Consultant
Rothesay, NB

Christine Ottawa
Mathematics Consultant
Winnipeg, MB

Chris Van Bergeyk
School District 23
(Central Okanagan)
Kelowna, BC

Reviewers

Sheila Cunningham
Saskatchewan Rivers S.D.
Prince Albert, SK

Lori Edwards
St. James-Assiniboia S.D.
Winnipeg, MB

Michael Freed
Edmonton Public Schools
Edmonton, AB

Terry Kaminski
Northern Lights S.D. 69
Cold Lake, AB

Catherine Kaye
Winnipeg School Division
Winnipeg, MB

April Popple
Southwest Horizon School Division
Souris, MB

Sandra Rietchel
Coquitlam School District 43
Coquitlam (Port Moody), BC

Patrick Sproul
Calgary Catholic School District
Calgary, AB

Christer Tamm
School District 68
(Nanaimo-Ladysmith)
Nanaimo, BC

CONTENTS

BUILD GOOD STUDY HABITS NOW.

1. Know What You Need to Learn

Use a **highlighter** to reinforce the **Big Ideas** of the chapter.

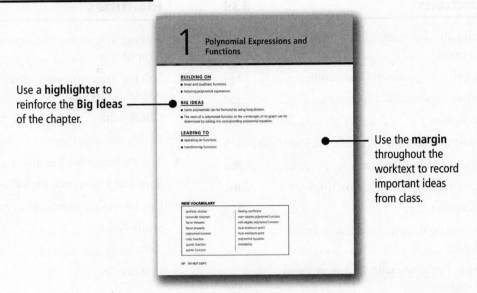

Use the **margin** throughout the worktext to record important ideas from class.

2. Build Your Understanding

Use a **highlighter** to reinforce the lesson **Focus**.

Use your worktext like a notebook. Write **solutions** on the page wherever you see the ✐.

Need extra space? Use the Additional Workspace page at the end of each lesson.

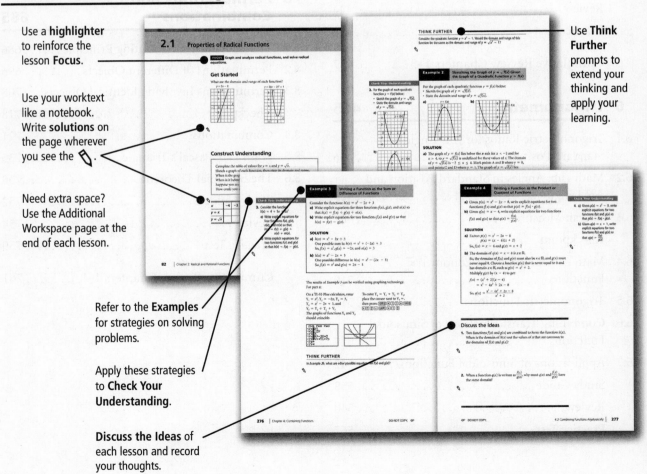

Use **Think Further** prompts to extend your thinking and apply your learning.

Refer to the **Examples** for strategies on solving problems.

Apply these strategies to **Check Your Understanding**.

Discuss the Ideas of each lesson and record your thoughts.

PRACTICAL TIPS FOR USING myWORKTEXT

3. Practise What You've Learned

Try a range of the exercise questions.

Use **Multiple-Choice** questions to help you prepare for exams.

Record **Study Notes** to summarize your learning.

Answers to **Check Your Understanding** and **Exercises** are at the end of each lesson.

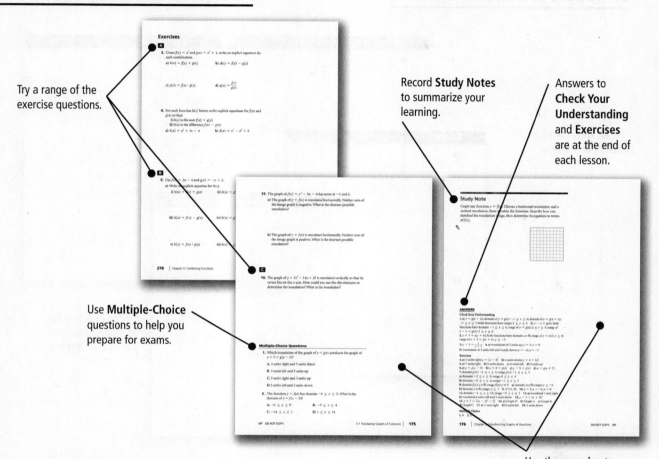

Use the **margins** to jot down notes about your thinking as the homework is taken up.

4. Develop Your Study Skills

Checkpoints occur at key intervals in the chapter to let you check your understanding so far.

The **Study Guide** summarizes important **Concepts** and key **Skills** from the chapter. Use this as a model to make your own study guides.

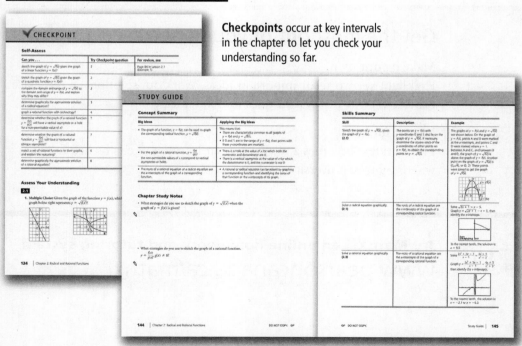

PRACTICAL TIPS FOR USING myWORKTEXT

5. Prepare for Tests and Exams

Use **Review** pages for additional practice.

Try the **Practice Test** as a sample before you take a class test.

Get the most out of your worktext

Make it your own.
Highlight key words or important ideas. Work out solutions in the space provided. Write down your questions and ideas.

Keep it for later.
The worktext becomes a record of your learning. It can be helpful later, when you take university math courses.

Try MathXL, an online homework and tutoring system.
www.pearsoncanada.ca/mathxl

1 Polynomial Expressions and Functions

BUILDING ON

- linear and quadratic functions
- factoring polynomial expressions

BIG IDEAS

- Some polynomials can be factored by using long division.
- The zeros of a polynomial function or the *x*-intercepts of its graph can be determined by solving the corresponding polynomial equation.

LEADING TO

- operating on functions
- transforming functions

NEW VOCABULARY

synthetic division	leading coefficient
remainder theorem	even-degree polynomial function
factor theorem	odd-degree polynomial function
factor property	local maximum point
polynomial function	local minimum point
cubic function	polynomial equation
quartic function	multiplicity
quintic function	

1.1 Dividing a Polynomial by a Binomial

FOCUS Use different strategies to divide a polynomial by a binomial.

Get Started

Use long division to determine each quotient. Verify the answer.

$2748 \div 13$ $\qquad\qquad$ $4212 \div 27$

What does a remainder of 0 mean?

Construct Understanding

Divide. Assume each divisor never equals zero.

Compare the strategies you used with those for dividing real numbers.

$(3x^2 - 4x + 5) \div (x - 2)$ $\qquad$ $(2x^3 - x^2 - 2x + 1) \div (x + 1)$

Long division can be used to divide a polynomial by a binomial. Since division by zero is not possible, assume that the divisor is never 0.

To divide $x^2 + 2x + 5$ by $x - 1$:

$$
\begin{array}{r}
x + 3 \\
x - 1 \overline{)\ x^2 + 2x + 5} \\
-(x^2 - x) \\
\hline
3x + 5 \\
-(3x - 3) \\
\hline
8
\end{array}
$$

— Divide x^2 by x.
← Divide $3x$ by x.

Multiply the divisor, $x - 1$, by x, then subtract.

Multiply the divisor, $x - 1$, by 3, then subtract.

The remainder is 8.

So, the quotient is $x + 3$ and the remainder is 8.

Before dividing, write the polynomial and the binomial divisor in descending order.

Example 1   Dividing a Polynomial by a Binomial

Check Your Understanding

1. Divide: $2x^3 + 5 - 2x + 3x^2$ by $x - 1$

Divide: $-x + 3x^3 - 6 + 2x^2$ by $x + 2$

SOLUTION

Write the polynomial in descending order: $3x^3 + 2x^2 - x - 6$
Use long division to divide.

$$
\begin{array}{r}
3x^2 - 4x + 7 \\
x + 2 \overline{)\ 3x^3 + 2x^2 - x - 6} \\
-(3x^3 + 6x^2) \\
\hline
-4x^2 - x \\
-(-4x^2 - 8x) \\
\hline
7x - 6 \\
-(7x + 14) \\
\hline
-20
\end{array}
$$

$3x^3 \div x = 3x^2$
Subtract: $3x^2(x + 2)$
$-4x^2 \div x = -4x$
Subtract: $-4x(x + 2)$
$7x \div x = 7$
Subtract: $7(x + 2)$

So, the quotient is $3x^2 - 4x + 7$ and the remainder is -20.

To verify the answer in *Example 1*, multiply the quotient by the divisor, then add the remainder.

$(x + 2)(3x^2 - 4x + 7) + (-20)$
$= x(3x^2 - 4x + 7) + 2(3x^2 - 4x + 7) - 20$
$= 3x^3 - 4x^2 + 7x + 6x^2 - 8x + 14 - 20$
$= 3x^3 + 2x^2 - x - 6$

Since this is the original polynomial, the answer is correct.

In *Example 1*, note that the dividend is a polynomial of degree 3, and the quotient is a polynomial of degree 2. In general, when a polynomial is divided by a divisor of the form $x - a$, the degree of the quotient is 1 less than the degree of the dividend.

THINK FURTHER

When is it not necessary to use long division to divide a polynomial by a binomial?

When a polynomial is divided by a binomial, the *division statement* relates the original polynomial and the divisor to the quotient and remainder. This is how the answer to the polynomial division in *Example 1* was verified.

Division Statement for Division by $x - a$

$P(x) = (x - a)Q(x) + R$, where $P(x)$ is the original polynomial, $(x - a)$ is the binomial divisor, $Q(x)$ is the quotient polynomial (which has degree 1 less than $P(x)$), and R is the remainder (which is a constant).

THINK FURTHER

In the division statement, when R = 0, how are P(x) and (x − a) related?

The polynomial may have some powers of the variable missing. Since adding 0 to a polynomial does not change its value, terms with coefficient 0 are inserted to hold the places of missing terms.

Example 2   **Using Zero as a Place Holder**

Divide: $-4x^4 + 2x^2 - x - 3$ by $x - 3$
Write the division statement.

2. Divide: $3x^4 - x^3 + 3x - 20$ by $x + 2$
Write the division statement.

SOLUTION

The polynomial does not have an x^3-term. Write $0x^3$ as a place holder:
$-4x^4 + 0x^3 + 2x^2 - x - 3$

$$
\begin{array}{r}
-4x^3 - 12x^2 - 34x - 103 \\
x - 3 \overline{)\, -4x^4 + 0x^3 + 2x^2 - x - 3} \\
\underline{-(-4x^4 + 12x^3)} \\
-12x^3 + 2x^2 \\
\underline{-(-12x^3 + 36x^2)} \\
-34x^2 - x \\
\underline{-(-34x^2 + 102x)} \\
-103x - 3 \\
\underline{-(-103x + 309)} \\
-312
\end{array}
$$

So, $-4x^4 + 2x^2 - x - 3 = (x - 3)(-4x^3 - 12x^2 - 34x - 103) - 312$

Synthetic division can be used to divide a polynomial by a binomial of the form $x - a$, $a \in \mathbb{Z}$. In this method, the variables are removed and only the coefficients are recorded. To divide $5x^2 + 7x - 4$ by $x - 2$:

Compare $x - 2$ to $x - a$:

$a = 2$

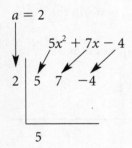

$$
\begin{array}{c|ccc}
2 & 5 & 7 & -4 \\
& & & \\
\hline
& 5 & &
\end{array}
$$

Write the value of a on the left. Write the coefficients of the polynomial on the right. Bring down the first coefficient, 5.

$$
\begin{array}{c|ccc}
2 & 5 & 7 & -4 \\
& & 10 & \\
\hline
& 5 & 17 &
\end{array}
$$

Multiply 5 by the value of a, 2. Record the product, 10, beneath the second coefficient, 7, then add.

$$
\begin{array}{c|ccc}
2 & 5 & 7 & -4 \\
& & 10 & 34 \\
\hline
& 5 & 17 & 30
\end{array}
$$

Multiply the sum, 17, by the value of a, 2. Record the product, 34, beneath the third coefficient, -4, then add.

The numbers below the line are the coefficients of the quotient polynomial and the remainder. Since the dividend is a polynomial of degree 2, the quotient is a polynomial of degree 1. So, the quotient is $5x + 17$ and the remainder is 30.

All the steps in a synthetic division can be recorded in one diagram.

Check Your Understanding

3. Divide: $-3x^4 + 2x^3 + 3x^2 - 4x + 5$ by $x + 2$
Write the division statement.

Example 3   **Using Synthetic Division to Divide**

Divide: $2x^3 + 4x^2 - 5x - 6$ by $x + 1$
Write the division statement.

SOLUTION

Compare $x + 1$ to $x - a$: $a = -1$

$$
\begin{array}{r|rrrr}
-1 & 2 & 4 & -5 & -6 \\
   & \downarrow & -2 & -2 & 7 \\
\hline
   & 2 & 2 & -7 & 1
\end{array}
$$

Write the value of a on the left.
Write the coefficients of the polynomial on the right.
Bring down the first coefficient, 2.

Multiply 2 by -1. Record the product, -2, beneath the second coefficient, 4, then add.
Multiply the sum, 2, by -1. Record the product, -2, beneath the third coefficient, -5, then add.
Multiply the sum, -7, by -1. Record the product, 7, beneath the fourth coefficient, -6, then add.
Since the dividend is a polynomial of degree 3, the quotient is a polynomial of degree 2.
So, $2x^3 + 4x^2 - 5x - 6 = (x + 1)(2x^2 + 2x - 7) + 1$

THINK FURTHER

How could you use synthetic division to divide $6x^3 + 4x^2 + 8$ by $2x + 4$?

Discuss the Ideas

1. What strategies can you use to divide a polynomial by a binomial?

2. How is long division of a polynomial by a binomial related to synthetic division?

Exercises

A

3. Divide.

a) $(2x^2 - x - 6) \div (x - 2)$ b) $(x^2 - 49) \div (x + 7)$

c) $(2x^2 + 9x - 18) \div (x + 6)$ d) $(x^2 - 10x + 25) \div (x - 5)$

1.1 Dividing a Polynomial by a Binomial |

4. When each division is performed using synthetic division, the result is as shown. Write the quotient and the remainder.

    a) $(2x^3 - 5x^2 + 3x - 7) \div (x - 3)$; 2   1   6   11

    b) $(5x^2 - 7x - 3) \div (x + 4)$; 5   −27   105

    c) $(3x^4 + 9x^3 - 8x^2 + x - 9) \div (x - 2)$; 3   15   22   45   81

    d) $(-5x^5 - 3x^3 + 11x^2 - 19x) \div (x + 1)$;
    −5   5   −8   19   −38   38

5. Divide. Verify your answers.

    a) $(x^2 + x - 2) \div (x - 3)$ **b)** $(2x^3 + 5x^2 - 2x + 4) \div (x + 3)$

6. A polynomial is divided by $x - 3$. The quotient is $x^2 + 5x - 2$ and the remainder is -3. What is the original polynomial?

B

7. Use long division to divide. Write the division statement.

a) $(-8x^2 - 27x + 4x^3 + 45) \div (x - 3)$

b) $(-7x + 2x^4 + 13x^3) \div (x + 2)$

8. Use synthetic division to divide. Write the division statement.

    a) $(-21x^2 + 5x^4 - 12 - 40x + 12x^3) \div (x + 3)$

    b) $(-11x^3 + 6x^4 + 5 - x^5) \div (1 + x)$

9. Divide the polynomial $2x^5 - x^4 + 2x^3 - 3x^2 + 2x + 10$ by each binomial.

    a) $x - 2$

    b) $4 + x$

10. Look at the exercises for which there was no remainder when a polynomial was divided by a binomial. What relationship is there among the constant terms of the dividend, divisor, and quotient?

11. a) Determine the quotient and remainder when $4x^3 + 5x^2 - 6x + 5$ is divided by each binomial.

    i) $x + 1$ **ii)** $x - 1$

    b) Use your answers to part a to determine the quotient and remainder when $4x^3 + 5x^2 - 6x + 5$ is divided by each binomial. Explain your strategy.

    i) $-x + 1$

    ii) $-x - 1$

12. Here is a student's solution for dividing $3x^4 - 4x^3 + 5x^2 - 6x + 10$ by $x - 1$ using synthetic division. Identify the error in the solution. Write a correct solution.

$$
\begin{array}{r|rrrrr}
-1 & 3 & -4 & 5 & -6 & 10 \\
   &   & -3 & 7 & -12 & 18 \\
\hline
   & 3 & -7 & 12 & -18 & 28
\end{array}
$$

So, $3x^4 - 4x^3 + 5x^2 - 6x + 10 = (x - 1)(3x^3 - 7x^2 + 12x - 18) + 28$

13. A polynomial is divided by $x - a$, $a \in \mathbb{Z}$, and has quotient $2x^2 - 3x + 5$ and remainder 7. Determine a possible polynomial. How many different polynomials can you determine? Explain.

C

14. Divide.

$(-4x^4 + 17x^2 + 6x^5 - 27x + 10 - 21x^3) \div (x^3 - 2)$

Multiple-Choice Questions

1. What is the remainder when $-3x^3 + x^2 - 2x + 3 + 2x^4$ is divided by $x + 1$?

    A. -11 **B.** 11 **C.** 8 **D.** -8

2. When $2x^4 - x^3 - 3x^2 + x - p$ is divided by $x - 2$, the remainder is 0. What is the value of p?

    A. -14 **B.** 7 **C.** -7 **D.** 14

Study Note

What do you need to check before you divide a polynomial by a binomial?

ANSWERS

Check Your Understanding

1. $2x^2 + 5x + 3$ R8
2. $3x^4 - x^3 + 3x - 20 = (x + 2)(3x^3 - 7x^2 + 14x - 25) + 30$
3. $-3x^4 + 2x^3 + 3x^2 - 4x + 5 = (x + 2)(-3x^3 + 8x^2 - 13x + 22) - 39$

Exercises

3. a) $2x + 3$ b) $x - 7$ c) $2x - 3$ d) $x - 5$ **4. a)** $2x^2 + x + 6$ R11
b) $5x - 27$ R105   c) $3x^3 + 15x^2 + 22x + 45$ R81
d) $-5x^4 + 5x^3 - 8x^2 + 19x - 38$ R38   **5. a)** $x + 4$ R10   b) $2x^2 - x + 1$ R1
6. $x^3 + 2x^2 - 17x + 3$ **7. a)** $4x^3 - 8x^2 - 27x + 45 = (x - 3)(4x^2 + 4x - 15)$
b) $2x^4 + 13x^3 - 7x = (x + 2)(2x^3 + 9x^2 - 18x + 29) - 58$
8. a) $5x^4 + 12x^3 - 21x^2 - 40x - 12 = (x + 3)(5x^3 - 3x^2 - 12x - 4)$
b) $-x^5 + 6x^4 - 11x^3 + 5 = (x + 1)(-x^4 + 7x^3 - 18x^2 + 18x - 18) + 23$
9. a) $2x^4 + 3x^3 + 8x^2 + 13x + 28$ R66
b) $2x^4 - 9x^3 + 38x^2 - 155x + 622$ R(-2478)
11. a) i) $4x^2 + x - 7$ R12   ii) $4x^2 + 9x + 3$ R8   b) i) $-4x^2 - 9x - 3$ R8
ii) $-4x^2 - x + 7$ R12
12. $3x^4 - 4x^3 + 5x^2 - 6x + 10 = (x - 1)(3x^3 - x^2 + 4x - 2) + 8$
14. $6x^2 - 4x - 21$ R($29x^2 - 35x - 32$)

Multiple Choice

1. B   2. D

FOCUS Use the remainder theorem and factor theorem to factor polynomials.

Get Started

Factor each polynomial.

$6x^2 + 7x - 3$ $2x^3 - 3x^2 - 14x$ $49x^2 - 36y^4$

Construct Understanding

For each polynomial below, divide to determine whether the given binomial is a factor. Each binomial has the form $x - a$. Evaluate each polynomial when $x = a$.

- $3x^2 - 2x - 1$ $x - 1$
- $3x^3 - 8x^2 - x - 2$ $x - 3$
- $2x^4 - x^3 - 17x^2 - 11x + 6$ $x + 2$

How might you tell whether the binomial is a factor without dividing?

When a polynomial is divided by a binomial of the form $x - a$, the remainder is related to the polynomial and the constant term of the divisor. For example,

$$
\begin{array}{r}
5x^2 + 8x + 24 \\
x - 2\overline{)5x^3 - 2x^2 + 8x - 1} \\
\underline{5x^3 - 10x^2} \\
8x^2 + 8x \\
\underline{8x^2 - 16x} \\
24x - 1 \\
\underline{24x - 48} \\
47
\end{array}
$$

The divisor is $x - 2$.
Let $P(x) = 5x^3 - 2x^2 + 8x - 1$

Evaluate the polynomial for $x = 2$.
$P(2) = 5(2)^3 - 2(2)^2 + 8(2) - 1$
$\qquad = 40 - 8 + 16 - 1$
$\qquad = 47$

The value of the polynomial when $x = 2$ is equal to the remainder when the polynomial is divided by $x - 2$. This is called the **remainder theorem**.

Remainder Theorem

When a polynomial, $P(x)$, is divided by a binomial, $x - a, a \in \mathbb{Z}$, the remainder is $P(a)$.

To illustrate why this works, use the division statement.
$P(x) = (x - a)Q(x) + R$
Substitute: $x = a$
$P(a) = (a - a)Q(a) + R$
$P(a) = (0)Q(a) + R$
$P(a) = R$

| Example 1 | Determining the Remainder without Dividing |

Determine the remainder when $3x^4 + 7x^3 - x^2 + 14x - 3$ is divided by each binomial.

a) $x - 1$ **b)** $x + 3$

1. Determine the remainder when $2x^4 - 5x^3 - 5x^2 + 5x + 3$ is divided by each binomial.

a) $x - 3$ **b)** $x + 2$

SOLUTION

Let $P(x) = 3x^4 + 7x^3 - x^2 + 14x - 3$ and use the remainder theorem.

a) When $P(x)$ is divided by $x - 1$, the remainder is $P(1)$.

$$P(1) = 3(1)^4 + 7(1)^3 - (1)^2 + 14(1) - 3$$
$$= 3 + 7 - 1 + 14 - 3$$
$$= 20$$

The remainder is 20.

b) Write $x + 3$ in the form $x - a$: $x - (-3)$

When $P(x)$ is divided by $x + 3$, the remainder is $P(-3)$.

$$P(-3) = 3(-3)^4 + 7(-3)^3 - (-3)^2 + 14(-3) - 3$$
$$= 3(81) + 7(-27) - 9 - 42 - 3$$
$$= 243 - 189 - 9 - 42 - 3$$
$$= 0$$

The remainder is 0.

THINK FURTHER

Does a polynomial have to be written in descending order to use the remainder theorem?

In *Example 1b*, the remainder was 0. This means that the divisor, $x + 3$, is a factor of the polynomial. This special case of the remainder theorem is called the **factor theorem**.

Factor Theorem

For $a \in \mathbb{Z}$, $x - a$ is a factor of the polynomial $P(x)$ if $P(a) = 0$.

2. Which binomials are factors of $x^3 - 6x^2 + 5x + 12$?

a) $x + 1$ b) $x - 3$

c) $x - 4$ d) $x + 4$

Which binomials are factors of $x^3 + 2x^2 - 13x + 10$?

a) $x - 1$ b) $x - 2$

c) $x + 2$ d) $x + 5$

SOLUTION

Let $P(x) = x^3 + 2x^2 - 13x + 10$ and use the factor theorem.

a) $P(1) = (1)^3 + 2(1)^2 - 13(1) + 10$
$$= 0$$
Since $P(1) = 0$, $x - 1$ is a factor of $x^3 + 2x^2 - 13x + 10$.

b) $P(2) = (2)^3 + 2(2)^2 - 13(2) + 10$
$$= 0$$
Since $P(2) = 0$, $x - 2$ is a factor of $x^3 + 2x^2 - 13x + 10$.

c) $P(-2) = (-2)^3 + 2(-2)^2 - 13(-2) + 10$
$$= 36$$
Since $P(-2) \neq 0$, $x + 2$ is not a factor of $x^3 + 2x^2 - 13x + 10$.

d) $P(-5) = (-5)^3 + 2(-5)^2 - 13(-5) + 10$
$$= 0$$
Since $P(-5) = 0$, $x + 5$ is a factor of $x^3 + 2x^2 - 13x + 10$.

From *Example 2*, there are three binomial factors of $x^3 + 2x^2 - 13x + 10$: $x - 1, x - 2, x + 5$
The product of these factors is the original polynomial:
$(x - 1)(x - 2)(x + 5) = x^3 + 2x^2 - 13x + \mathbf{10}$
The constant term in each binomial is a factor of the constant term in the polynomial; that is, each of $1, 2$, and -5 is a factor of 10.

This leads to the **factor property**.

Factor Property

If $x - a, a \in \mathbb{Z}$, is a factor of a polynomial, then a is a factor of the constant term in the polynomial.

Example 3   **Factoring a Polynomial**

Factor fully: $2x^3 - 9x^2 + 7x + 6$

3. Factor fully: $3x^3 - 4x^2 - 5x + 2$

SOLUTION

Let $P(x) = 2x^3 - 9x^2 + 7x + 6$ and use the factor theorem.
List the factors of the constant term, 6: $1, -1, 2, -2, 3, -3, 6, -6$
Use mental math to substitute $x = 1$, then $x = -1$ to determine that
neither $x - 1$ nor $x + 1$ is a factor.
Try $x = 2$: $P(2) = 2(2)^3 - 9(2)^2 + 7(2) + 6$
$\qquad\qquad\quad = 2(8) - 9(4) + 14 + 6$
$\qquad\qquad\quad = 0$
So, $x - 2$ is a factor of $2x^3 - 9x^2 + 7x + 6$.
Divide to determine the other factor.

$$
\begin{array}{r|rrrr}
2 & 2 & -9 & 7 & 6 \\
  &   & 4 & -10 & -6 \\
\hline
  & 2 & -5 & -3 & 0
\end{array}
$$

Since $P(x)$ is a polynomial of degree 3, the quotient is a polynomial
of degree 2.
So, $2x^3 - 9x^2 + 7x + 6 = (x - 2)(2x^2 - 5x - 3)$
Factor the trinomial: $2x^2 - 5x - 3 = (x - 3)(2x + 1)$
So, $2x^3 - 9x^2 + 7x + 6 = (x - 2)(x - 3)(2x + 1)$

THINK FURTHER

In *Example 3*, how do you know that neither $x - 1$ nor $x + 1$ is a factor of $2x^2 - 5x - 3$?

Discuss the Ideas

1. How can you determine whether a binomial of the form $x - a$ is a
factor of a polynomial?

2. How do you decide whether to use synthetic division or the factor theorem to help you factor a polynomial?

Exercises

A

3. Write each binomial in the form $x - a$. What is the value of a?

   a) $x + 4$ **b)** $x - 1$

   c) $11 + x$ **d)** $-7 + x$

4. a) Determine the remainder when $x^3 - 4x^2 - 7x + 10$ is divided by each binomial.

   i) $x - 1$ **ii)** $x + 3$

   iii) $x + 2$ **iv)** $x - 2$

b) Which binomials in part a are factors of $x^3 - 4x^2 - 7x + 10$? How do you know?

5. Which values of a, $a \in \mathbb{Z}$, should be chosen to test for binomial factors of the form $x - a$ of the polynomial $x^4 + 3x^3 - 8x^2 - 12x + 16$? How did you choose the values?

B

6. a) Determine the remainder when each polynomial is divided by $x - 2$.

    i) $x^2 - 7x + 11$ **ii)** $2x^3 - 3x^2 - 6x + 8$

    iii) $3x^3 - 2x^2 - 10x + 6$ **iv)** $x^4 - 2x^3 + 3x^2 - 8$

b) Explain the relationship between the remainder when a polynomial $P(x)$ is divided by $x - a$, $a \in \mathbb{Z}$, and $P(a)$.

7. Determine the remainder.

a) $(2x^3 - x^2 + 3x - 2) \div (x - 3)$ b) $(3x^3 - 2x^2 - 4x + 6) \div (x - 2)$

8. When $2x^3 + kx^2 - 3x + 2$ is divided by $x - 2$, the remainder is 4. Determine the value of k.

9. Determine one binomial factor of each polynomial.

a) $x^4 + 6x^3 + 5x^2 - 24x - 36$

b) $x^5 + 3x^4 - 5x^3 - 15x^2 + 4x + 12$

10. a) Show that $x + 5$ is a factor of $x^3 + 4x^2 - 11x - 30$.

b) Determine the other binomial factors of the polynomial.
Verify that the factors are correct.

11. Fully factor each polynomial.

a) $x^3 + 6x^2 + 3x - 10$

b) $x^4 - 5x^2 + 4$

12. a) What value of b will ensure $x + 3$ is a factor of $bx^3 - 2x^2 + x - 6$?

b) What value of d will ensure $x + 2$ is a factor of
$3x^5 - dx^4 + 4x^3 - 2dx^2 + x + 10$?

13. Determine whether $x + b$ is a factor of $(x + b)^5 + (x + p)^5 + (b - p)^5$,
$b, p \in \mathbb{R}$.

14. When $mx^3 - 2x^2 + nx - 4$ is divided by $x + 2$, the remainder is 4.
When $mx^3 - 2x^2 + nx - 4$ is divided by $x - 1$, the remainder is
-11. Determine the values of m and n.

15. Determine each remainder.

   a) $(8x^2 - 6x + 3) \div (4x + 1)$

   b) $(3x^3 + 2x^2 - 6x - 1) \div (3x + 2)$

1. Which binomial is not a factor of $2x^4 + 3x^3 - 12x^2 - 7x + 6$?

   A. $x - 2$ B. $x + 3$

   C. $x - 1$ D. $x + 1$

2. Which product of factors is equal to $x^3 - 8x^2 + x + 42$?

   A. $(x + 2)(x - 7)(x - 3)$ B. $(x - 2)(x + 7)(x - 3)$

   C. $(x - 2)(x - 7)(x + 3)$ D. $(x + 2)(x + 7)(x + 3)$

Study Note

How are the remainder theorem and factor theorem related?

ANSWERS

Check Your Understanding

1. a) 0   b) 45   2. a) yes   b) yes   c) yes   d) no
3. $3x^3 - 4x^2 - 5x + 2 = (x + 1)(x - 2)(3x - 1)$

Exercises

3. a) -4 b) 1   c) -11 d) 7   4. a) i) 0   ii) -32 iii) 0   iv) -12
b) $x - 1$ and $x + 2$ 5. $\pm 1, \pm 2, \pm 4, \pm 8, \pm 16$ 6. a) i) 1   ii) 0   iii) 2   iv) 4
7. a) 52   b) 14   8. $k = -2$ 9. a) $x + 2, x - 2,$ or $x + 3$
b) $x - 1, x + 1, x - 2, x + 2,$ or $x + 3$ 10. b) $x + 2$ and $x - 3$
11. a) $(x - 1)(x + 2)(x + 5)$ b) $(x - 1)(x + 1)(x - 2)(x + 2)$
12. a) $b = -1$ b) $d = -5$ 13. yes   14. $m = -1; n = -4$ 15. a) 5   b) 3

Multiple Choice

1. C   2. A

Additional Workspace

✔ CHECKPOINT

Self-Assess

Can you . . .	Try *Checkpoint* question	For review, see
divide a polynomial by a binomial using long division?	2	Page 3 in Lesson 1.1 (Example 1)
divide a polynomial by a binomial using synthetic division?	3	Page 6 in Lesson 1.1 (Example 3)
use the remainder theorem to determine the remainder when a polynomial is divided by a binomial?	5	Page 17 in Lesson 1.2 (Example 1)
use the factor theorem to determine whether a binomial is a factor of a given polynomial?	5	Page 18 in Lesson 1.2 (Example 2)
use the factor theorem to determine a binomial factor of a polynomial?	6	Page 19 in Lesson 1.2 (Example 3)
apply the factor theorem to write a polynomial as a product of factors?	7	Page 19 in Lesson 1.2 (Example 3)

Assess Your Understanding

1.1

1. **Multiple Choice** When synthetic division is used to divide $x^4 - 7x^2 + 2x + 3$ by $x + 1$, the result is: $1 \quad -1 \quad -6 \quad 8 \quad -5$
   Which is the correct division statement?

   A. $x^4 - 7x^2 + 2x + 3 = (x + 1)(x^4 - x^3 - 6x^2 + 8x - 5) + 0$

   B. $x^4 - 7x^2 + 2x + 3 = (x + 1)(x^3 - x^2 - 6x + 8) - 5$

   C. $x^4 - 7x^2 + 2x + 3 = (x + 1)(x^3 - x^2 - 6x + 8) + 5$

   D. $x^4 - 7x^2 + 2x - 2 = (x + 1)(x^3 - x^2 - 6x + 8)$

2. **a)** Use long division to divide:

   i) $2x^2 - 11x - 19$ by $x - 7$ **ii)** $3x^3 + 4x^2 - 15x + 30$ by $x + 4$

b) Verify the answer to one division in part a.

3. Use synthetic division to divide $2x^4 - 7x^3 - 29x^2 - 8x + 12$ by each binomial.

   a) $x - 1$

   b) $x - 6$

   c) $x + 2$

   d) $x + 3$

4. **Multiple Choice** When a polynomial $P(x)$ is divided by $x + 3$, the remainder is -4. Which statement is true?

   A. $P(-4) = -3$ B. $P(3) = -4$

   C. $P(-3) = -4$ D. $P(-3) = 0$

5. a) Determine the remainder when $3x^4 + 8x^3 - 15x^2 - 32x + 12$ is divided by $x + 1$.

   b) Is $x + 1$ a factor of the polynomial in part a? If your answer is yes, explain how you know. If your answer is no, determine a binomial of the form $x - a$, $a \in \mathbb{Z}$, that is a factor.

6. For each polynomial, determine one factor of the form $x - a$, $a \in \mathbb{Z}$.

   a) $x^3 - 5x^2 - 17x + 21$

   b) $4x^4 - 15x^3 - 32x^2 + 33x + 10$

7. Factor this polynomial.

$$4x^4 - 12x^3 + 3x^2 + 13x - 6$$

ANSWERS

1. B   **2. a) i)** $2x + 3$ R2   **ii)** $3x^2 - 8x + 17$ R(-38)

3. a) $2x^3 - 5x^2 - 34x - 42$ R(-30) **b)** $2x^3 + 5x^2 + x - 2$

c) $2x^3 - 11x^2 - 7x + 6$ **d)** $2x^3 - 13x^2 + 10x - 38$ R126   **4.** C   **5. a)** 24

b) no; $x - 2$, $x + 2$, or $x + 3$ **6. a)** $x - 1$, $x + 3$, or $x - 7$ **b)** $x - 1$, $x + 2$, or $x - 5$

7. $(x + 1)(x - 2)(2x - 3)(2x - 1)$

1.3 Graphing Polynomial Functions

FOCUS Use technology to graph polynomial functions.

Get Started

For the graph of each quadratic function, identify the coordinates of the vertex, the domain, the range, the direction of opening, and the intercepts.

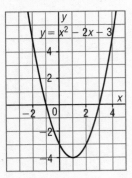

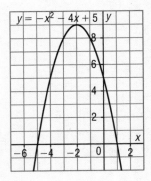

Construct Understanding

Use graphing technology to investigate the graphs of some polynomial functions.

A. Graph each polynomial function of degree 3, then sketch its graph.

    i) $f(x) = 2x^3 + 3x^2 - 3x - 2$ **ii)** $g(x) = -x^3 + 7x + 6$

A **polynomial function** of degree 3 is a **cubic function**.

iii) $h(x) = x^3 - 3x^2 + 2x + 3$ **iv)** $j(x) = x^3 - 4x^2 - 3x + 18$

v) $k(x) = -3x^3 + 19x^2 - 33x + 9$ **vi)** $m(x) = -3x^3 + x^2 - 5x - 7$

B. Complete the table below for the graphs in Part A.

Graph	Number of x-intercepts	Number of hills	Number of valleys	y-intercept
i				
ii				
iii				
iv				
v				
vi				

For each graph:

- when x is positive and very large, how does y change as x increases?

- when x is negative and $|x|$ is very large, how does y change as $|x|$ increases?

How do the changes in x and y relate to the sign of the x^3-term in the equation?

C. What generalizations can you make about the graph of a cubic function? How could you predict the *y*-intercept of the graph from its equation?

D. Write the equation of a different cubic function. Use your generalization from Part C to predict what the graph might look like. Then graph to check your predictions.

Assess Your Understanding

1. a) Use graphing technology. Graph each polynomial function of degree 4, then sketch its graph.

  i) $f(x) = -x^4 + 3x^3 + 4x^2 - 12x - 2$

> A polynomial function of degree 4 is a **quartic function**.

  ii) $g(x) = x^4 - 2x^3 - 3x^2 + 8x + 9$

  iii) $h(x) = -2x^4 + 4x^3 - 8x + 10$

iv) $j(x) = 2x^4 - 7x^2 - 5x$

b) How does the sign of the x^4-term affect the shape of the graph?

c) How does the value of the constant term affect the graph of the function?

d) How are the graphs of quartic functions like the graphs of quadratic functions? How are they different?

2. a) Use graphing technology. Graph each polynomial function of degree 5, then sketch its graph.

   i) $f(x) = x^5 + 2x^4 - 7x^3 - 8x^2 + 12x - 1$

   A polynomial function of degree 5 is a **quintic function**.

ii) $g(x) = -x^5 + 2x^4 + 5x^3 - 3x^2 - 4x + 8$

iii) $h(x) = 2x^5 - x^4 + 3x^3 + 5x^2 + x - 3$

iv) $j(x) = -2x^5 + x^3 - x^2 + 3x$

THINK FURTHER
....

How does the range of a function of degree 1, 3, or 5 differ from the range of a function of degree 2 or 4?

b) How does the sign of the x^5-term affect the shape of the graph?

c) How does the value of the constant term affect the graph of the function?

d) How are the graphs of quintic functions like the graphs of cubic functions? How are they different?

FOCUS Identify characteristics of polynomial functions and their graphs.

Get Started

Match each quadratic equation to a graph below.
What characteristics did you use?

$y = x^2 + 4$

$y = -3(x - 1)^2 + 7$

$y = -x^2 + 4$

$y = 2(x + 1)(x + 2)$

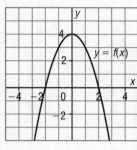

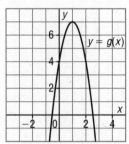

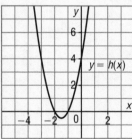

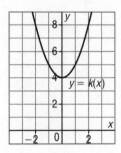

Construct Understanding

Match each graph with its equation.
Justify your choices.

$y = -x^5 + 5x^3 - 4x + 4$ $y = 2x^4 - 2x^3 - 5x^2 + 3x + 4$

$y = x^3 - 4x^2 - x + 4$ $y = -x^4 + 2x^3 + 3x^2 - 8x + 4$

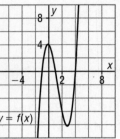

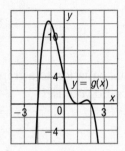

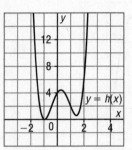

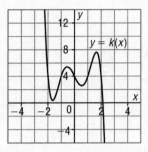

Linear, quadratic, cubic, quartic, and quintic functions are polynomial functions.

The *degree* of a polynomial function is the highest power of the variable in the equation. For example, the function $f(x) = -2x^3 + 3x^5 - 3 + x^2$ has degree 5 because the highest power of x is x^5.

> ## Polynomial Functions
>
> A polynomial function of degree n can be written in standard form as:
> $f(x) = a_n x^n + a_{n-1} x^{n-1} + a_{n-2} x^{n-2} + \ldots + a_1 x + a_0$, where n is a whole number and $a_n, a_{n-1}, a_{n-2}, \ldots, a_1, a_0$ are real numbers.
>
> The coefficient of the highest power of x is the **leading coefficient**.

The graph of a polynomial function is smooth and continuous, which means it has no sharp corners and can be drawn without lifting the pencil from the paper.

A polynomial function can be described by its degree:
even-degree polynomial function or **odd-degree polynomial function.**

Degree	Type	Positive leading coefficient	Negative leading coefficient
1	Linear Odd-degree polynomial function	$f(x) = x - 2$ 	$f(x) = -x + 3$
2	Quadratic Even-degree polynomial function	$f(x) = 2x^2 + x - 2$ 	$f(x) = -2x^2 - 3x + 1$
3	Cubic Odd-degree polynomial function	$f(x) = x^3 + 2x^2 + x - 2$ 	$f(x) = -x^3 - 2x^2 + 5$

4	Quartic Even-degree polynomial function	$f(x) = x^4 - 5x^2 + 2$ 	$f(x) = -2x^4 - 3x^3 + 2x^2 - 4x + 1$
5	Quintic Odd-degree polynomial function	$f(x) = x^5 + 2x^4 - 3x^3 - 4x^2 + x - 3$ 	$f(x) = -7x^5 + x^2 - 3$

The end behaviour of a graph refers to the behaviour of the graph as $|x|$ becomes very large. For positive values of x, as x becomes very large, we say x approaches infinity. We write: $x \rightarrow \infty$

For negative values of x, as $|x|$ becomes very large, we say x approaches negative infinity. We write: $x \rightarrow -\infty$

The end behaviour of the graphs of polynomial functions can be summarized.

Odd-Degree Polynomial Functions

Leading Coefficient	End Behaviour of Graph
positive	As $x \rightarrow -\infty$, the graph falls to the left, and as $x \rightarrow \infty$, the graph rises to the right
negative	As $x \rightarrow -\infty$, the graph rises to the left, and as $x \rightarrow \infty$, the graph falls to the right

Even-Degree Polynomial Functions

Leading Coefficient	End Behaviour of Graph
positive	As $x \rightarrow -\infty$, the graph rises to the left, and as $x \rightarrow \infty$, the graph rises to the right
negative	As $x \rightarrow -\infty$, the graph falls to the left, and as $x \rightarrow \infty$, the graph falls to the right

When a graph rises to the left and rises to the right, the graph *opens up*. When a graph falls to the left and falls to the right, the graph *opens down*.

For the graph of a polynomial function:

- A point where the graph changes from increasing to decreasing is called a **local maximum point**. The y-value of this point is greater than those of neighbouring points.

- A point where the graph changes from decreasing to increasing is called a **local minimum point**. The y-value of this point is less than those of neighbouring points.

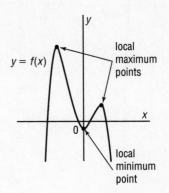

An inspection of the graphs of polynomial functions in this lesson and in Lesson 1.3 illustrates that the graph of a polynomial function of degree n can have at most n x-intercepts and at most $(n - 1)$ local maximum or minimum points. For example, the graph of a cubic function can have at most 3 x-intercepts and at most 2 local maximum or local minimum points.

To sketch the graph of a polynomial function, use a table of values and knowledge of the end behaviour of its graph.

Example 1	Using a Table of Values to Sketch the Graph of a Polynomial Function

Remember that a sketch does not have to be accurate.

Sketch the graph of each polynomial function.

a) $f(x) = -2x^3 + 4x + 4$ **b)** $g(x) = x^4 - x^3 - 3x^2$

Check Your Understanding

1. Sketch the graph of each polynomial function.

a) $f(x) = x^3 - 3x^2$

b) $g(x) = -x^4 - 6x^3 - 9x^2 + 3$

SOLUTION

a) The equation represents an odd-degree polynomial function. Since the leading coefficient is negative, as $x \to -\infty$, the graph rises and as $x \to \infty$, the graph falls. The constant term is 4, so the y-intercept is 4. Use a table of values to create the graph.

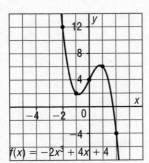

x	f(x)
-2	12
-1	2
0	4
1	6
2	-4

b) The equation represents an even-degree polynomial function. Since the leading coefficient is positive, the graph opens up. The constant term is 0, so the y-intercept is 0. Use a table of values to create the graph.

1.4 Relating Polynomial Functions and Equations | **41**

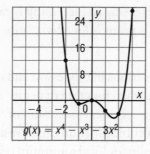

x	g(x)
−2	12
−1	−1
0	0
1	−3
2	−4
3	27

$g(x) = x^4 - x^3 - 3x^2$

2. Sketch the graph of the polynomial function:

$f(x) = x^3 + x^2 - 6x$

Example 2 — Using Intercepts to Sketch the Graph of a Polynomial Function

Sketch the graph of the polynomial function:
$f(x) = 2x^4 - x^3 - 14x^2 + 19x - 6$

SOLUTION

Factor the polynomial. Use the factor theorem.
List the factors of the constant term, -6:
$1, -1, 2, -2, 3, -3, 6, -6$
Use mental math. When $x = 1$, $f(1) = 0$
So, $x - 1$ is a factor of $2x^4 - x^3 - 14x^2 + 19x - 6$.
Divide to determine the other factor.

$$
\begin{array}{r|rrrrr}
1 & 2 & -1 & -14 & 19 & -6 \\
  &   & 2 & 1   & -13 & 6 \\
\hline
  & 2 & 1 & -13 & 6   & 0
\end{array}
$$

So, $2x^4 - x^3 - 14x^2 + 19x - 6 = (x - 1)(2x^3 + x^2 - 13x + 6)$
Factor the cubic polynomial. Use the factor theorem.
Let $P(x) = 2x^3 + x^2 - 13x + 6$
Use mental math.
When $x = 1$, $P(1) \neq 0$
When $x = -1$, $P(-1) \neq 0$
So, neither $x - 1$ nor $x + 1$ is a factor.
Try $x = 2$: $P(2) = 2(2)^3 + (2)^2 - 13(2) + 6$
$\qquad\qquad\quad = 16 + 4 - 26 + 6$
$\qquad\qquad\quad = 0$
So, $x - 2$ is a factor of $2x^3 + x^2 - 13x + 6$.
Divide to determine the other factor.

$$
\begin{array}{r|rrrr}
2 & 2 & 1 & -13 & 6 \\
  &   & 4 & 10 & -6 \\
\hline
  & 2 & 5 & -3 & 0
\end{array}
$$

$2x^4 - x^3 - 14x^2 + 19x - 6 = (x - 1)(x - 2)(2x^2 + 5x - 3)$

Factor the trinomial: $2x^2 + 5x - 3 = (x + 3)(2x - 1)$

So, $f(x) = (x - 1)(x - 2)(x + 3)(2x - 1)$

Determine the zeros of $f(x)$. Let $f(x) = 0$.

$0 = (x - 1)(x - 2)(x + 3)(2x - 1)$ Solve the equation.

So, $x - 1 = 0$ or $x - 2 = 0$ or $x + 3 = 0$ or $2x - 1 = 0$

         $x = 1$ $x = 2$ $x = -3$ $x = \dfrac{1}{2}$

The zeros are: $1, 2, -3, \dfrac{1}{2}$

So, the x-intercepts of the graph are: $1, 2, -3$, and $\dfrac{1}{2}$

Plot points at the intercepts.

The equation has degree 4, so it is an even-degree polynomial function. The leading coefficient is positive, so the graph opens up. The constant term is -6, so the y-intercept is -6.

Draw a smooth curve through the points, beginning at the top left and ending at the top right.

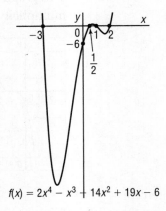

$f(x) = 2x^4 - x^3 + 14x^2 + 19x - 6$

THINK FURTHER

Suppose the graph of a polynomial function is symmetrical about the y-axis. What do you know about the function?

In *Example 2*, the equation $0 = (x - 1)(x - 2)(x + 3)(2x - 1)$ is the factored form of a **polynomial equation**. This *Example* illustrates that when the equation of a polynomial function is factorable, the x-intercepts of its graph can be determined by factoring.

The x-intercepts are the zeros of the polynomial function because they are the values of x when the function is 0. The zeros of the function are the roots of the related polynomial equation.

A polynomial equation may have a repeated root. Here are two examples:

$x^2 - 2x + 1 = 0$ can be written as $(x - 1)^2 = 0$.

The equation has root: $x = 1$

The exponent of the factor $(x - 1)$ is 2, so 1 is a root with **multiplicity** 2.

The related function has a zero of multiplicity 2.

$x^3 - 3x^2 + 3x - 1 = 0$ can be written as $(x - 1)^3 = 0$.

The equation has root: $x = 1$

The exponent of the factor $(x - 1)$ is 3, so 1 is a root with multiplicity 3.

The related function has a zero of multiplicity 3.

The behaviour of the graph at a zero depends on its multiplicity.

Here are the graphs of $f(x) = (x - 1)^2$ and $g(x) = (x - 1)^3$.

This graph has a zero of
multiplicity 2.

This graph has a zero of
multiplicity 3.

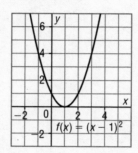

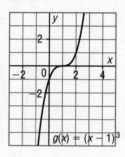

Both graphs have x-intercept 1.

The graph of $f(x) = (x - 1)^2$ touches the x-axis at $x = 1$, but does not cross the axis at this point.

The graph of $g(x) = (x - 1)^3$ crosses the x-axis at $x = 1$.

This difference in behaviour is related to the multiplicity of the zero.

In general, when a zero has even multiplicity, the graph touches the x-axis at the related x-intercept, but does not cross it; we say that the graph "just touches" the x-axis.

When a zero has odd multiplicity, the graph crosses the x-axis at the related x-intercept.

Sketch the graph of each polynomial function.

a) $f(x) = (x - 1)^2(x + 3)^2$ **b)** $g(x) = -(x + 2)^3(x - 1)^2$

3. Sketch the graph of each polynomial function.

a) $f(x) = (x + 1)^4(x - 2)$

b) $g(x) = -(x + 1)^3(x - 3)$

SOLUTION

a) $f(x) = (x - 1)^2(x + 3)^2$

To determine the zeros, solve $f(x) = 0$.

$0 = (x - 1)^2(x + 3)^2$

The roots of the equation are $x = 1$ and $x = -3$.

So, the zeros of the function are 1 and −3.

The zero 1 has multiplicity 2.

The zero −3 has multiplicity 2.

So, the graph just touches the x-axis at $x = 1$ and at $x = -3$.

The equation has degree 4, so it is an even-degree polynomial function. The leading coefficient is positive, so the graph opens up. The y-intercept is: $(-1)^2(3)^2 = 9$

Plot points at the intercepts, then draw a smooth curve that rises to the left and rises to the right.

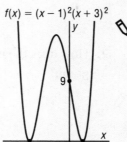

$f(x) = (x - 1)^2(x + 3)^2$

b) $g(x) = -(x + 2)^3(x - 1)^2$

To determine the zeros, solve $g(x) = 0$.

$0 = -(x + 2)^3(x - 1)^2$

The roots of the equation are $x = -2$ and $x = 1$.

So, the zeros of the function are −2 and 1.

The zero −2 has multiplicity 3.

The zero 1 has multiplicity 2.

So, the graph crosses the x-axis at $x = -2$, and just touches the x-axis at $x = 1$.

The equation has degree 5, so it is an odd-degree polynomial function.

The leading coefficient is negative, so as $x \to -\infty$, the graph rises and as $x \to \infty$, the graph falls.

The y-intercept is: $-(2)^3(-1)^2 = -8$

Plot points at the intercepts, then draw a smooth curve that rises to the left and falls to the right.

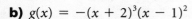

$g(x) = -(x + 2)^3(x - 1)^2$

Discuss the Ideas

1. Suppose $x - a$ is a factor of a polynomial. What else do you know about the corresponding polynomial equation and the graph of the corresponding polynomial function?

2. How does the multiplicity of a zero of a polynomial function affect its graph?

Exercises

A

3. Which functions are polynomial functions? Justify your choices.

   a) $f(x) = 2\sqrt{x} - x^2$

   b) $g(x) = 6x^3 - x^2 + 3x - 7$

   c) $h(x) = 7x^2 + 2x^3 - x - \dfrac{1}{2}$

   d) $k(x) = 3^x + 5$

   e) $p(x) = 5x^2 - 7x + \dfrac{2}{x}$

4. Which graphs are graphs of polynomial functions? Justify your answers.

a)

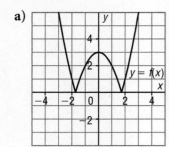

b)

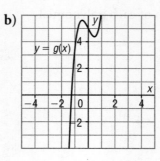

c)

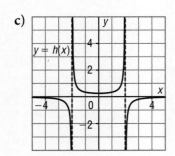

d)

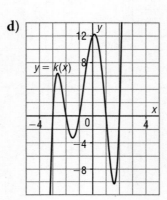

5. Complete the table below. The first row has been done for you.

	Equation	Degree	Odd or Even Degree	Type	Leading coefficient	y-intercept of its graph
	$f(x) = 3x^2 - 2x + 1$	2	even	quadratic	3	1
a)	$g(x) = 5x + x^5 - 2x^3$					
b)	$h(x) = 2x^2 - 3x^3 - 7$					
c)	$k(x) = 5 - x^4 - 3x$					

6. Use a table of values to sketch the graph of each polynomial function.

a) $f(x) = x^3 - 7x + 6$

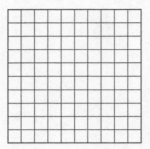

b) $g(x) = -x^4 + 5x^2 - 4$

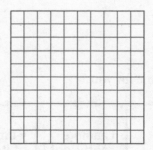

7. Use intercepts to sketch the graph of each polynomial function.

a) $f(x) = 2x^3 + 3x^2 - 2x$

b) $h(x) = 2x^4 + 7x^3 + 4x^2 - 7x - 6$

8. Identify the graph that corresponds to each function. Justify your choices.

a) $f(x) = -x^3 + 3x^2 + x - 3$ b) $g(x) = x^4 - 3x^2 - 3$

c) $h(x) = x^5 + 3x^3 - 3$ d) $k(x) = -x^2 + 4x - 3$

i) Graph A

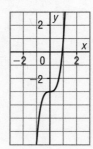

ii) Graph B

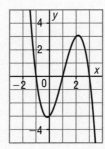

iii) Graph C

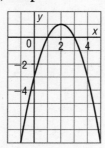

iv) Graph D

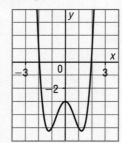

9. Determine the zeros of each polynomial function. State the multiplicity of each zero. How does the graph of each function behave at the related x-intercepts?
Use graphing technology to check.

a) $f(x) = (x + 3)^3$ b) $g(x) = (x - 2)^2(x + 3)^2$

c) $h(x) = (x - 1)^4(2x + 1)$ **d)** $j(x) = (x - 4)^3(x + 1)^2$

10. Sketch the graph of this polynomial function.
$$h(x) = (x + 1)^2(x - 1)(x + 2)$$

11. a) Write an equation in standard form for each polynomial function described below.

 i) a cubic function with zeros 3, −3, and 0

 ii) a quartic function with zeros −2 and 1 of multiplicity 1, and a zero 2 of multiplicity 2

b) Is there more than one possible equation for each function in part a? Explain.

12. Sketch a possible graph of each polynomial function.

   a) cubic function; leading coefficient is positive; zero of 4 has multiplicity 3

   b) quintic function; leading coefficient is positive; zero of 3 has multiplicity 2; zero of -2 has multiplicity 2; zero of -4 has multiplicity 1

   c) quartic function; leading coefficient is negative; zero of -4 has multiplicity 3; zero of 3 has multiplicity 1

13. A cubic function has zeros 2, 3, and -1. The y-intercept of its graph is -18. Sketch the graph, then determine an equation of the function.

C

14. Investigate pairs of graphs of even-degree polynomial functions of the form shown below for different values of the variables a, b, c, and $d \in \mathbb{Z}$. Describe one graph as a transformation image of the other graph. What conclusions can you make?
$h(x) = (x + a)(x + b)(x + c)(x + d)$ and
$k(x) = (x - a)(x - b)(x - c)(x - d)$

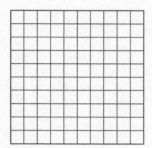

15. Investigate pairs of graphs of odd-degree polynomial functions of the form shown below for different values of the variables a, b, c, d, and $e \in \mathbb{Z}$. Describe one graph as a transformation image of the other graph. What conclusions can you make?
$h(x) = (x + a)(x + b)(x + c)(x + d)(x + e)$ and
$k(x) = (x - a)(x - b)(x - c)(x - d)(x - e)$

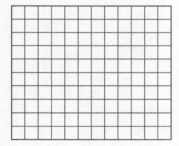

16. Each of the functions $f(x) = x^3 - 27x + 54$ and
$g(x) = x^3 - 27x - 54$ has one zero of multiplicity 2 and one
different zero. Use only this information to determine the values of
b for which the function $h(x) = x^3 - 27x + b$ has each number of
zeros. Explain your strategy.

a) 3 different zeros

b) 1 zero of multiplicity 1 and no other zeros

Multiple-Choice Questions

1. The graph of a polynomial function rises to the left and falls to the
right. Which statement describes the function?

A. The function has an odd degree and its leading coefficient is
positive.

B. The function has an even degree and its leading coefficient is
positive.

C. The function has an odd degree and its leading coefficient is
negative.

D. The function has an even degree and its leading coefficient is
negative.

2. The graph of a polynomial function of degree 4 is shown. Which statements are true?

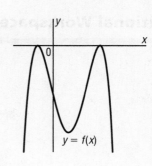

I. The function has an even degree.

II. The function has a zero of multiplicity 3.

III. The y-intercept is negative.

IV. The function is a quartic function.

A. I, II, IV   **B.** I, III, IV

C. I, II   **D.** I, III

Study Note

Generalize the rules for graphing polynomial functions of odd or even degree.

ANSWERS

Exercises

3. a) no   **b)** yes   **c)** yes   **d)** no   **e)** no   **4. a)** no   **b)** yes   **c)** no   **d)** yes

5. a) 5; odd; quintic; 1; 0   **b)** 3; odd; cubic; −3; −7   **c)** 4; even; quartic; −1; 5

8. a) B   **b)** D   **c)** A   **d)** C   **9. a)** −3, multiplicity 3

b) 2, multiplicity 2; −3, multiplicity 2   **c)** 1, multiplicity 4; −0.5, multiplicity 1

d) 4, multiplicity 3; −1, multiplicity 2   **11. b)** yes

13. $y = -3x^3 + 12x^2 - 3x - 18$ **16. a)** $-54 < b < 54$ **b)** $b > 54$ or $b < -54$

Multiple Choice

1. C   **2.** B

Additional Workspace

1.5

Modelling and Solving Problems with Polynomial Functions

FOCUS Analyze the graph of a polynomial function to solve a problem.

Get Started

This graph represents the path of a ball kicked into the air.

What was the maximum height of the ball?

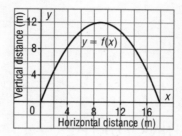

How far had the ball travelled horizontally when it reached this height?

What total horizontal distance did the ball travel?

Construct Understanding

Use graphing technology.

A certain airline's regulations state that the sum of the length, width, and depth of a piece of carry-on luggage must not exceed 100 cm. Several models of carry-on luggage have length 10 cm greater than their depth.

Write a polynomial function to represent the volume of this luggage. Graph the function.

To the nearest cubic centimetre, what is the maximum possible volume of this luggage? What are its dimensions to the nearest tenth of a centimetre? What assumptions did you make?

THINK FURTHER

In the problem above, suppose the sum of the length, width, and depth was halved. Would the maximum volume also be halved? Explain.

Polynomial functions and their graphs can be used to solve real-world problems.

Example 1	Using the Graph of a Cubic Function to Solve a Problem

A piece of sheet metal 25 cm long and 18 cm wide is used to make a box with no lid. Equal squares of side length x centimetres are cut from the corners and the sides are folded up.

a) Write a polynomial function to represent the volume, V, of the box in terms of x.
b) Graph the function. What is the domain?
c) To the nearest cubic centimetre, what is the maximum volume of the box? What size of square should be cut out to create a box with this volume? To the nearest tenth of a centimetre, what are the dimensions of the box?

DO NOT COPY. ©P

SOLUTION

a) Sketch a diagram.
The box has height x centimetres, width $(18 - 2x)$ centimetres, and length $(25 - 2x)$ centimetres.
So, a polynomial function that represents the volume, V, of the box is: $V(x) = x(18 - 2x)(25 - 2x)$

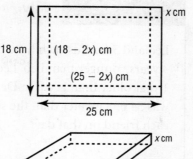

b) Graph the function. What is the domain?

c) To the nearest cubic centimetre, what is the maximum volume of the box? What size of square should be cut out to create a box with this volume? To the nearest tenth of a centimetre, what are the dimensions of the box?

b) Use a graphing calculator. Enter the equation:
$y = x(18 - 2x)(25 - 2x)$
The dimensions of the box are positive.
The sheet metal has width 18 cm.
So, the side length of a square cut from each corner must be less than $\frac{18 \text{ cm}}{2}$, or 9 cm.
So, the domain is: $0 < x < 9$
Use these window settings:

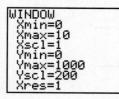 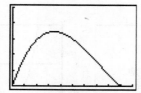

c) To determine the maximum volume, press: [2nd] [TRACE] [4], then use the arrow keys to move the cursor to determine the approximate coordinates of the local maximum point.

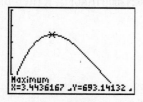

So, the maximum volume of the box is approximately 693 cm³.
This occurs when each square that is cut out has a side length of approximately 3.4 cm.
The approximate dimensions of the box are:
Height: 3.4 cm
Width: 18 cm − 2(3.4 cm) = 11.2 cm
Length: 25 cm − 2(3.4 cm) = 18.2 cm
So, for maximum volume, the dimensions of the box are approximately 18.2 cm by 11.2 cm by 3.4 cm.

Example 2 **Using the Graph of a Quartic Function to Solve a Problem**

2. Clara and 3 friends were born on March 11. Lesley is 5 years younger than Clara. Mike is 2 years younger than Clara. Thomas is 3 years older than Clara. On March 11, 2011, the product of their ages was 61 136 greater than the sum of their ages. How old was Clara and each friend on that day?

Leo and 3 friends each have birthdays on December 13. Sanda is 3 years younger than Leo. Leo is 4 years younger than Vince. Hunter is 1 year older than Leo. On December 13, 2010, the product of their ages was 54 658 greater than the sum of their ages. How old was Leo and each friend on that day?

SOLUTION

Let Leo's age in years be x.

Then, Sanda's age in years is $x - 3$, Vince's age in years is $x + 4$, and Hunter's age in years is $x + 1$. The sum of their ages is:

$x + (x - 3) + (x + 4) + (x + 1) = 4x + 2$

Sum of ages + 54 658 = product of ages

So, $4x + 2 + 54\,658 = x(x - 3)(x + 4)(x + 1)$

$0 = x(x - 3)(x + 4)(x + 1) - 4x - 54\,660$

Enter the equation $y = x(x - 3)(x + 4)(x + 1) - 4x - 54\,660$ into a graphing calculator. Graph the function using these window settings:

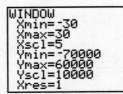 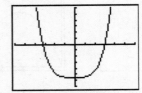

Since age cannot be negative, the positive x-intercept of the graph represents Leo's age.

To determine the positive x-intercept, press: [2nd] [TRACE] [2], then use the arrow keys. The x-intercept is 15.

So, Leo was 15 years old on that day.

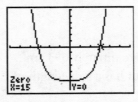

The ages of the other friends, in years, were: Sanda: $15 - 3 = 12$

Vince: $15 + 4 = 19$

Hunter: $15 + 1 = 16$

On December 13, 2010, Leo was 15, Sanda was 12, Vince was 19, and Hunter was 16.

Discuss the Ideas

1. Why might the domain and range of a polynomial function differ from the domain and range of a function that models a situation using the same polynomial?

2. When you use a graphing calculator to graph a polynomial function, how do you determine the window settings?

Exercises

Use technology to graph the functions.

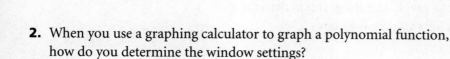

3. A box has length $(x + 2)$ units, width $(x - 5)$ units, and height $(2x + 3)$ units. Write a polynomial function to represent its volume, V, in terms of x.

1.5 Modelling and Solving Problems with Polynomial Functions |

4. a) Write a polynomial function to represent the volume, V, of this square prism in terms of x.

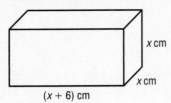

x cm
x cm
$(x + 6)$ cm

b) Graph the function. Sketch the graph. Use the graph to determine the dimensions of the prism if its volume is 81 cm³.

B

5. A piece of cardboard 36 cm long and 28 cm wide is used to make an open box. Equal squares of side length x centimetres are cut from the corners and the sides are folded up.

a) Write expressions to represent the length, width, and height of the box in terms of x.

b) Write a polynomial function to represent the volume of the box in terms of x.

c) Graph the function. Sketch the graph. What is the domain?

d) What is the maximum volume of the box? What is the side length of the square that should be cut out to create a box with this volume? Give your answers to the nearest tenth.

6. The volume, in cubic centimetres, of an expandable gift box can be represented by the polynomial function $V(x) = -x^3 + 35x^2 + 200x$. The height of the box in centimetres is $40 - x$. Assume the length is greater than the width.

    a) Determine binomial expressions for the length and width of the box in terms of x.

    b) Graph the function. Sketch the graph. What do the x-intercepts represent?

    c) To the nearest cubic centimetre, what is the maximum volume of the gift box?

7. Fred and Ted are twins. They were born 3 years after their older sister, Bethany. This year, the product of their three ages is 5726 greater than the sum of their ages. How old are the twins?

8. Ann, Stan, and Fran are triplets. They were born 4 years before their sister, Kim. This year, the product of their four ages is 49 092 greater than the sum of their ages. How old is Kim?

9. A carton of juice has dimensions 6.4 cm by 3.8 cm by 10.9 cm. The manufacturer wants to design a box with double the capacity by increasing each dimension by x centimetres. To the nearest tenth of a centimetre, what are the dimensions of the larger carton?

10. A package sent by a courier has the shape of a square prism. The sum of the length of the prism and the perimeter of its base is 100 cm.

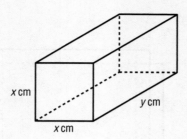

a) Write a polynomial function to represent the volume V of the package in terms of x.

b) Graph the function. Sketch the graph.

c) To the nearest tenth of a centimetre, what are the dimensions of the package for which its volume is maximized?

C

11. An open box with locking tabs is to be made from a square piece of cardboard with side length 28 cm. This is done by cutting equal squares of side length x centimetres from the corners and folding along the dotted lines as shown.

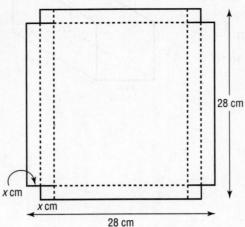

28 cm

x cm

x cm

28 cm

a) Write a polynomial function to represent the volume, V, of the box in terms of x.

b) Graph the function. Sketch the graph. State the domain.

c) To the nearest centimetre, what is the value of x for the box with maximum volume?

12. A manufacturer designs a cylindrical can with no top. The surface area of the can is 300 cm^2. The can has base radius r centimetres.

a) Write a polynomial function to model the capacity, C cubic centimetres, of the can as a function of r.

b) Graph the function. Sketch the graph. To the nearest tenth of a centimetre, what are the radius and height of the can when it has a maximum capacity?

Multiple-Choice Questions

1. A box has the shape of a rectangular prism. The height of the box is x centimetres. The length of the box is $4x$ centimetres. The sum of its length, width, and height is 18 cm. What is a polynomial function that represents the volume, V, of the box?

A. $V(x) = x(4x)(18 - 5x)$ **B.** $V(x) = x(4x)(18 - 4x)$

C. $V(x) = x(4x)(18 - x)$ **D.** $V(x) = x(18 - 4x)(18 - 5x)$

2. Here is the graph of $y = 250x - \pi x^3$. Suppose y is the volume of a closed cylindrical can with radius x centimetres and surface area 500 cm^2. Which statements are correct?

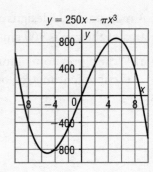

I. The maximum volume is approximately 858 cm^3.

II. The minimum volume is approximately -858 cm^3.

III. The volume is 0 when x is approximately 9 cm.

IV. The can has no maximum volume.

A. I and II   **B.** I and III

C. I and IV   **D.** II and IV

Study Note

Which characteristics of the graph of a polynomial function may be used to solve a problem, involving volume, that is modelled by a polynomial function?

ANSWERS

Check Your Understanding

1. a) $V(x) = x(25 - 2x)(30 - 2x)$ **b)** $0 < x < 12.5$ **c)** 1512 cm^3; 4.5 cm; 21.0 cm by 16.0 cm by 4.5 cm   **2.** In years: Clara: 17; Lesley: 12; Mike: 15; Thomas: 20

Exercises

3. $V(x) = (x + 2)(x - 5)(2x + 3)$ **4. a)** $V(x) = x^2(x + 6)$
b) 3 cm by 3 cm by 9 cm   **5. a)** height: x centimetres; length: $(36 - 2x)$ centimetres; width: $(28 - 2x)$ centimetres   **b)** $V(x) = x(36 - 2x)(28 - 2x)$ **c)** $0 < x < 14$
d) approximately 2342.9 cm^3; approximately 5.2 cm
6. a) length: $(x + 5)$ centimetres; width: x centimetres
c) approximately 11 284 cm^3 **7.** 17 years old   **8.** 12 years old
9. 8.0 cm by 5.4 cm by 12.5 cm   **10. a)** $V(x) = 4x^2(25 - x)$
c) approximately 16.7 cm by 16.7 cm by 33.3 cm   **11. a)** $V(x) = 8x(7 - x)(14 - x)$
b) $0 < x < 7$ **c)** 3 cm   **12. a)** $C(r) = \dfrac{300r - \pi r^3}{2}$ **b)** radius = height $\doteq$ 5.6 cm

Multiple Choice
1. A   **2.** B

Concept Summary

Big Ideas	Applying the Big Ideas
• Some polynomials can be factored by using long division.	This means that: • Polynomials can be divided by other polynomials. • When a polynomial P(x) is divided by a binomial of the form $x - a$, $a \in \mathbb{Z}$, the remainder is P(a). • A binomial is a factor of a polynomial when the division results in a remainder of 0.
• The zeros of a polynomial function or the x-intercepts of its graph can be determined by solving the corresponding polynomial equation.	• When a polynomial can be factored, the zeros of the related polynomial function or the x-intercepts of its graph can be determined by equating each factor to 0. • The behaviour of the graph of a polynomial function at its x-intercepts depends on the multiplicity of each zero of the function: – When a zero has even multiplicity, the graph just touches the x-axis at the related x-intercept. – When a zero has odd multiplicity, the graph crosses the x-axis at the related x-intercept.

Chapter Study Notes

• What do you need to remember when you divide a polynomial by a binomial?

• What characteristics of the graph of a polynomial function can be determined from its equation?

Skills Summary

Skill	Description	Example
Divide a polynomial by a binomial of the form $x - a$, $a \in \mathbb{Z}$. **(1.1)**	To divide using synthetic division, remove the variables and record only the coefficients. Include a 0 for any term that is not included in the polynomial.	Divide $4x^3 - 13x + 9$ by $x + 2$. $\begin{array}{r\|rrrr} -2 & 4 & 0 & -13 & 9 \\ & & -8 & 16 & -6 \\ \hline & 4 & -8 & 3 & 3 \end{array}$ So, $(4x^3 - 13x + 9) \div (x + 2)$ $= 4x^2 - 8x + 3$ R3
Use the remainder and factor theorems, and the factor property to factor a polynomial. **(1.2)**	If $x - a$ is a factor of a polynomial, then a is a factor of the constant term in the polynomial. The binomial $x - a$ is a factor of $P(x)$ if $P(a) = 0$.	Determine a binomial factor of $P(x) = 8x^3 + 6x^2 - 11x - 3$ The factors of -3 are: $1, -1, 3, -3$ Try $x = 1$: $P(1) = 8(1)^3 + 6(1)^2 - 11(1) - 3$ $\quad = 0$ So, $x - 1$ is a factor.
Sketch the graph of a polynomial function. **(1.4)**	In the equation of a polynomial function, the leading coefficient determines the end behaviour of the graph and the constant term is the y-intercept of the graph. The zeros of the function are the x-intercepts of the graph. The multiplicity of a zero determines the behaviour of the graph at the related x-intercept.	Sketch a graph of $f(x) = (x + 2)^2(x - 2)$. x-intercepts: $-2, 2$ The zero -2 has multiplicity 2; the graph just touches the x-axis at $x = -2$. The zero 2 has multiplicity 1; the graph crosses the x-axis at $x = 2$. The equation has degree 3, so it is an odd-degree polynomial function. The leading coefficient is positive, so as $x \to -\infty$, the graph falls and as $x \to \infty$, the graph rises. The constant term is -8, so the y-intercept is -8. $f(x) = (x + 2)^2(x - 2)$ *(graph showing curve with x-intercepts at −2 and 2, y-intercept at −8)*
Solve a problem by analyzing the graph of a polynomial function. **(1.5)**	Write a polynomial function to model the situation, then graph the function and analyze the graph to solve the problem.	A rectangular prism has width x metres, length $(x + 2)$ metres, and height $(x + 5)$ metres. What are the dimensions of a prism with volume 120 m³? A polynomial function that models the volume is: $y = x(x + 2)(x + 5)$ Graph the function and $y = 120$. Determine the x-coordinate of the point of intersection: $(3, 120)$ The prism has dimensions 3 m by 5 m by 8 m.

1.1

1. Use long division to divide $7x^3 + 6x^4 - 7x - 9x^2 + 8$ by $x - 1$.
   Write the division statement.

2. Use synthetic division to divide. Write the division statement.

   a) $(2x^2 - 2x + x^3 - 3x^4 + 5) \div (x - 1)$

   b) $(-x^4 + 4x^5 - 16 - 4x) \div (1 + x)$

1.2

3. Determine the remainder when $x^4 - x^3 - 11x^2 + 9x + 18$ is divided by each binomial. Which binomials are factors of the polynomial? How do you know?

a) $x + 2$

b) $x + 3$

4. For each polynomial, determine one factor of the form $x - a, a \in \mathbb{Z}$.

a) $4x^3 - 5x^2 - 23x + 6$

b) $9x^4 - 37x^2 + 4$

5. Factor: $x^3 - 5x^2 - 2x + 24$

6. a) For each polynomial function below, predict the end behaviour of the graph. Justify your prediction, then use graphing technology to check.

   i) $g(x) = -2x^3 + 5x^2 - 8$

   ii) $h(x) = -x^4 + 2x^3 - 5x^2 + 9$

   iii) $k(x) = x^4 - 2x^3 + 5x^2 - 9$

b) What do you notice about the graphs and equations of the functions in part a, ii and iii?

7. Match each function to its graph. Justify your choices.

a) $y = x^4 - x^2 - 25x - 12$

b) $y = -x^4 + 8x^3 - 23x^2 + 28x - 12$

c) $y = x^5 - 3x^2 + 5$

d) $y = -x^3 + 2x + 5$

i) Graph A

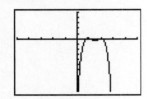

ii) Graph B

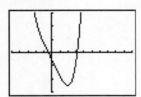

iii) Graph C

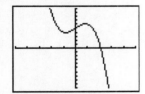

iv) Graph D

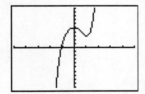

8. Sketch the graph of each polynomial function.

  a) $g(x) = -x^4 - 3x^3 + 11x^2 + 3x - 10$

  b) $f(x) = (x - 3)(x - 1)(x + 2)^2$

9. A piece of cardboard 26 cm long and 20 cm wide is used to make a gift box that has a top. The diagram shows the net for the box. The shaded parts are discarded. The squares cut from each corner have side length x centimetres. What is the maximum volume of the box? What is the side length of the square that should be cut out to create a box with this volume? Give your answers to the nearest tenth.

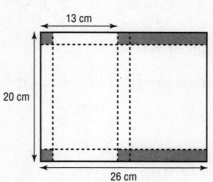

ANSWERS

1. $6x^4 + 7x^3 - 9x^2 - 7x + 8 = (x - 1)(6x^3 + 13x^2 + 4x - 3) + 5$

2. a) $-3x^4 + x^3 + 2x^2 - 2x + 5 = (x - 1)(-3x^3 - 2x^2 - 2) + 3$

b) $4x^5 - x^4 - 4x - 16 = (x + 1)(4x^4 - 5x^3 + 5x^2 - 5x + 1) - 17$

3. a) -20 **b)** 0 **4. a)** $x + 2$ or $x - 3$ **b)** $x - 2$ or $x + 2$

5. $x^3 - 5x^2 - 2x + 24 = (x - 4)(x - 3)(x + 2)$ **7. a)** B   **b)** A   **c)** D   **d)** C

9. approximately 433.6 cm^3; approximately 3.7 cm

1. **Multiple Choice** Which statement is true?

   A. When $2x^3 + 4x^2 - 2x - 1$ is divided by $x - 2$, the remainder is 3.

   B. The binomial $x + 1$ is a factor of $4x^4 - x^3 - 3x + 2$.

   C. When $2x^4 - 7x^3 + 6x^2 - 14x + 20$ is divided by $x - 3$, the remainder is -5.

   D. The binomial $x + 2$ is a factor of $5x^3 + 7x^2 + 12$.

2. **Multiple Choice** Which statement about the graph of a quartic function is false?

   A. The graph may open up.

   B. The graph may have a zero of multiplicity 3.

   C. The graph may fall to the left and rise to the right.

   D. The graph may have a zero of multiplicity 2.

3. Divide $2x^4 + 11x^3 - 10 - 5x + 14x^2$ by $x + 2$. Write the division statement.

4. Does the polynomial $x^4 - x^3 - 14x^2 + x + 16$ have a factor of $x + 3$? How do you know?

5. Factor: $4x^4 - 20x^3 + 17x^2 + 26x - 15$

6. Sketch the graph of this polynomial function.

$$g(x) = 4x^4 + 11x^3 - 7x^2 - 11x + 3$$

7. Canada Post defines a small packet as one for which the sum of its length, width, and height is less than or equal to 90 cm. A company produces several different small packets, each with length 15 cm longer than its height.

    a) Write a polynomial function to represent possible volumes of one of these packets in terms of its height x. Assume the sum of the dimensions is maximized.

    b) Graph the function.

    c) To the nearest cubic centimetre, what is the maximum possible volume of one of these packets? What are its dimensions to the nearest tenth of a centimetre?

ANSWERS

1. D   **2.** C   **3.** $2x^4 + 11x^3 + 14x^2 - 5x - 10 = (x + 2)(2x^3 + 7x^2 - 5)$

4. no   **5.** $(x + 1)(x - 3)(2x - 5)(2x - 1)$ **7. a)** $V(x) = x(x + 15)(75 - 2x)$

c) 25 347 cm³; 38.1 cm by 28.8 cm by 23.1 cm

2 Radical and Rational Functions

BUILDING ON

- graphing polynomial functions
- solving radical and rational equations algebraically
- simplifying rational expressions

BIG IDEAS

- The graph of a function, $y = f(x)$, can be used to graph the corresponding radical function, $y = \sqrt{f(x)}$.
- For the graph of a rational function, $y = \dfrac{f(x)}{g(x)}$, the non-permissible values of x correspond to vertical asymptotes or holes.
- The roots of a rational equation or radical equation are the x-intercepts of the graph of a corresponding function.

LEADING TO

- curve sketching using calculus

NEW VOCABULARY

radical function	rational function
invariant point	oblique (slant) asymptote

2.1 Properties of Radical Functions

FOCUS Graph and analyze radical functions, and solve radical equations.

Get Started

What are the domain and range of each function?

$y = 3x - 2$

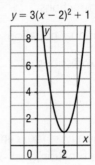

$y = 3(x - 2)^2 + 1$

Construct Understanding

> Complete the table of values for $y = x$ and $y = \sqrt{x}$.
> Sketch a graph of each function, then state its domain and range.
> When is the graph of $y = \sqrt{x}$ above the graph of $y = x$?
> When is it below?
> Suppose you are given the graph of $y = x$.
> How could you use it to graph $y = \sqrt{x}$?

x	−4	−3	−2	−1	−0.25	0	0.25	1	2	3	4
$y = x$											
$y = \sqrt{x}$											

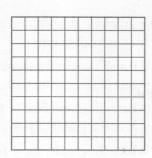

A **radical function** has the form $y = \sqrt{f(x)}$, where $f(x)$ is a function.
The square root of a number is only defined for non-negative numbers,
so the domain of $y = \sqrt{f(x)}$ is the set of values of x for which $f(x) \geq 0$.

Here is the graph of $y = \sqrt{x}$.
The domain of $y = \sqrt{x}$ is $x \geq 0$ and the
range is $y \geq 0$.
The graph starts at the origin and extends
in only one direction.

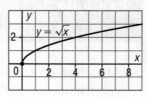

Here are the graphs of two linear functions and their related radical
functions.

$y = x + 4$ and $y = \sqrt{x + 4}$

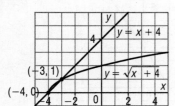

$y = -x + 2$ and $y = \sqrt{-x + 2}$

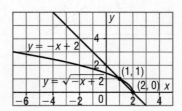

The points $(-4, 0)$ and $(-3, 1)$ lie
on both graphs. Between these
points, the graph of $y = \sqrt{x + 4}$
lies above the graph of $y = x + 4$.
Since $x + 4 \geq 0$
then $x \geq -4$
So, the domain of $y = \sqrt{x + 4}$
is $x \geq -4$; and the range is $y \geq 0$.
The graph of $y = \sqrt{x + 4}$ opens
to the right.

The points $(1, 1)$ and $(2, 0)$ lie on
both graphs. Between these points,
the graph of $y = \sqrt{-x + 2}$ lies
above the graph of $y = -x + 2$.
Since $-x + 2 \geq 0$
then $x \leq 2$
So, the domain of $y = \sqrt{-x + 2}$
is $x \leq 2$; and the range is $y \geq 0$.
The graph of $y = \sqrt{-x + 2}$
opens to the left.

The graphs at the bottom of page 83 illustrate characteristics that are common to all graphs of $y = f(x)$ and $y = \sqrt{f(x)}$.

- If 0 and 1 are in the range of $y = f(x)$, then points with these y-coordinates lie on both graphs; these are **invariant points**.
- Where the graph of $y = f(x)$ lies between the graph of $y = 1$ and the x-axis, the graph of $y = \sqrt{f(x)}$ lies above the graph of $y = f(x)$.
- Where the graph of $y = f(x)$ lies above the graph of $y = 1$, the graph of $y = \sqrt{f(x)}$ lies below the graph of $y = f(x)$.
- Where the graph of $y = f(x)$ lies below the x-axis, the graph of $y = \sqrt{f(x)}$ does not exist.

These characteristics can be used to sketch a graph of $y = \sqrt{f(x)}$ when the graph of $y = f(x)$ is given.

THINK FURTHER

Why does the graph of $y = \sqrt{f(x)}$ lie above the graph of $y = f(x)$ between the invariant points?

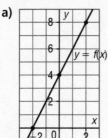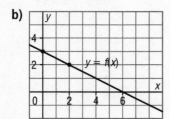

Example 1	Sketching the Graph of $y = \sqrt{f(x)}$ Given the Graph of a Linear Function $y = f(x)$

For each graph of $y = f(x)$ below:
- Sketch the graph of $y = \sqrt{f(x)}$.
- State the domain and range of $y = \sqrt{f(x)}$.

a)
b)

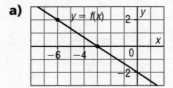

SOLUTION

a) From the graph:
$f(x) \geq 0$ for all values of $x \leq -3$,
so the domain of $y = \sqrt{f(x)}$ is $x \leq -3$.
Mark the points where $y = 0$ or $y = 1$;
the graph of $y = \sqrt{f(x)}$ lies above the graph of $y = f(x)$ between these points. Identify the coordinates of another point that lies above the x-axis on the graph of $y = \sqrt{f(x)}$:

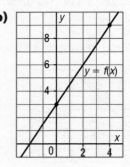

x	$y = f(x)$	$y = \sqrt{f(x)}$
-6	2	$\sqrt{2} \doteq 1.4$

Join the points with a smooth curve for the graph of $y = \sqrt{f(x)}$.
The range of $y = \sqrt{f(x)}$ is $y \geq 0$.

b) From the graph:

$f(x) \geq 0$ for all values of $x \geq -2$, so the domain of $y = \sqrt{f(x)}$ is $x \geq -2$.

Mark the points where $y = 0$ or $y = 1$. Identify the coordinates of other points that lie above the x-axis on the graph of $y = \sqrt{f(x)}$:

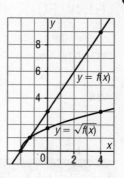

x	$y = f(x)$	$y = \sqrt{f(x)}$
0	3	$\sqrt{3} \doteq 1.7$
4	9	$\sqrt{9} = 3$

Join the points with a smooth curve for the graph of $y = \sqrt{f(x)}$. The range of $y = \sqrt{f(x)}$ is $y \geq 0$.

In *Example 1b*, the functions $y = f(x)$ and $y = \sqrt{f(x)}$ have different domains because the square root of a negative number is not defined; and, if $x < -2$, then $f(x)$ is negative and $\sqrt{f(x)}$ is not defined. The ranges are different because $\sqrt{f(x)}$ is the principal square root of $f(x)$, which is always 0 or positive.

Here are tables of values for and graphs of $y = x^2 + 1$ and $y = \sqrt{x^2 + 1}$.

x	$y = x^2 + 1$	$y = \sqrt{x^2 + 1}$
-3	10	$\sqrt{10} \doteq 3.2$
-2	5	$\sqrt{5} \doteq 2.2$
-1	2	$\sqrt{2} \doteq 1.4$
0	1	$\sqrt{1} = 1$
1	2	$\sqrt{2} \doteq 1.4$
2	5	$\sqrt{5} \doteq 2.2$
3	10	$\sqrt{10} \doteq 3.2$

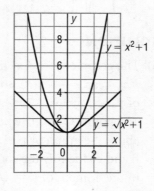

THINK FURTHER

Describe the graph of a linear function, $y = f(x)$, for which the graph of $y = \sqrt{f(x)}$ is a horizontal line, and $\sqrt{f(x)} > f(x)$ for all real values of x.

The domain of $y = x^2 + 1$ is $x \in \mathbb{R}$, and the range is $y \geq 1$.
The domain of $y = \sqrt{x^2 + 1}$ is $x \in \mathbb{R}$, and the range is $y \geq 1$.
The only invariant point is $(0, 1)$.

Consider the quadratic function $y = x^2 - 1$. Would the domain and range of this function be the same as the domain and range of $y = \sqrt{x^2 - 1}$?

Example 2	Sketching the Graph of $y = \sqrt{f(x)}$ Given the Graph of a Quadratic Function $y = f(x)$

2. For the graph of each quadratic function $y = f(x)$ below:
• Sketch the graph of $y = \sqrt{f(x)}$.
• State the domain and range of $y = \sqrt{f(x)}$.

a)
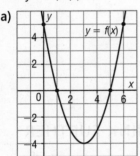

b)
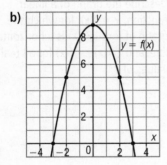

For the graph of each quadratic function $y = f(x)$ below:
• Sketch the graph of $y = \sqrt{f(x)}$.
• State the domain and range of $y = \sqrt{f(x)}$.

a)
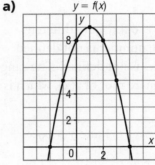

b)
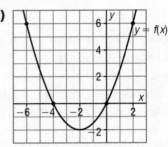

SOLUTION

a) The graph of $y = f(x)$ lies below the x-axis for $x < -2$ and for $x > 4$, so $y = \sqrt{f(x)}$ is undefined for these values of x. The domain of $y = \sqrt{f(x)}$ is $-2 \leq x \leq 4$. Mark points A and B where $y = 0$, and points C and D where $y = 1$. The graph of $y = \sqrt{f(x)}$ lies above the graph of $y = f(x)$ between A and C, and between B and D. Identify the coordinates of another point with x-coordinate in the domain of $y = \sqrt{f(x)}$.

x	$y = f(x)$	$y = \sqrt{f(x)}$
1	9	$\sqrt{9} = 3$

Join the points with a smooth curve for the graph of $y = \sqrt{f(x)}$.

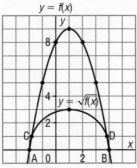

The range of $y = \sqrt{f(x)}$ is $0 \leq y \leq 3$.

b) The graph of $y = f(x)$ lies below the x-axis for $-4 < x < 0$, so $y = \sqrt{f(x)}$ is undefined for these values of x. The domain of $y = \sqrt{f(x)}$ is $x \leq -4$ or $x \geq 0$. Mark points A and B where $y = 0$ and points C and D where $y = 1$. The graph of $y = \sqrt{f(x)}$ lies above the graph of $y = f(x)$ between A and C, and between B and D. Identify the coordinates of other points with x-coordinates in the domain of $y = \sqrt{f(x)}$.

x	$y = f(x)$	$y = \sqrt{f(x)}$
-6	6	$\sqrt{6} \doteq 2.4$
2	6	$\sqrt{6} \doteq 2.4$

Join the points with two smooth curves for the graph of $y = \sqrt{f(x)}$.

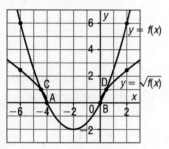

The range of $y = \sqrt{f(x)}$ is $y \geq 0$.

To sketch the graph of a radical function, it may not always be necessary to determine the coordinates of additional points beyond those with y-coordinates 0 and 1.

THINK FURTHER

The graph of a radical function $y = \sqrt{g(x)}$ is the point $(2, 0)$. What is an explicit equation for a possible quadratic function $y = g(x)$?

Example 3

Example 3 | **Sketching the Graph of $y = \sqrt{f(x)}$ Given the Graph of a Cubic Function $y = f(x)$**

3. For the graph of the cubic function $y = f(x)$:

- Sketch the graph of $y = \sqrt{f(x)}$.

- State the domain and range of $y = \sqrt{f(x)}$.

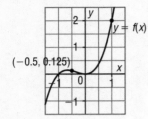

For the graph of the cubic function $y = f(x)$:

- Sketch the graph of $y = \sqrt{f(x)}$.
- State the domain and range of $y = \sqrt{f(x)}$.

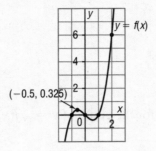

SOLUTION

The graph of $y = f(x)$ lies below the x-axis for $x < -1$ and for $0 < x < 1$, so the graph of $y = \sqrt{f(x)}$ is undefined for these values of x.

The domain of $y = \sqrt{f(x)}$ is $-1 \leq x \leq 0$ or $x \geq 1$.

Mark the three points where $y = 0$ and the point where $y = 1$.

Identify the coordinates of other points on the graph of $y = \sqrt{f(x)}$.

x	$y = f(x)$	$y = \sqrt{f(x)}$
-0.5	0.325	$\sqrt{0.325} \doteq 0.6$
2	6	$\sqrt{6} \doteq 2.4$

Join the points with two smooth curves for the graph of $y = \sqrt{f(x)}$.

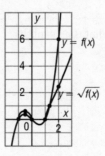

The range of $y = \sqrt{f(x)}$ is $y \geq 0$.

The graph of a radical function can be used to solve a related radical equation. The zeros of the graph are the roots of the equation.

Example 4 | Solving a Radical Equation Graphically

Use graphing technology to solve: $\sqrt{2x - 1} = x - 4$
Give the solution to the nearest tenth.

4. Use graphing technology to solve: $\sqrt{3x + 2} = -6 + x$
Give the solution to the nearest tenth.

SOLUTION

$\sqrt{2x - 1} = x - 4$
Move all the terms to one side of the equation.
$\sqrt{2x - 1} - x + 4 = 0$
Graph the related function:
$f(x) = \sqrt{2x - 1} - x + 4$
The solution of the equation $\sqrt{2x - 1} = x - 4$
is the zero of the related function; that is, the value
of x for which $f(x) = 0$.
Use the zero feature from the CALC menu to approximate the zero:
7.8284271
So, the solution of $\sqrt{2x - 1} = x - 4$ is: $x \doteq 7.8$

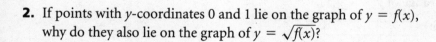

```
Zero
X=7.8284271   Y=0
```

Discuss the Ideas

1. Why is the function $y = \sqrt{f(x)}$ undefined for $f(x) < 0$?
Is the function $y = \sqrt[3]{f(x)}$ also undefined when $f(x) < 0$?

2. If points with y-coordinates 0 and 1 lie on the graph of $y = f(x)$,
why do they also lie on the graph of $y = \sqrt{f(x)}$?

3. What is the relationship between the roots of a radical equation and
the x-intercepts of the graph of the corresponding radical function?

Exercises

A

4. a) Complete the table of values.

x	−4	−2	−1	0	1	2	4
$y = -x$							
$y = \sqrt{-x}$							

b) For each function in part a, sketch its graph then state its domain and range.

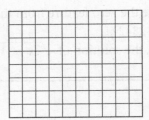

c) How are the graphs in part b related?

5. For each graph of $y = g(x)$ below:

   i) Mark points where $y = 0$ or $y = 1$.

   ii) Sketch the graph of $y = \sqrt{g(x)}$.

   iii) Identify the domain and range of $y = \sqrt{g(x)}$.

a)

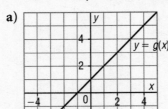

b)

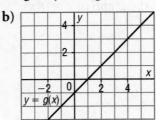

c)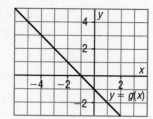

d)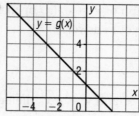

6. a) Use technology to graph each function. Sketch each graph.

    i) $y = \sqrt{2x + 3}$ **ii)** $y = \sqrt{-2x + 3}$

    iii) $y = \sqrt{-2x - 3}$ **iv)** $y = \sqrt{0.5x + 4}$

    v) $y = \sqrt{-0.5x - 4}$ **vi)** $y = \sqrt{0.5x - 4}$

  b) Given a linear function of the form $f(x) = ax + b, a, b \neq 0$

    i) For which values of a does the graph of $y = \sqrt{f(x)}$ open to the right? Use examples to support your answer.

ii) For which values of *a* does the graph of $y = \sqrt{f(x)}$ open to the left? Use examples to support your answer.

7. a) Complete this table of values for $y = x^2$ and $y = \sqrt{x^2}$, then graph the functions on the same grid.

x	−3	−2	−1	0	1	2	3
$y = x^2$							
$y = \sqrt{x^2}$							

b) What other function describes the graph of $y = \sqrt{x^2}$? Explain why.

8. a) For the graph of each quadratic function $y = f(x)$ below:
   • Sketch the graph of $y = \sqrt{f(x)}$.
   • State the domain and range of $y = \sqrt{f(x)}$.

   i)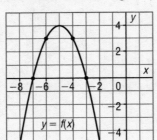

   ii)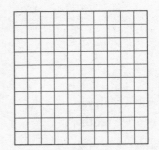

b) Choose one pair of functions $y = f(x)$ and $y = \sqrt{f(x)}$ from part a. If the domains are different and the ranges are different, explain why.

9. Solve each radical equation by graphing. Give the solution to the nearest tenth where necessary.

a) $x - 5 = 2\sqrt{x + 3}$

b) $x = \sqrt{4 - x} + 2$

c) $3\sqrt{2x + 1} = x + 4$

d) $1 + \sqrt{x - 3} = \sqrt{2x - 6}$

10. For the graph of each cubic function $y = g(x)$ below:
- Sketch the graph of $y = \sqrt{g(x)}$.
- State the domain and range of $y = \sqrt{g(x)}$.

a)

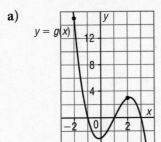

b)

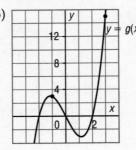

11. a) Sketch the graph of a linear function $y = g(x)$ for which $y = \sqrt{g(x)}$ is not defined. Explain how you know that $y = \sqrt{g(x)}$ is not defined.

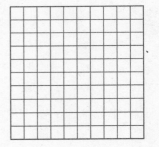

b) Sketch the graph of a quadratic function $y = f(x)$ for which $y = \sqrt{f(x)}$ is not defined. Explain how you know that $y = \sqrt{f(x)}$ is not defined.

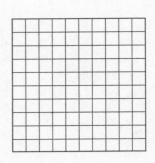

c) For every cubic function $y = g(x)$, the function $y = \sqrt{g(x)}$ exists. Explain why.

12. For each graph of $y = g(x)$, sketch the graph of $y = \sqrt{g(x)}$.

a)

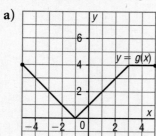

b)

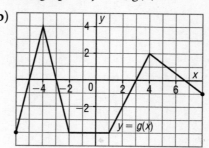

13. When a satellite is h kilometres above Earth, the time for one complete orbit, t minutes, can be calculated using this formula:
$$t = 1.66 \times 10^{-4}\sqrt{(h + 6370)^3}$$
A communications satellite is to be positioned so that it is always above the same point on Earth's surface. It takes 24 h for this satellite to complete one orbit. What should the height of the satellite be?

14. Given the graph of $y = f(x)$, sketch the graph of $y = \sqrt[3]{f(x)}$ without using graphing technology. What are the invariant points on the graph of $y = \sqrt[3]{f(x)}$?

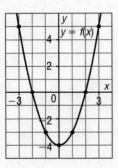

Multiple-Choice Questions

1. For the function $y = f(x)$ shown below, what are the domain and range of $y = \sqrt{f(x)}$?

   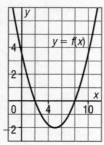

   A. domain: $2 \leq x \leq 8$;
   range: $y \geq 0$

   B. domain: $2 \leq x \leq 8$;
   range: $y > 0$

   C. domain: $x \leq 2$ or $x \geq 8$;
   range: $y \geq 0$

   D. domain $x \leq 2$ or $x \geq 8$;
   range: $y > 0$

2. For the function $y = f(x)$ shown below, which graph best represents $y = \sqrt{f(x)}$?

   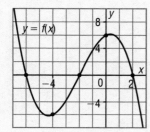

   A.

   B.

   C.

   D.

Study Note

Explain the strategy you use to sketch the graph of $y = \sqrt{f(x)}$, given the graph of $y = f(x)$. Illustrate your response using your choice of $f(x)$.

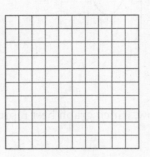

ANSWERS

Check Your Understanding

1. a) domain: $x \geq -2$; range: $y \geq 0$ **b)** domain: $x \leq 6$; range: $y \geq 0$
2. a) domain: $x \leq 1$ or $x \geq 5$; range: $y \geq 0$ **b)** domain: $-3 \leq x \leq 3$;
range: $0 \leq y \leq 3$ **3.** domain: $x \geq -1$; range: $y \geq 0$ **4.** $x \doteq 12.2$

Exercises

4. b) For $y = -x$, domain: $x \in \mathbb{R}$; range: $y \in \mathbb{R}$; for $y = \sqrt{-x}$, domain: $x \leq 0$;
range: $y \geq 0$ **5. a) iii)** domain: $x \geq -1$; range: $y \geq 0$
b) iii) domain: $x \geq 1$; range: $y \geq 0$ **c) iii)** domain: $x \leq -1$; range: $y \geq 0$
d) iii) domain: $x \leq 1$; range: $y \geq 0$ **6. b) i)** $a > 0$ **ii)** $a < 0$ **7. b)** $y = |x|$
8. a) i) domain: $-7 \leq x \leq -3$; range: $0 \leq y \leq 2$ **ii)** domain: $x \in \mathbb{R}$; range: $y \geq 2$
9. a) $x = 13$ **b)** $x = 3$ **c)** $x \doteq 0.8, x \doteq 9.2$ **d)** $x \doteq 8.8$
10. a) domain: $x \leq -1$ or $1 \leq x \leq 3$; range: $y \geq 0$
b) domain: $-2 \leq x \leq 0$ or $x \geq 2$; range: $y \geq 0$ **13.** approximately 35 849 km
14. $y = 0, \pm 1$

Multiple Choice

1. C **2.** B

2.2 Graphing Rational Functions

FOCUS Use technology to investigate non-permissible values of rational functions.

Get Started

Explain why each graph below has asymptotes, and identify their equations.

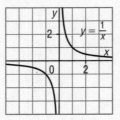

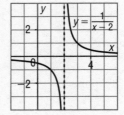

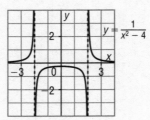

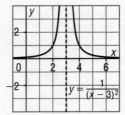

Construct Understanding

Use graphing technology.

A. Graph each function. Input brackets around a binomial or trinomial. For a graphing calculator, use these window settings: $-9.4 \le X \le 9.4$, and $-6.2 \le Y \le 6.2$.
Use the TABLE feature to check for any non-permissible values of x, and to examine the behaviour of the graph when $|x|$ is large. Complete the tables below.

Group I

Function	Sketch of graph	Vertical asymptotes	Horizontal asymptote	Non-permissible values of x
$y = \dfrac{x^2 - 1}{x + 1}$				
$y = \dfrac{x^2 + x - 2}{x + 2}$				
$y = \dfrac{x^2}{x - 1}$				
$y = \dfrac{x^2 + 2x + 1}{x + 2}$				
$y = \dfrac{2x^2 - 4x}{x - 2}$				

Group II

Function	Sketch of graph	Vertical asymptotes	Horizontal asymptote	Non-permissible values of x
$y = \dfrac{3x}{x - 1}$				
$y = \dfrac{x^2 - 1}{x^2 - 4}$				
$y = \dfrac{-2x + 4}{x - 1}$				

Group III

Function	Sketch of graph	Vertical asymptotes	Horizontal asymptote	Non-permissible values of x
$y = \dfrac{6}{x^2 + 2}$				
$y = \dfrac{2}{-x^2 + 2x + 3}$				
$y = \dfrac{4}{x^2}$				

$y = \dfrac{2x}{x^2}$				
$y = \dfrac{4x}{x^2 + 1}$				

B. Analyze the functions and their graphs in Part A.

- All the functions in Part A are **rational functions**. Why do you think this name is appropriate?

- For a rational function, how can you determine the non-permissible values of x from its graph?

- From the equation of a rational function, how can you tell whether its graph has an asymptote or a hole at a non-permissible value of x?

- From the equation of a rational function, how can you tell whether its graph has a horizontal asymptote?

THINK FURTHER

Determine an equation for a rational function whose graph lies on a horizontal line and has exactly 2 non-permissible values of x.

Assess Your Understanding

Use graphing technology to check your answers.

1. Without graphing, predict whether the graph of each function has a hole. State the related non-permissible value.

   a) $y = \dfrac{x^2 - 16}{x + 4}$

   b) $y = \dfrac{x^2 + 5}{x^2 - 25}$

2. Without graphing, predict the equations of any vertical asymptotes for the graph of each function.

   a) $y = \dfrac{2x + 1}{x}$

   b) $y = \dfrac{x^2 - 2}{x^2 - 16}$

   c) $y = \dfrac{3x}{x^2 + 2}$

   d) $y = \dfrac{x - 2}{x^2 + 7x + 10}$

3. Without graphing, predict which graphs of these functions have horizontal asymptotes.

   a) $y = \dfrac{x + 3}{2x^2 + 6x}$

   b) $y = \dfrac{2x^2 + 6x}{x + 3}$

ANSWERS

1. a) hole; $x = -4$ b) no holes   2. a) $x = 0$ b) $x = \pm 4$ d) $x = -2; x = -5$
3. The graph in part a has a horizontal asymptote.

FOCUS Determine the characteristics of the graphs of rational functions, and solve rational equations.

Get Started

Identify the equations of the asymptotes of the graph of this rational function. What are the domain and range of the function?

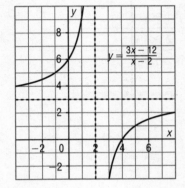

$$y = \frac{3x - 12}{x - 2}$$

Construct Understanding

Use graphing technology.

For a TI-83 Plus or TI-84 graphing calculator, set the WINDOW to $-9.4 \le X \le 9.4$ and $-6.2 \le Y \le 6.2$. If your calculator is different, set it to show holes.

Graph each function, then sketch it.

Complete each table of values.

Identify the non-permissible values of x, and describe the graph near these values.

Determine the equation of any horizontal asymptote, and describe the graph near the asymptote.

$$y = \frac{x^2 - 4}{x - 2}$$

x	y
1.9	
1.99	
1.999	
2.001	
2.01	
2.1	

$$y = \frac{x - 4}{x - 2}$$

x	y
1.9	
1.99	
1.999	
2.001	
2.01	
2.1	

x	y
−1000	
−100	
−50	
50	
100	
1000	

Rational Function

A *rational function* has the form $y = \frac{f(x)}{g(x)}$, where $f(x)$ and $g(x)$ are polynomial functions, and $g(x) \neq 0$.

The characteristics of the graph of a rational function can be determined from an equation of the function.

Characteristic 1: Non-permissible values of *x*

Consider the function

$$y = \frac{x + 3}{(x - 3)(x + 1)}$$

Since the denominator cannot be 0, $x \neq 3$ and $x \neq -1$
The numerator and denominator have no common factors, so there are vertical asymptotes at $x = 3$ and at $x = -1$.

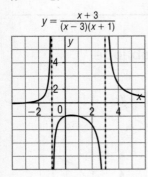

Consider the function

$$y = \frac{(x - 3)(x + 1)}{x - 3}$$

Since the denominator cannot be 0, $x \neq 3$
The numerator and denominator have a common factor $(x - 3)$, so the equation can be simplified and written as:
$y = x + 1, x \neq 3$
The graph is the line $y = x + 1$, with a hole at $x = 3$.

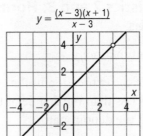

THINK FURTHER

Would the graph of the function $y = \frac{(x - 3)^2(x + 1)}{x - 3}$ have an asymptote or a hole at $x = 3$?

Note that $y = \dfrac{(x + 3)(x - 3)}{(x - 3)^2(x + 1)}$ can be simplified as $y = \dfrac{x + 3}{(x - 3)(x + 1)}$, and the graphs of the functions are identical. In $y = \dfrac{(x + 3)(x - 3)}{(x - 3)^2(x + 1)}$, the denominator has a greater power of $(x - 3)$ than the numerator, so the graph has an asymptote at $x = 3$, and not a hole.

Example 1	Identifying Non-Permissible Values

Use the equation of each function to predict whether its graph has vertical asymptotes or holes. Use graphing technology to verify.

a) $y = \dfrac{x^2}{9 - x^2}$

b) $y = \dfrac{x^2 - x - 2}{x + 1}$

SOLUTION

a) $y = \dfrac{x^2}{9 - x^2}$

The function is undefined when:
$$9 - x^2 = 0$$
$$x^2 = 9$$
$$x = \pm 3$$

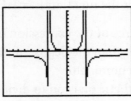

The non-permissible values are $x = 3$ and $x = -3$.
Since the numerator and denominator have no common factors, the graph has vertical asymptotes at $x = -3$ and $x = 3$.

Check Your Understanding

1. Use the equation of each function to predict whether its graph has vertical asymptotes or holes. Use graphing technology to verify.

a) $y = \dfrac{x^2 - 25}{x + 5}$

b) $y = \dfrac{4x + 2}{x - 2}$

b) $y = \dfrac{x^2 - x - 2}{x + 1}$

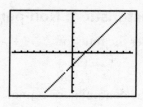

The function is undefined when:

$x + 1 = 0$

$x = -1$

Factor the numerator.

$y = \dfrac{(x + 1)(x - 2)}{x + 1}$

Since $(x + 1)$ is a common factor, the equation can be written as:

$y = x - 2, x \neq -1$

The graph has a hole at $x = -1$.

THINK FURTHER

Suppose the graph of a rational function has the shape of a parabola with a hole.
What is an equation of a possible function and what are the coordinates of the hole?

Characteristics 2 and 3: Horizontal and oblique asymptotes

Consider the function: $y = \dfrac{-4}{x + 4}$

The degree of the expression in the numerator is less than the degree of the expression in the denominator.
So, as $|x| \to \infty$, $y \to 0$, and the graph has a horizontal asymptote at $y = 0$.

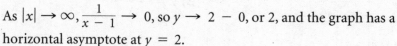

Consider the function: $y = \dfrac{2x - 3}{x - 1}$

The expressions in the numerator and the denominator have the same degree.
Use synthetic division to divide.

```
1  | 2    -3
   |       2
   ‾‾‾‾‾‾‾‾‾‾
     2    -1
```

The quotient is 2 and the remainder is -1.
The remainder can be written as a fraction of the divisor, so $y = \dfrac{2x - 3}{x - 1}$ can be written as $y = 2 - \dfrac{1}{x - 1}$.

As $|x| \to \infty$, $\dfrac{1}{x - 1} \to 0$, so $y \to 2 - 0$, or 2, and the graph has a horizontal asymptote at $y = 2$.

Consider the function $y = \dfrac{x^2}{x + 1}$.

The degree of the expression in the numerator is greater than the degree of the expression in the denominator.
Use synthetic division to divide.

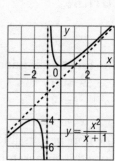

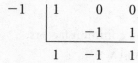

```
-1 | 1     0     0
   |      -1     1
   ‾‾‾‾‾‾‾‾‾‾‾‾‾‾‾‾
     1    -1     1
```

The quotient is $x - 1$ and the remainder is 1.

The remainder can be written as a fraction of the divisor, so $y = \dfrac{x^2}{x + 1}$

can be written as $y = x - 1 + \dfrac{1}{x + 1}$.

As $|x| \to \infty$, $\dfrac{1}{x + 1} \to 0$, so $y \to x - 1 + 0$, or $x - 1$, and the graph

has an *oblique asymptote* with equation $y = x - 1$.

An **oblique** (or **slant**) **asymptote** is an oblique line that a graph
approaches as $|x|$ becomes very large.

Horizontal and Oblique Asymptotes

The graph of a rational function $y = \dfrac{f(x)}{g(x)}$, where $f(x)$ and $g(x)$ have
no common factors, has:

- a horizontal asymptote at $y = 0$ if the degree of $f(x)$ is less than
  the degree of $g(x)$;

- a horizontal asymptote at $y = \dfrac{a}{b}$, where a is the leading coefficient
  of $f(x)$, and b is the leading coefficient of $g(x)$, if the degrees of
  $f(x)$ and $g(x)$ are equal;

- an oblique asymptote if the degree of $f(x)$ is 1 more than the
  degree of $g(x)$.

Example 2	Identifying Horizontal and Oblique Asymptotes

Use the equation of each function to predict whether its graph has
horizontal or oblique asymptotes. Write the equations of these
asymptotes. Use graphing technology to verify.

a) $y = \dfrac{x}{9 - x^2}$ **b)** $y = \dfrac{-x^2 + 4}{x - 3}$

SOLUTION

a) $y = \dfrac{x}{9 - x^2}$

The degree of the numerator is less than the degree of the
denominator.

So, there is a horizontal asymptote with equation $y = 0$.

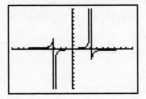

Check Your Understanding

2. Use the equation of each
   function to predict whether its
   graph has horizontal or oblique
   asymptotes. Write the
   equations of these asymptotes.
   Use graphing technology to
   verify.

   a) $y = \dfrac{x^2 + 6x - 7}{x + 2}$

   b) $y = \dfrac{x + 2}{x^2 + 6x - 7}$

b) $y = \dfrac{-x^2 + 4}{x - 3}$

There are no common factors. Since the degree of the numerator is 1 more than the degree of the denominator, there is an oblique asymptote.

Determine: $(-x^2 + 4) \div (x - 3)$

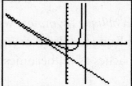

$$
\begin{array}{r|rrr}
3 & -1 & 0 & 4 \\
  &   & -3 & -9 \\
\hline
  & -1 & -3 & -5
\end{array}
$$

The quotient is $-x - 3$ and the remainder is -5.

The function can be written as: $y = -x - 3 - \dfrac{5}{x - 3}$

As $|x| \to \infty$, $\dfrac{5}{x - 3} \to 0$, so $y \to -x - 3 - 0$, or $-x - 3$, and the graph has an oblique asymptote with equation $y = -x - 3$.

Check Your Understanding

3. For the graph of each function below

　i) Determine any non-permissible values of x, and whether each indicates a hole or a vertical asymptote.

　ii) Determine the equations of any horizontal or oblique asymptotes.

　iii) Determine the domain.

Use graphing technology to verify the characteristics.

a) $y = \dfrac{x - 4}{x^2 - 4}$

b) $y = \dfrac{x^2 - 4}{x^2 - 9}$

Example 3　Identifying the Characteristics of the Graph of a Rational Function

For the graph of each function below

　i) Determine any non-permissible values of x, and whether each indicates a hole or a vertical asymptote.

　ii) Determine the equations of any horizontal or oblique asymptotes.

　iii) Determine the domain.

Use graphing technology to verify the characteristics.

a) $y = \dfrac{x^2 + x - 2}{x + 1}$　　　　　**b)** $y = \dfrac{x^2 - 3x + 2}{1 - x^2}$

SOLUTION

a) $y = \dfrac{x^2 + x - 2}{x + 1}$

　i) The function is undefined when:

　　$x + 1 = 0$

　　　　$x = -1$

　　The non-permissible value is $x = -1$.

　　Factor the numerator.

　　$y = \dfrac{(x - 1)(x + 2)}{x + 1}$

　　Since the numerator and denominator have no common factors, there are no holes. There is a vertical asymptote at $x = -1$.

---

ii) The degree of the numerator is 1 more than the degree of the denominator, so there is an oblique asymptote.

Determine: $(x^2 + x - 2) \div (x + 1)$

$$\begin{array}{c|rrr} -1 & 1 & 1 & -2 \\ & & -1 & 0 \\ \hline & 1 & 0 & -2 \end{array}$$

The quotient is x and the remainder is -2.

The function can be written as: $y = x - \dfrac{2}{x + 1}$

As $|x| \to \infty$, $\dfrac{2}{x + 1} \to 0$,

and $y \to x - 0$

So, the oblique asymptote has equation $y = x$.

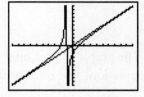

iii) Since the non-permissible value is $x = -1$, the domain is: $x \neq -1$

b) $y = \dfrac{x^2 - 3x + 2}{1 - x^2}$

i) The function is undefined when:

$$1 - x^2 = 0$$
$$x^2 = 1$$
$$x = \pm 1$$

The non-permissible values are $x = 1$ and $x = -1$.

Factor the equation.

$$y = \frac{(x - 2)(x - 1)}{(1 + x)(1 - x)} \text{ or } y = \frac{-(x - 2)(x - 1)}{(x + 1)(x - 1)}$$

Since the numerator and denominator have a common factor of $(x - 1)$, there is a hole at $x = 1$ and a vertical asymptote at $x = -1$.

ii) The degrees of the numerator and denominator are equal, so there is a horizontal asymptote. Write the function as:

$$y = \frac{x^2 - 3x + 2}{-x^2 + 1}$$

The leading coefficients of the numerator and denominator are 1 and -1 respectively. So, the equation of the horizontal asymptote is: $y = \dfrac{1}{-1}$, or $y = -1$

iii) Since the non-permissible values are $x = 1$ and $x = -1$, the domain is: $x \neq \pm 1$

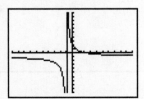

THINK FURTHER

Write an equation of another rational function that has both a hole and a vertical asymptote. Identify the coordinates of the hole and the equation of the asymptote.

The graph of a rational function can be used to solve a related rational equation. The zeros of the function are the roots of the equation.

4. Use graphing technology to solve:

$$\frac{8}{x^2 + 1} = x$$

Give the solution to the nearest tenth.

Use graphing technology to solve: $x + 6 = \dfrac{x - 1}{x + 1}$

Give the solution to the nearest tenth.

SOLUTION

$x + 6 = \dfrac{x - 1}{x + 1}$ Move all the terms to one side of the equation.

$x + 6 - \dfrac{x - 1}{x + 1} = 0$

Graph the related function: $f(x) = x + 6 - \dfrac{x - 1}{x + 1}$

The roots of the equation $x + 6 - \dfrac{x - 1}{x + 1} = 0$ are the zeros of the related function; that is, the values of x for which $f(x) = 0$.
Use the CALC menu to determine the zeros.

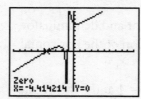 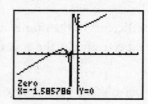

The approximate roots of the equation are:
$x = -4.4142\ldots$ and $x = -1.5857\ldots$
So, $x \doteq -4.4$ and $x \doteq -1.6$

Discuss the Ideas

1. For the graph of a rational function, $y = \dfrac{f(x)}{g(x)}$, how can you tell whether a non-permissible value of x corresponds to a vertical asymptote or a hole?

2. For the graph of a rational function, $y = \dfrac{f(x)}{g(x)}$, how can you determine the equation of a horizontal asymptote?

3. What is the relationship between the roots of a rational equation and the x-intercepts of the graph of the corresponding rational function? Explain.

Exercises

A

4. For the graph of each rational function below:

    i) Write the equations of any asymptotes.

    ii) State the domain.

a)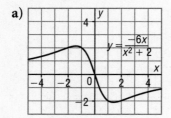

b)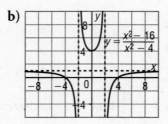

c)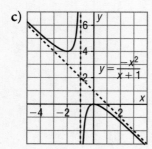

d)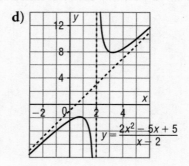

5. For the graph of each rational function:

    i) Write the coordinates of any hole.

    ii) Write the equations of any vertical asymptotes.

a) $y = \dfrac{x^2 - 4}{x + 2}$ **b)** $y = \dfrac{x^2 + x - 2}{x^2 - 2x - 3}$

c) $y = \dfrac{x^2 - 4}{x^2 + 4}$ **d)** $y = \dfrac{x^2 - 5x + 4}{x - 1}$

6. For each rational function, determine whether its graph has a horizontal asymptote. If it does, write its equation.

a) $y = \dfrac{4x}{x + 2}$ **b)** $y = \dfrac{x^2 - 16}{x^2 + 4}$

c) $y = \dfrac{x}{x^2 - 25}$
  d) $y = \dfrac{x - 2}{x - 4}$

7. For each rational function, determine whether its graph has an oblique asymptote. If it does, write its equation.

a) $y = \dfrac{x^2 - 2x - 5}{x - 1}$
  b) $y = \dfrac{x^2 - 7x + 10}{x - 5}$

c) $y = \dfrac{x^2}{4 - x}$
  d) $y = \dfrac{-2x^2 + 3x + 1}{x + 2}$

8. Solve each rational equation by graphing.
Give the solutions to the nearest tenth where necessary.

a) $\dfrac{4}{x + 2} + 1 = 0$ **b)** $\dfrac{x - 2}{x - 4} = x + 3$

c) $\dfrac{x^2 - x - 2}{x^2 - 4} = x + 6$ **d)** $\dfrac{4}{3x^2 - 1} = 2 + \dfrac{10}{6x - 1}$

9. Match each function to its graph. Justify your choice.

i) Graph A

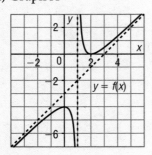

ii) Graph B

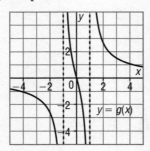

iii) Graph C

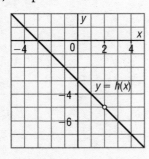

iv) Graph D

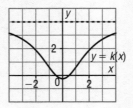

v) Graph E

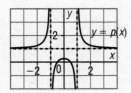

vi) Graph F

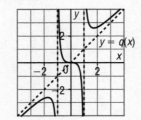

a) $y = \dfrac{x^2 + x - 6}{2 - x}$

b) $y = \dfrac{x^2 - 4x + 4}{x - 1}$

c) $y = \dfrac{x^3}{x^2 - 1}$

d) $y = \dfrac{4x}{x^2 - 1}$

e) $y = \dfrac{4x^2 - 1}{x^2 + 4}$

f) $y = \dfrac{4x^2 - 1}{4x^2 - 4}$

10. For the graph of each function:

    i) Determine the equations of any asymptotes and the coordinates of any hole.

    ii) Determine the domain.

    iii) Use graphing technology to verify the characteristics, and to explain the behaviour of the graph close to the non-permissible values.

a) $y = \dfrac{2x^2 - 4}{x^2}$

b) $y = \dfrac{x^2 + 2x - 15}{3 - x}$

c) $y = \dfrac{x - 4}{x^2 + 2}$

11. The speed of a boat in still water is 10 km/h. It travels 25 km upstream and 25 km downstream in 6 h. This equation models the total time for the journey in terms of the speed of the current, v kilometres per hour: $\dfrac{25}{10 - v} + \dfrac{25}{10 + v} = 6$
What is the speed of the current, to the nearest whole number?

C

12. Create an equation for a rational function whose graph has the given characteristics.

   a) The graph is the line $y = x$ with two holes.

   b) The graph has a horizontal asymptote with equation $y = -6$, and no vertical asymptotes.

   c) The graph has an oblique asymptote with equation $y = x + 1$, and a vertical asymptote with equation $x = 2$.

d) The graph has two vertical asymptotes, a horizontal asymptote that is not the x-axis, two holes, and:

i) the y-axis is a line of symmetry

ii) the y-axis is not a line of symmetry

Multiple-Choice Questions

1. Which function has a graph with an oblique asymptote?

A. $y = \dfrac{x^2 + 7x + 10}{x + 5}$

B. $y = \dfrac{x - 5}{x^2 + 7x + 10}$

C. $y = \dfrac{x^2 + 7x + 10}{x^2 - 5}$

D. $y = \dfrac{x^2 + 7x + 10}{x - 5}$

2. Which characteristic applies to the graph of $y = \dfrac{2x^2 + 4x - 30}{x - 3}$?

A. The vertical asymptote has equation $x = 3$.

B. The horizontal asymptote has equation $y = 2$.

C. There is a hole at $x = 3$.

D. The oblique asymptote has equation $y = x + 5$.

Study Note

List possible characteristics of the graph of a rational function $y = \dfrac{f(x)}{g(x)}$, then describe how to determine them.

ANSWERS

Check Your Understanding

1. a) hole at $x = -5$ **b)** asymptote: $x = 2$

2. a) oblique asymptote: $y = x + 4$ **b)** horizontal asymptote: $y = 0$

3. a) i) asymptotes $x = -2$ and $x = 2$ **ii)** $y = 0$ **iii)** $x \neq \pm 2$

b) i) asymptotes $x = -3$ and $x = 3$ **ii)** $y = 1$ **iii)** $x \neq \pm 3$

4. $x \doteq 1.8$

Exercises

4. a) i) $y = 0$ **ii)** $x \in \mathbb{R}$ **b) i)** $x = -2, x = 2; y = 1$ **ii)** $x \neq \pm 2$

c) i) $x = -1; y = -x + 1$ **ii)** $x \neq -1$ **d) i)** $x = 2; y = 2x - 1$ **ii)** $x \neq 2$

5. a) i) $(-2, -4)$ **b) ii)** $x = 3, x = -1$ **d) i)** $(1, -3)$ **6. a)** $y = 4$ **b)** $y = 1$

c) $y = 0$ **d)** $y = 1$ **7. a)** $y = x - 1$ **c)** $y = -x - 4$ **d)** $y = -2x + 7$

8. a) $x = -6$ **b)** $x \doteq -2.3, x \doteq 4.3$ **c)** $x \doteq -4.6, x \doteq -2.4$

d) $x \doteq -1.3, x \doteq -0.1, x \doteq 0.8$ **9. a)** Graph C **b)** Graph A **c)** Graph F

d) Graph B **e)** Graph D **f)** Graph E **10. a) i)** $x = 0; y = 2$ **ii)** $x \neq 0$

b) i) $(3, -8)$ **ii)** $x \neq 3$ **c) i)** $y = 0$ **ii)** $x \in \mathbb{R}$ **11.** approximately 4 km/h

Multiple Choice

1. D **2.** C

Additional Workspace

✔ CHECKPOINT

Self-Assess

Can you . . .	Try *Checkpoint* question	For review, see
sketch the graph of $y = \sqrt{f(x)}$ given the graph of a linear function $y = f(x)$?	2	Page 84 in Lesson 2.1 (Example 1)
sketch the graph of $y = \sqrt{f(x)}$ given the graph of a quadratic function $y = f(x)$?	2	Page 86 in Lesson 2.1 (Example 2)
compare the domain and range of $y = \sqrt{f(x)}$ to the domain and range of $y = f(x)$, and explain why they may differ?	2	Page 85 in Lesson 2.1
determine graphically the approximate solution of a radical equation?	3	Page 89 in Lesson 2.1 (Example 4)
graph a rational function with technology?	4	Page 101 in Lesson 2.2
determine whether the graph of a rational function $y = \dfrac{f(x)}{g(x)}$ will have a vertical asymptote or a hole for a non-permissible value of x?	7	Page 107 in Lesson 2.3 (Example 1)
determine whether the graph of a rational function $y = \dfrac{f(x)}{g(x)}$ will have a horizontal or oblique asymptote?	7	Page 109 in Lesson 2.3 (Example 2)
match a set of rational functions to their graphs, and explain the reasoning?	6	Page 117 in Lesson 2.3 (Question 9)
determine graphically the approximate solution of a rational equation?	8	Page 112 in Lesson 2.3 (Example 4)

Assess Your Understanding

2.1

1. **Multiple Choice** Given the graph of the function $y = f(x)$, which graph below right represents $y = \sqrt{f(x)}$?

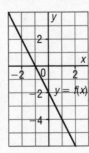
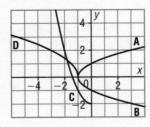

2. For each function $y = f(x)$ graphed below:

- Sketch the graph of $y = \sqrt{f(x)}$.
- State the domain and range of $y = \sqrt{f(x)}$.
- Explain why the domains are different and the ranges are different.

a)

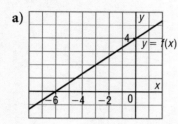

b)

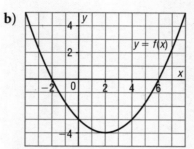

3. Solve each radical equation by graphing. Give the solution to the nearest tenth.

  a) $-x + 3 = \sqrt{2x - 1}$ **b)** $\sqrt{x + 2} = 5 - \sqrt{3x + 4}$

2.2

4. Use graphing technology to graph each rational function. Identify any non-permissible values of x and the equations of any horizontal asymptotes.

  a) $y = \dfrac{3x}{x + 4}$ **b)** $y = \dfrac{3x}{x^2 - 4}$

  c) $y = \dfrac{x^2 - 4}{3x}$ **d)** $y = \dfrac{x^2 - 4x}{3x}$

2.3

5. Multiple Choice Which function has a graph with a hole?

  A. $y = \dfrac{x + 4}{2x^2 + 8x}$ **B.** $y = \dfrac{x - 4}{2x^2 + 8x}$

  C. $y = \dfrac{4x + 4}{2x^2 + 8x}$ **D.** $y = \dfrac{x + 4}{2x^2 - 8x}$

6. Match each function to its graph. Justify your choice.

i) Graph A

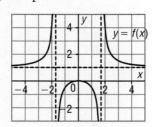

ii) Graph B

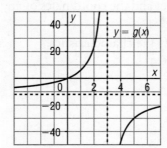

iii) Graph C

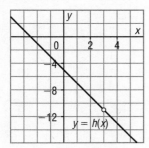

iv) Graph D

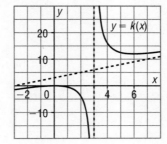

a) $y = \dfrac{-12x}{x - 3}$

b) $y = \dfrac{2x^2 - x - 15}{3 - x}$

c) $y = \dfrac{x^2}{x - 3}$

d) $y = \dfrac{x^2}{x^2 - 3}$

7. For the graph of each rational function below, determine without technology:

     i) the equations of any asymptotes and the coordinates of any hole
    ii) the domain of the function
    Use graphing technology to verify the characteristics.

a) $y = \dfrac{2x^2}{25 - x^2}$

b) $y = \dfrac{-2x^2 - 6x}{x + 3}$

8. Solve each rational equation by graphing. Give the solution to the nearest tenth.

a) $x - 2 = \dfrac{3x - 5}{x - 3}$ **b)** $\dfrac{x^2 + 3x - 5}{x - 1} = -5$

ANSWERS

1. D   **2. a)** domain: $x \geq -6$; range: $y \geq 0$
b) domain: $x \leq -2$ or $x \geq 6$; range: $y \geq 0$ **3. a)** $x \doteq 1.6$ **b)** $x \doteq 1.8$
4. a) $x \neq -4$; $y = 3$ **b)** $x \neq \pm 2$; $y = 0$ **c)** $x \neq 0$ **d)** $x \neq 0$
5. A   **6. a)** Graph B   **b)** Graph C   **c)** Graph D   **d)** Graph A
7. a) i) $x = 5, x = -5$; $y = -2$ **ii)** $x \neq \pm 5$ **b) i)** $(-3, 6)$ **ii)** $x \neq -3$
8. a) $x \doteq 1.8, x \doteq 6.2$ **b)** $x \doteq -9.1, x \doteq 1.1$

Get Started

For each rational function, determine the non-permissible values of x and the intercepts of its graph.

$$y = \frac{x^2 - 9}{2x}$$

$$y = \frac{x - 2}{x^2 - 2x - 3}$$

Construct Understanding

> Use the characteristics of the graph of $y = \dfrac{x - 1}{x^2 - 1}$ and its intercepts to sketch the graph.

To sketch the graph of a rational function, determine then use:

- the non-permissible values of x (holes and vertical asymptotes),
- the equation of the horizontal or oblique asymptote,
- the behaviour of the graph near the asymptotes, and
- the intercepts

Example 1   Sketching a Graph with a Hole

Check Your Understanding

1. Sketch the graph of this rational function, then state the domain and range.
$$y = \frac{x^2 - 5x + 4}{1 - x}$$

Sketch the graph of this rational function, then state the domain and range.
$$y = \frac{x^2 - x - 12}{4 - x}$$

SOLUTION

$$y = \frac{x^2 - x - 12}{4 - x}$$

Factor:
$$y = \frac{(x - 4)(x + 3)}{(4 - x)}, \text{ or } y = \frac{-(x - 4)(x + 3)}{(x - 4)}$$

There is a hole at $x = 4$.

Simplify:
$$y = -(x + 3), x \neq 4$$
$$y = -x - 3, x \neq 4$$

For the y-coordinate of the hole, substitute $x = 4$ in $y = -x - 3$ to get $y = -7$. So, the hole has coordinates $(4, -7)$.

The x-intercept is -3. The y-intercept is -3.

Draw an open circle at $(4, -7)$, then draw the line with equation $y = -x - 3$ on either side of the hole.

The domain is: $x \neq 4$

The range is: $y \neq -7$

Example 2 | Sketching a Graph with Horizontal and Vertical Asymptotes

Sketch the graph of this rational function, then state the domain.

$$y = \frac{x^2}{x^2 + 2x - 8}$$

SOLUTION

$$y = \frac{x^2}{x^2 + 2x - 8}$$

The function is undefined when:

$x^2 + 2x - 8 = 0$

$(x + 4)(x - 2) = 0$

$x = -4$ or $x = 2$

The numerator and denominator have no common factors, so there are no holes.

The vertical asymptotes have equations: $x = -4$ and $x = 2$

The degrees of the numerator and denominator are equal, so there is a horizontal asymptote. Both leading coefficients of the numerator and denominator are 1, so the horizontal asymptote has equation $y = 1$.

Draw broken lines for the asymptotes:

$x = -4$, $x = 2$, and $y = 1$

Determine the behaviour of the graph near the asymptotes.

Approximate the y-values where necessary.

x	-4.01	-3.99	1.99	2.01	-100	100
y	268	-266	-66	67	1.02	0.98

When x is to the left of the asymptote $x = -4$, y is positive.

When x is to the right of the asymptote $x = -4$, y is negative.

When x is to the left of the asymptote $x = 2$, y is negative.

When x is to the right of the asymptote $x = 2$, y is positive.

For this graph:

When $x < 0$, and $|x|$ is large, the graph lies above the asymptote $y = 1$.

When $x > 0$, and $|x|$ is large, the graph lies below the asymptote $y = 1$.

Determine the intercepts.

When $x = 0$, $y = 0$, so the graph passes through the origin.

Determine the coordinates of some other points: $(-8, 1.6)$, $(-2, -0.5)$, $(4, 1)$

Plot a point at $(0, 0)$. Join all the points to form 3 smooth curves.

The domain is: $x \neq -4$ or $x \neq 2$

2. Sketch the graph of this rational function, then state the domain.

$$y = \frac{-2x^2}{x^2 - 25}$$

Example 3 | Sketching a Graph with an Oblique Asymptote

3. Sketch the graph of this rational function, then state the domain and range.

$$y = \frac{-2x^2 + 5x - 2}{x - 1}$$

Sketch the graph of this rational function, then state the domain and range.

$$y = \frac{2x^2 + 5x - 12}{x + 2}$$

SOLUTION

$$y = \frac{2x^2 + 5x - 12}{x + 2}$$

Factor: $y = \dfrac{(x + 4)(2x - 3)}{x + 2}$

There are no common factors, so there are no holes.

The vertical asymptote has equation: $x = -2$

There is an oblique asymptote because the degree of the numerator is 1 more than the degree of the denominator.

Determine: $(2x^2 + 5x - 12) \div (x + 2)$

$$
\begin{array}{r|rrr}
-2 & 2 & 5 & -12 \\
   &   & -4 & -2 \\
\hline
   & 2 & 1 & -14
\end{array}
$$

The quotient is $2x + 1$, so the equation of the oblique asymptote is $y = 2x + 1$.

Determine the behaviour of the graph near the vertical asymptote.

Approximate the y-values.

x	-2.01	-1.99
y	1397	-1403

Determine the intercepts.

When $x = 0$, $y = -6$

When $y = 0$, $2x^2 + 5x - 12 = 0$

$\qquad\qquad (x + 4)(2x - 3) = 0$

$\qquad\qquad x = -4 \text{ or } x = 1.5$

Plot points at $(0, -6)$, $(-4, 0)$, and $(1.5, 0)$.

Draw broken lines for the asymptotes.

Determine the coordinates of some other points:

$(-6, -7.5)$, $(-3, 9)$, $(-1, -15)$, $(5, 9)$

Join the points to form 2 smooth curves; one curve to the right of the asymptotes and one curve to the left of the asymptotes.

The domain is: $x \neq -2$

From the graph, the range is: $y \in \mathbb{R}$

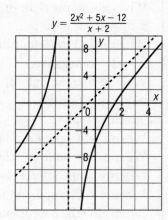

$y = \dfrac{2x^2 + 5x - 12}{x + 2}$

Example 4　　**Sketching a Graph with Asymptotes and a Hole**

Sketch the graph of this rational function, then state the domain and range.

$$y = \frac{2x + 3}{2x^2 + 9x + 9}$$

4. Sketch the graph of this rational function, then state its domain and range.
$$y = \frac{x + 3}{x^2 - 9}$$

SOLUTION

$$y = \frac{2x + 3}{2x^2 + 9x + 9}$$

Factor: $y = \dfrac{2x + 3}{(2x + 3)(x + 3)}$

There is a vertical asymptote with equation $x = -3$.

There is a hole at $x = -\dfrac{3}{2}$.

The function can be written as:

$$y = \frac{1}{x + 3}, x \neq -\frac{3}{2}$$

The y-coordinate of the hole is:

$$y = \frac{1}{\left(-\dfrac{3}{2}\right) + 3}, \text{ or } \frac{2}{3}$$

The degree of the numerator is less than that of the denominator, so there is a horizontal asymptote at $y = 0$.

Determine the behaviour of the graph close to the asymptotes. Approximate the y-values.

$y = \dfrac{2x + 3}{2x^2 + 9x + 9}$

x	-3.01	-2.99	-100	100
y	-100	100	-0.01	0.01

Determine the intercepts.
When $x = 0, y = \dfrac{1}{3}$

Since the numerator of the function is 1, $y \neq 0$, so there is no x-intercept.

Plot a point at $\left(0, \dfrac{1}{3}\right)$. Draw an open circle at $\left(-\dfrac{3}{2}, \dfrac{2}{3}\right)$.

Draw a broken line for the vertical asymptote.

Plot points on either side of the ends of the asymptotes, to illustrate the behaviour of the graph near the asymptotes.

Since the graph is that of a reciprocal function, with a hole, draw 2 smooth curves at the top right and bottom left.

The domain is: $x \neq -3, x \neq -\dfrac{3}{2}$

From the graph, the range is: $y \neq 0, y \neq \dfrac{2}{3}$

THINK FURTHER

Write an equation of a rational function whose graph has an oblique asymptote and a hole.

Discuss the Ideas

1. When you sketch the graph of a rational function, why is it important to identify the behaviour of the graph near the asymptotes?

2. Can the graph of a rational function have an oblique asymptote and a horizontal asymptote?

Exercises

A

3. Sketch the graph of each function.

a) $y = \dfrac{(x-2)(x+1)}{x+1}$

b) $y = \dfrac{(-2x+4)(x-2)}{x-2}$

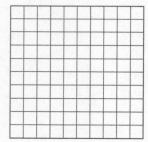
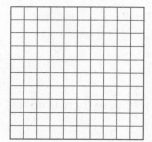

4. Sketch the graph of each function.

a) $y = \dfrac{x - 2}{x + 1}$

b) $y = \dfrac{-2x + 4}{x}$

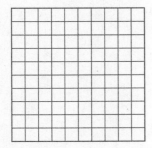

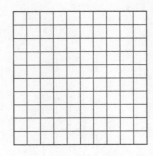

5. Sketch the graph of each function, then state the domain.

a) $y = \dfrac{-4x}{x^2 - 9}$

b) $y = \dfrac{x^2 - 9}{-x^2}$

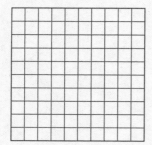

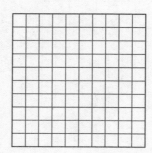

c) $y = \dfrac{x^2 + 2x - 8}{-x - 4}$

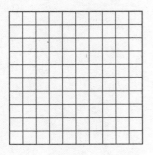

d) $y = \dfrac{2x^2 - 3x + 1}{x - 2}$

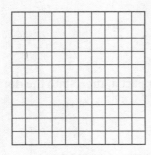

6. a) How are these functions different from other functions in this lesson?

i) $y = \dfrac{x^2 - 1}{x^3 - x}$ **ii)** $y = \dfrac{x^3 - x}{x^2 - 1}$

b) Sketch the graph of each function in part a, then state the domain and range.

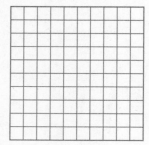 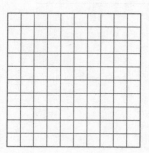

7. For a rational function, when the degree of the numerator is 2 or more than the degree of the denominator, the graph has no horizontal or oblique asymptotes. Without using graphing technology, determine a strategy to sketch the graph of $y = \dfrac{x^3}{x + 2}$ then graph the function. State the domain.

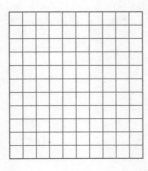

C

8. Sketch the graph of each function, then state the domain.

a) $y = \dfrac{x^2}{x^3 - 3x^2 - x + 3}$

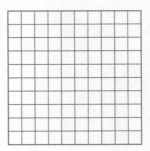

b) $y = \dfrac{x^3 - 2x^2 - x + 2}{x^2 - 4}$

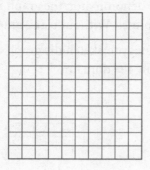

Multiple-Choice Questions

1. Which function describes this graph?

A. $y = \dfrac{-x}{x^2 - 9}$

B. $y = \dfrac{x}{x^2 - 9}$

C. $y = \dfrac{x^2}{x^2 - 9}$

D. $y = \dfrac{-x^2}{x^2 - 9}$

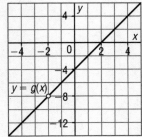

2. Which graph represents the function $y = \dfrac{2x^2 - 8}{x - 2}$?

A.

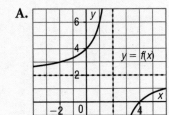

B.

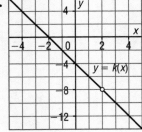

C.

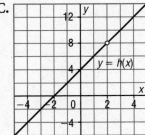

D.

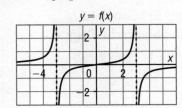

Study Note

Write your own rational function, different from any in Lessons 2.2 to 2.4, that you know you can sketch without using graphing technology. Sketch the function, and describe your strategy. Identify the domain.

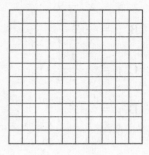

ANSWERS

Check Your Understanding

1. domain: $x \neq 1$; range: $y \neq 3$ 2. domain: $x \neq \pm 5$

3. domain: $x \neq 1$; range: $y \in \mathbb{R}$ 4. domain: $x \neq \pm 3$; range: $y \neq 0, y \neq -\frac{1}{6}$

Exercises

5. a) $x \neq \pm 3$ b) $x \neq 0$ c) $x \neq -4$ d) $x \neq 2$

6. b) i) domain: $x \neq \pm 1, x \neq 0$; range: $y \neq \pm 1, y \neq 0$

ii) domain: $x \neq \pm 1$; range: $y \neq \pm 1$ 7. $x \neq -2$

8. a) $x \neq -1, x \neq 1, x \neq 3$ b) $x \neq \pm 2$

Multiple Choice

1. A   2. C

2.4 Sketching Graphs of Rational Functions |

Concept Summary

Big Ideas	Applying the Big Ideas
• The graph of a function, $y = f(x)$, can be used to graph the corresponding radical function, $y = \sqrt{f(x)}$.	This means that: • There are characteristics common to all graphs of $y = f(x)$ and $y = \sqrt{f(x)}$. • If 0 and 1 are in the range of $y = f(x)$, then points with these y-coordinates are invariant.
• For the graph of a rational function, $y = \dfrac{f(x)}{g(x)}$, the non-permissible values of x correspond to vertical asymptotes or holes.	• There is a hole at the value of x for which both the numerator and denominator are 0. • There is a vertical asymptote at the value of x for which the denominator is 0, and the numerator is not 0.
• The roots of a rational equation or a radical equation are the x-intercepts of the graph of a corresponding function.	• A rational or radical equation can be solved by graphing a corresponding function and identifying the zeros of that function or the x-intercepts of its graph.

Chapter Study Notes

• What strategies do you use to sketch the graph of $y = \sqrt{f(x)}$ when the graph of $y = f(x)$ is given?

• What strategies do you use to sketch the graph of a rational function, $y = \dfrac{f(x)}{g(x)}, g(x) \neq 0$?

Skills Summary

Skill	Description	Example
Sketch the graph of $y = \sqrt{f(x)}$, given the graph of $y = f(x)$. **(2.1)**	The points on $y = f(x)$ with y-coordinates 0 and 1 also lie on the graph of $y = \sqrt{f(x)}$. If necessary, determine the square roots of the y-coordinates of other points on $y = f(x)$, to obtain the corresponding points on $y = \sqrt{f(x)}$.	The graphs of $y = f(x)$ and $y = \sqrt{f(x)}$ are shown below. On the graph of $y = f(x)$, points A and B are labelled at the x-intercepts, and points C and D are labelled where $y = 1$. Between A and C, and between B and D, the graph of $y = \sqrt{f(x)}$ is above the graph of $y = f(x)$. Another point on the graph of $y = \sqrt{f(x)}$ is $(0, \sqrt{4})$, or $(0, 2)$. These points were joined to get the graph of $y = \sqrt{f(x)}$.
Solve a radical equation graphically. **(2.1)**	The roots of a radical equation are the x-intercepts of the graph of a corresponding radical function.	Solve $\sqrt{2x + 1} = x - 5$. Graph $y = \sqrt{2x + 1} - x + 5$, then identify the x-intercept. Zero X=9.4641016 Y=0 To the nearest tenth, the solution is: $x = 9.5$
Solve a rational equation graphically. **(2.3)**	The roots of a rational equation are the x-intercepts of the graph of a corresponding rational function.	Solve $\dfrac{2x^2 + 3x - 1}{x - 1} = \dfrac{4x + 5}{x^2 + 3}$. Graph $y = \dfrac{2x^2 + 3x - 1}{x - 1} - \dfrac{4x + 5}{x^2 + 3}$, then identify the x-intercepts. To the nearest tenth, the solution is: $x = -2.1$ or $x = -0.3$

2.1

1. a) For each graph of $y = f(x)$ below:
- Sketch the graph of $y = \sqrt{f(x)}$.
- State the domain and range of $y = \sqrt{f(x)}$.

i)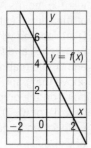

ii)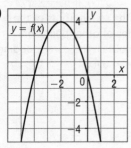

iii)

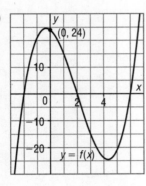

iv)

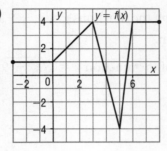

b) Choose one pair of graphs from part a for which the domains are different and the ranges are different.
- Explain the strategy you used to graph the radical function.
- Explain why the domains differ and the ranges differ.

2. Use graphing technology to graph the functions $y = x^2 - 9$ and $y = \sqrt{x^2 - 9}$ on the same screen.

a) State the domain and range of the function $y = \sqrt{x^2 - 9}$.

b) How is the domain of the function $y = \sqrt{x^2 - 9}$ related to the domain of $y = x^2 - 9$?

c) How are the zeros of $y = \sqrt{x^2 - 9}$ related to the zeros of $y = x^2 - 9$? Explain why.

d) What are the coordinates of the points of intersection of the two graphs? Explain your answer.

3. Solve each radical equation by graphing. Give the solution to the nearest tenth.

a) $x + 3 = \sqrt{5 - 2x}$ **b)** $\sqrt{4x} = \sqrt{3x + 1} - x$

2.2

4. Without graphing each rational function below, predict whether its graph has a hole and/or any horizontal or vertical asymptotes. State the related non-permissible values.

a) $y = \dfrac{x^2}{x^2 - 5x + 4}$

b) $y = \dfrac{x^2 - 5x + 4}{x - 4}$

c) $y = \dfrac{x^2 - 4x - 5}{x - 1}$

d) $y = \dfrac{x - 4}{x - 1}$

5. Match each function to its graph. Justify your choice.

i) Graph A

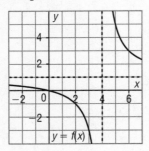

ii) Graph B

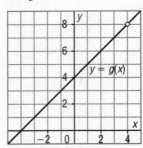

iii) Graph C

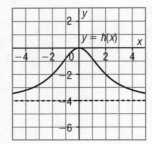

iv) Graph D

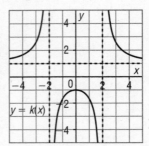

a) $y = \dfrac{-4x^2}{x^2 + 4}$

b) $y = \dfrac{x}{x - 4}$

c) $y = \dfrac{x^2 + 4}{x^2 - 4}$

d) $y = \dfrac{x^2 - 16}{x - 4}$

6. Solve each rational equation by graphing. Give the solution to the nearest tenth where necessary.

a) $\dfrac{2x - 1}{x + 3} = \dfrac{4}{x - 2}$

b) $\dfrac{x^2}{x^2 - 3} - \dfrac{x}{x + 2} = \dfrac{x}{2 - x}$

7. For the graph of each function below
i) Without graphing:
   - Determine the coordinates of any holes and the equations of any asymptotes.
   - Determine the domain.
ii) Use graphing technology to verify the characteristics and to explain the behaviour of the graph near the non-permissible values.

a) $y = \dfrac{-2x}{x^2 - 1}$

b) $y = \dfrac{3x^2 + 8x + 4}{x - 1}$

8. Without using graphing technology, sketch a graph of each function. State the domain.

a) $y = \dfrac{x^2 - x}{x + 1}$

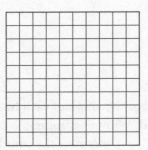

b) $y = \dfrac{-x^2}{x^2 - 9}$

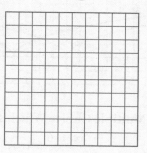

1. a) i) domain: $x \leq 2$; range: $y \geq 0$ **ii)** domain: $-4 \leq x \leq 0$; range: $y \geq 0$
iii) domain: $-2 \leq x \leq 2, x \geq 6$; range: $y \geq 0$
iv) domain: $-3 \leq x \leq 4, 5.5 \leq x \leq 8$; range: $0 \leq y \leq 2$
2. a) domain: $x \leq -3, x \geq 3$; range: $y \geq 0$ **d)** $(\pm 3, 0); (\pm\sqrt{10}, 1)$
3. a) $x \doteq -0.5$ **b)** $x \doteq 0.3$ **4. a)** $x \neq 1$ and $x \neq 4$ **b)** $x \neq 4$ **c)** $x \neq 1$
d) $x \neq 1$ **5. a)** Graph C   **b)** Graph A   **c)** Graph D   **d)** Graph B
6. a) $x \doteq -0.9, x \doteq 5.4$ **b)** $x \doteq -4.3, x \doteq -1.5, x = 0, x \doteq 1.8$
7. a) i) asymptotes: $x = \pm 1$; domain: $x \neq \pm 1$
b) i) asymptotes: $x = 1, y = 3x + 11$; domain: $x \neq 1$ **8. a)** $x \neq -1$ **b)** $x \neq \pm 3$

1. **Multiple Choice** Which graph represents $y = \sqrt{-0.5x - 2}$?

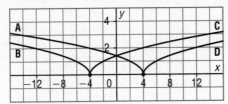

2. **Multiple Choice** Which statement about the graph of
$y = \dfrac{x^2 - 5x + 6}{x - 3}$ is true?

   A. There is a vertical asymptote with equation $y = 3$.

   B. There is an oblique asymptote with equation $y = x - 2$.

   C. There is a horizontal asymptote with equation $x = 2$.

   D. There is a hole at $(3, 1)$.

3. Without using graphing technology, graph the function
$y = \dfrac{x^2 + 3x + 2}{x^2 - x - 2}$. Identify any non-permissible values of x, the
equations of any asymptotes, and the domain.

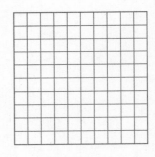

4. a) The graph of $y = f(x)$ is given. On the same grid, sketch the graph of $y = \sqrt{f(x)}$.

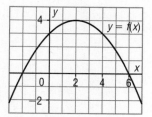

b) Identify the domain and range of each function in part a, then explain why the domains are different and the ranges are different.

5. Use graphing technology to solve each equation. Give the solution to the nearest tenth.

a) $x - 5 = \sqrt{2x + 1}$

b) $\dfrac{x - 2}{2x + 1} + 2 = \dfrac{x + 1}{x + 3}$

6. Without using graphing technology, match each function to its graph. Justify your choice.

i) Graph A

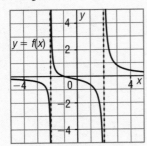

ii) Graph B

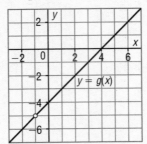

iii) Graph C

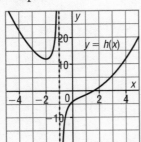

iv) Graph D

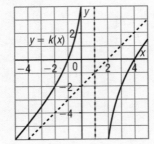

a) $y = \dfrac{x + 1}{x^2 - 4}$

b) $y = \dfrac{x^2 - 3x - 4}{x - 1}$

c) $y = \dfrac{x^2 - 3x - 4}{x + 1}$

d) $y = \dfrac{x^3 - 4}{x + 1}$

ANSWERS

1. B   **2.** D   **3.** $x \neq -1, x \neq 2$; asymptotes: $x = 2, y = 1$

4. b) for $y = f(x)$, domain: $x \in \mathbb{R}$; range: $y \leq 4$; for $y = \sqrt{f(x)}$,

domain: $-2 \leq x \leq 6$; range: $0 \leq y \leq 2$ **5. a)** $x \doteq 9.5$ **b)** $x \doteq -4.1, x \doteq 0.1$

6. a) Graph A   **b)** Graph D   **c)** Graph B   **d)** Graph C

1

1. Use long division to divide. Write the division statement.
$(-x^2 - 5x^3 + 2x - 3x^4 + 3) \div (x - 2)$

2. Use synthetic division to divide. Write the division statement.
$(7x + x^4 - 8x^3) \div (x - 5)$

3. Determine the remainder: $(4x^4 - 7x^3 + 2x^2 + x) \div (x + 1)$

4. Fully factor this polynomial: $6x^3 - 11x^2 - 3x + 2$

5. Sketch a graph of each polynomial function.

   a) $f(x) = x^4 - x^3 - 4x^2 + 4x$

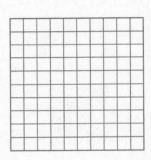

b) $g(x) = (x + 2)^3(x - 2)^2$

2

6. For the graph of the quadratic function $y = f(x)$ below:

   a) Sketch the graph of $y = \sqrt{f(x)}$.

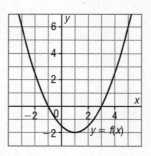

   b) State the domain and range of $y = \sqrt{f(x)}$.

7. Use graphing technology to solve each equation. Give the solution to the nearest tenth.

   a) $\sqrt{4 - x} + 3 = 2 + \sqrt{2x}$ **b)** $\dfrac{-3}{x^2 - 2} = \dfrac{5}{x - 2}$

8. Match each function below to its graph. Justify your choice.

i) Graph A

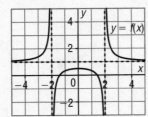

ii) Graph B

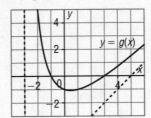

iii) Graph C

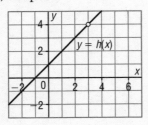

a) $y = \dfrac{x^2 - 2x - 3}{x + 3}$

b) $y = \dfrac{x^2 - 2}{x^2 - 4}$

c) $y = \dfrac{x^2 - 2x - 3}{x - 3}$

3 Transforming Graphs of Functions

BUILDING ON

- graphing functions
- transforming linear and quadratic functions

BIG IDEAS

- The graphs of functions can be translated, reflected, stretched, or compressed.

- When a function is written in the form $y - k = af(b(x - h))$, its graph is a transformation image of the graph of $y = f(x)$, and the transformations can be identified.

- The graphs of a relation and its inverse are reflections of each other in the line $y = x$.

LEADING TO

- the logarithmic function as the inverse of the exponential function
- transforming trigonometric functions

NEW VOCABULARY

inverse function

FOCUS Relate changes in the equation of a function to vertical and horizontal translations of its graph.

Get Started

Here is the graph of $y = x^2$.

How is the graph of $y = x^2 + q$ related to the graph of $y = x^2$ for each value of q?

• $q = 3$

• $q = -3$

How is the graph of $y = (x - h)^2$ related to the graph of $y = x^2$ for each value of h?

• $h = -3$

• $h = 4$

Construct Understanding

The graphs of $y = |x|$, $y - 1 = |x|$, $y + 1 = |x|$, $y - 3 = |x|$, and $y + 3 = |x|$ are shown on grid I.

The graphs of $y = |x|$, $y = |x + 1|$, $y = |x - 1|$, $y = |x + 3|$, and $y = |x - 3|$ are shown on grid II.

The graphs of $y = |x|$, $y - 1 = |x + 3|$, $y + 1 = |x - 2|$, $y + 3 = |x + 1|$, and $y - 2 = |x - 3|$ are shown on grid III.

Identify each graph. Use graphing technology to check that you have identified the graphs correctly.

How does the graph of $y - k = |x|$ compare to the graph of $y = |x|$? What is the effect of k? How does the graph of $y = |x - h|$ compare to the graph of $y = |x|$? What is the effect of h?

How does the graph of $y - k = |x - h|$ compare to the graph of $y = |x|$? What are the effects of h and k?

Grid I

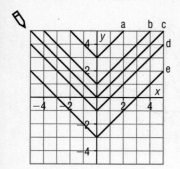

Grid II

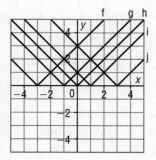

Grid III

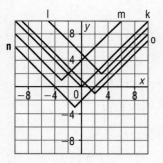

The graph of a function $y = f(x)$ may be translated vertically or horizontally.

For example, the graph of $y = \sqrt{x} + 2$ is the image of the graph of $y = \sqrt{x}$ after a vertical translation of 2 units up.
The graph of $y = \sqrt{x} - 1$ is the image of the graph of $y = \sqrt{x}$ after a vertical translation of 1 unit down.
The equations of the image graphs may be written as $y + 1 = \sqrt{x}$ and as $y - 2 = \sqrt{x}$.

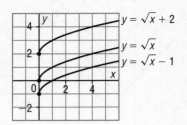

The graph of $y = (x + 2)^3$ is the image of the graph of $y = x^3$ after a horizontal translation of 2 units left.
The graph of $y = (x - 3)^3$ is the image of the graph of $y = x^3$ after a horizontal translation of 3 units right.

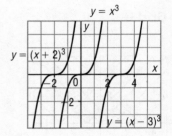

The image of the graph of a function $y = f(x)$ after a vertical or horizontal translation is congruent to the graph of $y = f(x)$, and both graphs have the same orientation.

Horizontal Translation

The graph of $y = f(x - h)$ is a horizontal translation of the graph of $y = f(x)$.
When $h > 0$, the graph of $y = f(x)$ is translated h units right.
When $h < 0$, the graph of $y = f(x)$ is translated $|h|$ units left.

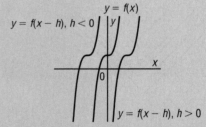

Vertical Translation

The graph of $y - k = f(x)$ is a vertical translation of the graph of $y = f(x)$.
When $k > 0$, the graph of $y = f(x)$ is translated k units up.
When $k < 0$, the graph of $y = f(x)$ is translated $|k|$ units down.

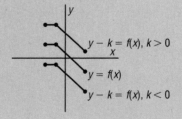

<table>
<tr><td>**Example 1**</td><td>**Sketching the Graph of a Function after a Single Translation**</td></tr>
</table>

Here is the graph of $y = f(x)$. Sketch the image graph after each translation. Write the equation of the image graph in terms of the function f.
State the domain and range of each function.

a) a translation of 3 units right
b) a translation of 2 units down

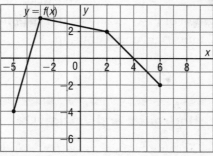

Check Your Understanding

1. Here is the graph of $y = g(x)$. Sketch the image graph after each translation. Write the equation of the image graph in terms of the function g. State the domain and range of each function.

a) a translation of 4 units left
b) a translation of 1 unit up

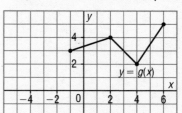

SOLUTION

a) Translate each point on the graph of $y = f(x)$ 3 units right. Since the translation is horizontal, the equation of the image graph has the form $y = f(x - h)$. The translation is 3 units right, so $h = 3$. The equation of the image graph is: $y = f(x - 3)$

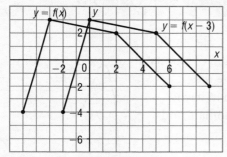

The domain of $y = f(x)$ is: $-5 \le x \le 6$
The domain of $y = f(x - 3)$ is: $-2 \le x \le 9$
Both functions have the same range: $-4 \le y \le 3$

b) Translate each point on the graph of $y = f(x)$ 2 units down. Since the translation is vertical, the equation of the image graph has the form $y - k = f(x)$. The translation is 2 units down, so $k = -2$. The equation of the image graph is: $y - (-2) = f(x)$, or $y + 2 = f(x)$

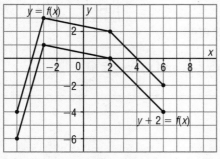

Both functions have the same domain: $-5 \le x \le 6$
The range of $y = f(x)$ is: $-4 \le y \le 3$
The range of $y + 2 = f(x)$ is: $-6 \le y \le 1$

The graph of a function $y = f(x)$ may be translated both horizontally and vertically. For example, the graph of $y - 4 = -(x - 2)^4$ is the image of the graph of $y = -x^4$ after a translation of 2 units right and 4 units up.

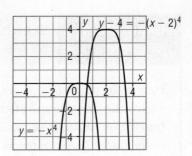

Horizontal and Vertical Translations

The graph of $y - k = f(x - h)$ is the image of the graph of $y = f(x)$ after a vertical translation of k units, and a horizontal translation of h units.

Check Your Understanding

2. Here is the graph of $y = j(x)$. Sketch the image graph after a translation of 4 units left and 5 units down. Write the equation of the image graph in terms of the function j. State the domain and range of each function.

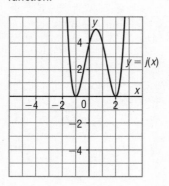

Example 2   **Sketching the Graph of a Function after a Combination of Translations**

Here is the graph of $y = f(x)$. Sketch the image graph after a translation of 5 units right and 3 units down. Write the equation of the image graph in terms of the function f. State the domain and range of each function.

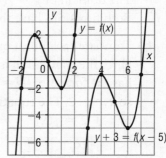

SOLUTION

Mark some lattice points on $y = f(x)$, translate each point 5 units right and 3 units down, then join the points with a smooth curve. Since the graph of $y = f(x)$ was translated horizontally and vertically, the equation of the image graph has the form $y - k = f(x - h)$, with $h = 5$ and $k = -3$.
So, the equation of the image graph is:
$y + 3 = f(x - 5)$
Both functions have domain $x \in \mathbb{R}$ and range $y \in \mathbb{R}$.

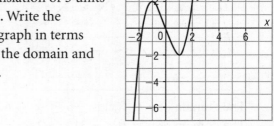

THINK FURTHER

Determine a function whose graph and image after a translation of h units right and k units up coincide.

An equation for a graph can be used to write an equation of its translation image.

An *explicit equation* is an equation that is written in terms of the independent variable.

Example 3 — Determining the Equation of an Image Graph after a Translation

The graph of $y = \sqrt{x}$ is translated 2 units right and 1 unit down. What is the equation of the image graph?

SOLUTION

The equation of the image graph has the form $y - k = \sqrt{x - h}$.
$h = 2$ and $k = -1$
So, the equation of the image graph is: $y + 1 = \sqrt{x - 2}$

Check Your Understanding

3. The graph of $y = \frac{1}{x}$ is translated 3 units left and 2 units up. What is the equation of the image graph?

Example 4 — Describing the Graph of a Function from Its Equation

Describe how the graph of $y = \frac{1}{x}$ could have been translated to create the graph of each function below. What are the equations of the asymptotes of each image graph? Use graphing technology to check.

a) $y = \dfrac{1}{x + 6}$ **b)** $y + 1 = \dfrac{1}{x - 2}$

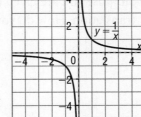

Check Your Understanding

4. Describe how the graph of $y = \frac{1}{x^2}$ could have been translated to create the graph of each function below. What are the equations of the asymptotes of each image graph?

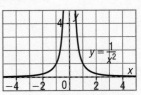

a) $y - 3 = \dfrac{1}{x^2}$

b) $y + 4 = \dfrac{1}{(x + 3)^2}$

SOLUTION

The graph of $y = \frac{1}{x}$ has a horizontal asymptote with equation $y = 0$ and a vertical asymptote with equation $x = 0$. The equation of a translation image of the graph of $y = \frac{1}{x}$ can be written in the form $y - k = \dfrac{1}{x - h}$.

a) Write $y = \dfrac{1}{x + 6}$ as $y = \dfrac{1}{x - (-6)}$, then compare to $y - k = \dfrac{1}{x - h}$: $h = -6$ and $k = 0$

So, the graph of $y = \dfrac{1}{x + 6}$ is the graph of $y = \frac{1}{x}$ after a translation of 6 units left.

The vertical asymptote was also translated 6 units left, so its equation is $x = -6$. Since the graph of $y = \frac{1}{x}$ was not translated vertically, the horizontal asymptote does not change.

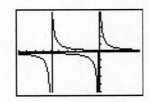

b) Write $y + 1 = \dfrac{1}{x - 2}$ as

$y - (-1) = \dfrac{1}{x - 2}$, then compare to

$y - k = \dfrac{1}{x - h}$: $h = 2$ and $k = -1$

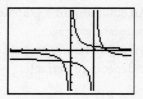

So, the graph of $y + 1 = \dfrac{1}{x - 2}$ is the

graph of $y = \dfrac{1}{x}$ after a translation of 2 units right and 1 unit down.
The horizontal asymptote was also translated 1 unit down, so its equation is $y = -1$.
The vertical asymptote was translated 2 units right, so its equation is $x = 2$.

THINK FURTHER

Why is the equation of a vertical asymptote not affected by a vertical translation?

Discuss the Ideas

1. Suppose you are given the graph of $y = f(x)$ and its image after a translation. How do you determine an equation of the image graph?

2. How do you recognize that one graph is the image of another after a vertical or horizontal translation, or a combination of translations?

3. When is the domain of a graph different from the domain of its image after a translation? When is the range of a graph different from the range of its image after a translation? How could you determine the domain and range of the image?

Exercises

A

4. On each grid, the graph of $y = |x|$ and its image after a single translation are shown. What was the translation? What is the equation of the image graph?

a) 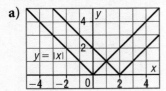 **b)**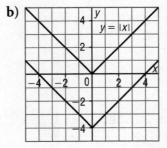

5. For each equation of a translation image, describe how the graph of $y = f(x)$ was translated.

a) $y = f(x - 7)$ **b)** $y + 5 = f(x)$

c) $y = f(x + 6)$ **d)** $y - 4 = f(x)$

6. The graph of $y = g(x)$ is translated as described below. Write the equation of each translation image in terms of the function g.

   a) a translation of 3 units right

   b) a translation of 8 units down

   c) a translation of 9 units up

   d) a translation of 7 units left

B

7. Here is the graph of $y = g(x)$. On the same grid, sketch the graph of each function below. State the domain and range of each function.

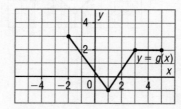

   a) $y - 1 = g(x)$ **b)** $y = g(x + 3)$

8. Here is the graph of $y = f(x)$. On the same grid, sketch the graph of each function below. State the domain and range of each function.

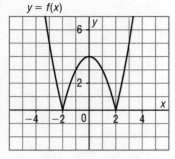

$y = f(x)$

a) $y + 3 = f(x + 2)$

b) $y - 1 = f(x - 2)$

9. The point A(3, 7) lies on the graph of $y = f(x)$. What are the coordinates of its image A′ on the graph of $y - 2 = f(x - 8)$? How do you know?

10. Here is the graph of $y = j(x)$. On the same grid, sketch the graph of $y - 3 = j(x + 2)$. Describe how the vertical and horizontal asymptotes are affected by the translations. What are the equations of the asymptotes of the image graph?

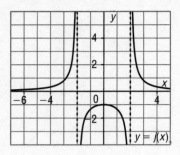

11. Use the graph of $y = p(x)$ to sketch the graph of each function below.

a) $y + 2 = p(x + 3)$

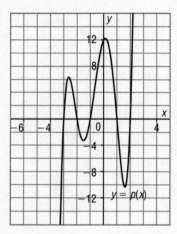

b) $y - 3 = p(x - 2)$

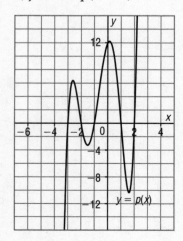

12. The function $y = f(x)$ has domain $-7 \leq x \leq 12$ and range $-1 \leq y \leq 10$. What are the domain and range of $y + 8 = f(x - 3)$?

13. Describe how the graph of $y = \sqrt{x}$ has been translated to create the graph of each function below. Use graphing technology to check.

a) $y = \sqrt{x - 1}$

b) $y = \sqrt{x + 4} - 2$

14. The graph of $y = x^3$ is translated 5 units left and 3 units up. What is the equation of the image graph?

15. The graph of $y = |x^2 - 2|$ is translated 2 units right and 7 units down. What is the equation of the image graph?

16. The graph of $y = f(x)$ has been translated to create the graphs below. Match each graph to its equation.

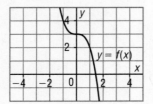

i) Graph A

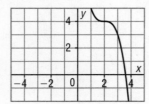

ii) Graph B

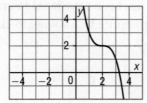

iii) Graph C

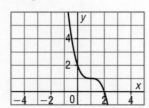

iv) Graph D

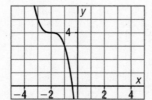

a) $y - 1 = f(x + 2)$

b) $y - 1 = f(x - 2)$

c) $y + 1 = f(x - 2)$

d) $y + 2 = f(x - 1)$

17. The graph of $f(x) = x^2 - 5x - 6$ has zeros at -1 and 6.

a) The graph of $y = f(x)$ is translated horizontally. Neither zero of the image graph is negative. What is the shortest possible translation?

b) The graph of $y = f(x)$ is translated horizontally. Neither zero of the image graph is positive. What is the shortest possible translation?

C

18. The graph of $y = 2x^2 - 12x + 23$ is translated vertically so that its vertex lies on the x-axis. How could you use the discriminant to determine the translation? What is the translation?

Multiple-Choice Questions

1. Which translation of the graph of $y = g(x)$ produces the graph of $y + 5 = g(x - 3)$?

A. 3 units right and 5 units down

B. 3 units left and 5 units up

C. 5 units right and 3 units up

D. 5 units left and 3 units down

2. The function $y = f(x)$ has domain $-4 \le x \le 9$. What is the domain of $y = f(x - 5)$?

A. $-4 \le x \le 9$ **B.** $-9 \le x \le 4$

C. $-14 \le x \le 1$ **D.** $1 \le x \le 14$

Study Note

Graph any function $y = f(x)$. Choose a horizontal translation and a vertical translation, then translate the function. Describe how you sketched the translation image, then determine its equation in terms of $f(x)$.

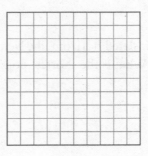

ANSWERS

Check Your Understanding

1. a) $y = g(x + 4)$; domain of $y = g(x)$: $-1 \leq x \leq 6$; domain of $y = g(x + 4)$: $-5 \leq x \leq 2$; both functions have range: $2 \leq y \leq 5$ **b)** $y - 1 = g(x)$; both functions have domain: $-1 \leq x \leq 6$; range of $y = g(x)$: $2 \leq y \leq 5$; range of $y - 1 = g(x)$: $3 \leq y \leq 6$

2. $y + 5 = j(x + 4)$; both functions have domain $x \in \mathbb{R}$; range of $y = j(x)$: $y \geq 0$; range of $y + 5 = j(x + 4)$: $y \geq -5$

3. $y - 2 = \dfrac{1}{x + 3}$ **4. a)** translation of 3 units up; $y = 3$; $x = 0$
b) translation of 3 units left and 4 units down; $y = -4$; $x = -3$

Exercises

4. a) 2 units right; $y = |x - 2|$ **b)** 4 units down; $y + 4 = |x|$
5. a) 7 units right   **b)** 5 units down   **c)** 6 units left   **d)** 4 units up
6. a) $y = g(x - 3)$ **b)** $y + 8 = g(x)$ **c)** $y - 9 = g(x)$ **d)** $y = g(x + 7)$
7. domain $g(x)$: $-2 \leq x \leq 5$; range $g(x)$: $-1 \leq y \leq 3$
a) domain: $-2 \leq x \leq 5$; range: $0 \leq y \leq 4$
b) domain: $-5 \leq x \leq 2$; range: $-1 \leq y \leq 3$
8. domain $f(x)$: $x \in \mathbb{R}$; range $f(x)$: $y \geq 0$ **a)** domain: $x \in \mathbb{R}$; range: $y \geq -3$
b) domain: $x \in \mathbb{R}$; range: $y \geq 1$ **9.** $A'(11, 9)$ **10.** $y = 3, x = -4, x = 0$
12. domain: $-4 \leq x \leq 15$; range: $-9 \leq y \leq 2$ **13. a)** translated 1 unit right
b) translated 4 units left and 2 units down   **14.** $y - 3 = (x + 5)^3$
15. $y + 7 = |(x - 2)^2 - 2|$ **16. a)** Graph D   **b)** Graph A   **c)** Graph B
d) Graph C   **17. a)** 1 unit right   **b)** 6 units left   **18.** 5 units down

Multiple Choice

1. A   **2.** D

FOCUS Relate changes in the equation of a function to reflections of its graph in the *x*- and *y*-axes.

Get Started

Write the coordinates of each point.

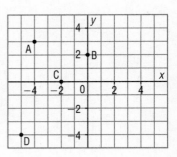

Reflect each point in the *x*-axis, then write the coordinates of the reflection image. What do you notice?

Reflect each given point in the *y*-axis, then write the coordinates of the reflection image. What do you notice?

Construct Understanding

On each grid below, reflect the original graph in the *x*-axis and in the *y*-axis. For each reflection, write an equation for the image graph. Describe any patterns in points on the graphs and the equations of the graphs.

Use the patterns to predict equations of the function $f(x) = |x^2 - 2x|$ after a reflection in the *x*-axis and in the *y*-axis. Use graphing technology to check your predictions.

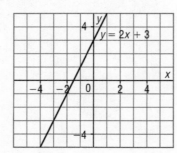

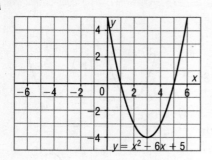

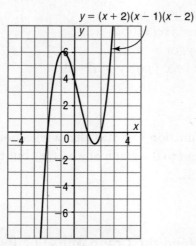

$y = (x + 2)(x - 1)(x - 2)$

The graph of a function $y = f(x)$ may be reflected in the x-axis or in the y-axis. For example, the graph of $y = -\sqrt{x - 2}$ is the image of the graph of $y = \sqrt{x - 2}$ after a reflection in the x-axis. The graph of $y = \sqrt{-x - 2}$ is the image of the graph of $y = \sqrt{x - 2}$ after a reflection in the y-axis.

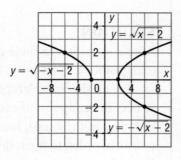

The point $(6, 2)$ lies on the graph of $y = \sqrt{x - 2}$.

The corresponding point on the graph of $y = \sqrt{-x - 2}$ is $(-6, 2)$, and the corresponding point on the graph of $y = -\sqrt{x - 2}$ is $(6, -2)$.

This example combined with the preceding examples can be generalized as follows.

Reflecting in the Axes

For a function $y = f(x)$

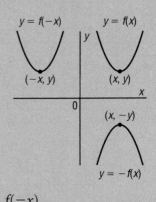

- The graph of $y = -f(x)$ is the image of the graph of $y = f(x)$ after a reflection in the x-axis. A point (x, y) on $y = f(x)$ corresponds to the point $(x, -y)$ on $y = -f(x)$.

- The graph of $y = f(-x)$ is the image of the graph of $y = f(x)$ after a reflection in the y-axis. A point (x, y) on $y = f(x)$ corresponds to the point $(-x, y)$ on $y = f(-x)$.

The image of the graph of a function $y = f(x)$ after a reflection in the x-axis or the y-axis is congruent to the graph of $y = f(x)$, but the graphs may have different orientations.

Example 1	Sketching the Graph of a Function after a Reflection

Check Your Understanding

1. Here is the graph of $y = g(x)$. Sketch the image graph after a reflection in the y-axis. State the domain and range of each function.

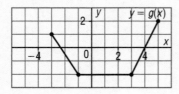

Here is the graph of $y = f(x)$. Sketch the image graph after a reflection in the x-axis. State the domain and range of each function.

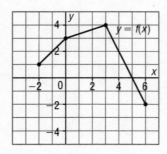

SOLUTION

After a reflection in the x-axis, the image of each point (x, y) on $y = f(x)$ is the point $(x, -y)$ on the image graph.
Reflect the endpoint of each line segment on $y = f(x)$ in the x-axis. Join corresponding points in order, to form the reflection image.
From the graph, both functions have domain: $-2 \le x \le 6$
The range of $y = f(x)$ is: $-2 \le y \le 4$
The range of the reflection image is: $-4 \le y \le 2$

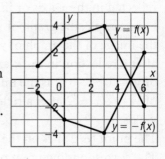

Here is the graph of $y = f(x)$. Sketch the graph of $y = f(-x)$. State the domain and range of each function.

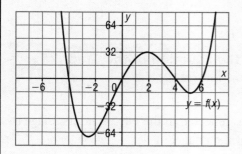

2. Here is the graph of $y = g(x)$. Sketch the graph of $y = -g(x)$. State the domain and range of each function.

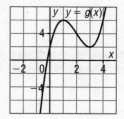

SOLUTION

The graph of $y = f(-x)$ is the image of the graph of $y = f(x)$ after a reflection in the y-axis. To sketch, use the transformation: (x, y) on $y = f(x)$ corresponds to $(-x, y)$ on $y = f(-x)$.

Estimate the coordinates of points on $y = f(x)$.

Point on $y = f(x)$	Point on $y = f(-x)$
$(-4, 0)$	$(4, 0)$
$(-3, -64)$	$(3, -64)$
$(-2, -64)$	$(2, -64)$
$(0, 0)$	$(0, 0)$
$(2, 32)$	$(-2, 32)$
$(4, 0)$	$(-4, 0)$
$(5, -16)$	$(-5, -16)$
$(6, 0)$	$(-6, 0)$

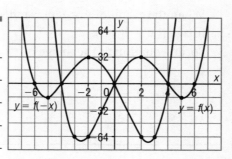

Plot the points, then draw a smooth curve through the points to form the graph of $y = f(-x)$.

Both functions have domain: $x \in \mathbb{R}$

Both functions have the same range. The approximate range is: $y \geq -68$

When the graph of a function is reflected in an axis, which points are invariant?

---

3. The graph of

$$y = \frac{1}{-2x^2 - 0.5}$$

was reflected in the x-axis and its image is shown. What is an equation of the image?

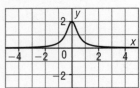

Example 3	Writing the Equation of the Graph of a Reflection Image

The graph of $y = \sqrt{x} - 3$ was reflected in the y-axis and its image is shown. What is an equation of the image?

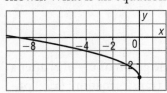

SOLUTION

When the graph of $y = f(x)$ is reflected in the y-axis, the equation of its image is $y = f(-x)$.

So, an equation of the image is:

$y = f(-x)$

$y = \sqrt{(-x)} - 3$

$y = \sqrt{-x} - 3$

THINK FURTHER

Suppose the graph of $y = f(x)$ is reflected in the x-axis, then its image is reflected in the y-axis. What is the equation of the final image?

When the equation of a function is given, the different reflections can be performed on a TI-83 Plus graphing calculator.

For example, to reflect the function in *Example 3*:

Define Y_1 as $\sqrt{x} - 3$.

To define Y_2 as $-f(x)$, set the cursor to the right of $Y_2 =$.

Press: (-) VARS ▶ 1 1

To define Y_3 as $f(-x)$, set the cursor to the right of $Y_3 =$.

Press: VARS ▶ 1 1 ((-) X,T,Θ,*n*)

Press: GRAPH
Here is what you should see:

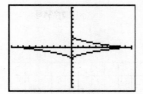

Discuss the Ideas

1. What is the relationship between the coordinates of a point and the coordinates of its image after a reflection in the *x*-axis and after a reflection in the *y*-axis?

2. What strategy do you use to remember which equation, $y = -f(x)$ or $y = f(-x)$, corresponds to a reflection in each axis?

Exercises

A

3. Here is the graph of $y = f(x)$. On the same grid, sketch its image after each reflection.

a) a reflection in the *x*-axis

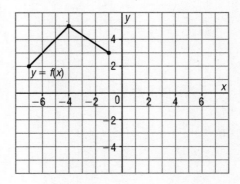

b) a reflection in the y-axis

4. Here is the graph of $y = g(x)$. On the same grid, sketch and label the graph of each function.

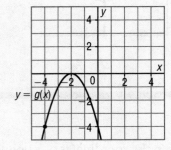

a) $y = -g(x)$

b) $y = g(-x)$

5. Here is the graph of $y = k(x)$. On the same grid, sketch and label the graph of each function below. State the domain and range of each function.

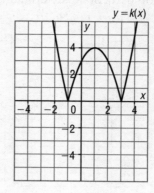

a) $y = -k(x)$

b) $y = k(-x)$

6. Sketch and label the graphs of each set of functions on the same grid. Describe the strategy you used. State the domain and range of each function.

   a) $y = |x - 3|$ $y = -|x - 3|$ $y = |-x - 3|$

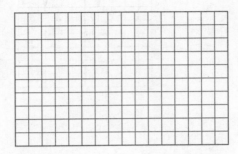

   b) $y = \sqrt{x - 4}$ $y = \sqrt{-x - 4}$ $y = -\sqrt{x - 4}$

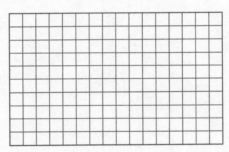

7. The graph of $y = \dfrac{1}{x - 2}$ was reflected in the x-axis and its image is shown. What is an equation of the image?

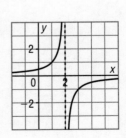

8. a) The graph of $y = x^3 + 3$ was reflected in the y-axis and its image is shown. What is an equation of the image? How can you verify your answer?

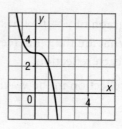

b) What is an equation of the image when the graph of $y = x^3 + 3$ is reflected in the x-axis?

9. Write an equation for the image of each function below after:
  i) a reflection of its graph in the x-axis
  ii) a reflection of its graph in the y-axis

a) $g(x) = -2x^3 + x^2 - 5x - 3$

b) $k(x) = \dfrac{1}{-(x + 3)^2 + 4}$

10. The graph of $y = f(x)$ has x-intercepts 5, 2, and -1, and y-intercept 10. What are the x-intercepts and y-intercept of the image graph after each reflection?

a) a reflection in the x-axis

b) a reflection in the y-axis

11. The function $y = f(x)$ has domain $-2 \leq x \leq 8$ and range $6 \leq y \leq 20$. Determine the domain and range of each function.

a) $y = -f(x)$

b) $y = f(-x)$

12. Determine where the graph of $f(x) = x^2 + x - 6$ intersects the graph of each function below. How do you know?

a) $y = -f(x)$

b) $y = f(-x)$

13. Here is the graph of $y = (x - 1)^3 + 2$. On the same grid, sketch
the graph of the final image after each pair of reflections.
Write the equation of the final image.

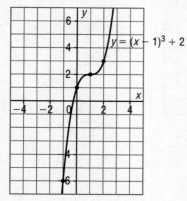

$y = (x - 1)^3 + 2$

a) a reflection in the y-axis, followed by a reflection in the x-axis

b) a reflection in the x-axis, followed by a reflection in the y-axis

c) Does the order in which the reflections are performed matter? Explain.

C

14. A function $f(x)$ is an *even function* when $f(x) = f(-x)$.

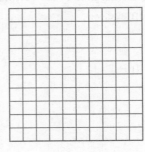

    a) Give 2 examples of even functions. Sketch their graphs.

    b) What property do all even functions share? Why?

15. A function $f(x)$ is an *odd function* when $f(-x) = -f(x)$.

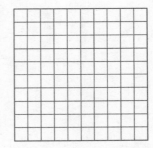

    a) Give 2 examples of odd functions. Sketch their graphs.

    b) What property do all odd functions share? Why?

Multiple-Choice Questions

    1. The graph of $y = g(x)$ is in Quadrants 1 and 2. In which quadrants is the graph of $y = -g(x)$?

       A. 1 and 2   **B.** 3 and 4   **C.** 2 and 4   **D.** 2 and 3

2. The graph of $y = -x^3 + 3x^2 - 4x + 1$ is reflected in the y-axis. What is an equation of its image?

A. $y = -x^3 - 3x^2 + 4x + 1$ **B.** $y = x^3 - 3x^2 + 4x + 1$

C. $y = -x^3 + 3x^2 - 4x + 1$ **D.** $y = x^3 + 3x^2 + 4x + 1$

Study Note

Describe relationships among the graphs of $y = f(x)$, $y = -f(x)$, and $y = f(-x)$.

ANSWERS

Check Your Understanding

1. domain of $y = g(x)$: $-3 \leq x \leq 5$; domain of reflection image: $-5 \leq x \leq 3$; both functions have range: $-2 \leq y \leq 2$

2. both functions have domain: $x \in \mathbb{R}$; both functions have range: $y \in \mathbb{R}$

3. $y = \dfrac{1}{2x^2 + 0.5}$

Exercises

5. $y = k(x)$: domain: $x \in \mathbb{R}$; range: $y \geq 0$

a) $y = -k(x)$: domain: $x \in \mathbb{R}$; range: $y \leq 0$

b) $y = k(-x)$: domain: $x \in \mathbb{R}$; range: $y \geq 0$

6. a) $y = |x - 3|$: domain $x \in \mathbb{R}$; range $y \geq 0$; $y = -|x - 3|$: domain $x \in \mathbb{R}$; range $y \leq 0$; $y = |-x - 3|$: domain $x \in \mathbb{R}$; range $y \geq 0$

b) $y = \sqrt{x - 4}$: domain $x \geq 4$; range $y \geq 0$; $y = \sqrt{-x - 4}$: domain $x \leq -4$; range $y \geq 0$; $y = -\sqrt{x - 4}$: domain $x \geq 4$; range $y \leq 0$

7. $y = \dfrac{1}{-x + 2}$ **8. a)** $y = -x^3 + 3$ **b)** $y = -x^3 - 3$

9. a) i) $y = 2x^3 - x^2 + 5x + 3$ **ii)** $y = 2x^3 + x^2 + 5x - 3$

b) i) $y = \dfrac{1}{(x + 3)^2 - 4}$ **ii)** $y = \dfrac{1}{-(-x + 3)^2 + 4}$

10. a) x-intercepts: $5, 2, -1$; y-intercept: -10

b) x-intercepts: $-5, -2, 1$; y-intercept: 10

11. a) domain: $-2 \leq x \leq 8$; range: $-20 \leq y \leq -6$

b) domain: $-8 \leq x \leq 2$; range: $6 \leq y \leq 20$ **12. a)** $(-3, 0), (2, 0)$ **b)** $(0, -6)$

13. a), b) $y = (x + 1)^3 - 2$ **c)** no   **14. b)** symmetrical about the y-axis

15. b) rotational symmetry of order 2 about the origin

Multiple Choice

1. B   **2.** D

FOCUS Relate changes in the equation of a function to stretches and compressions of its graph.

Get Started

Here is the graph of $y = x^2$.
How is the graph of $y = ax^2$ related to the
graph of $y = x^2$ for each value of a?

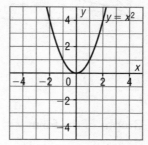

- $a = 0.5$

- $a = 2$

- $a = -0.5$

- $a = -2$

Construct Understanding

Look at the following graphs.
Each graph is the image of the graph of $y = \sqrt{x}$ after a transformation.
A point on the graph of $y = \sqrt{x}$ and its images are shown.
How does the graph of $y = a\sqrt{x}$ compare to the graph of $y = \sqrt{x}$?
What is the effect of a?
How does the graph of $y = \sqrt{bx}$ compare to the graph of $y = \sqrt{x}$?
What is the effect of b?
How does the graph of $y = a\sqrt{bx}$ compare to the graph of $y = \sqrt{x}$?
What are the effects of a and b?

Graphs of the form $y = a\sqrt{x}$

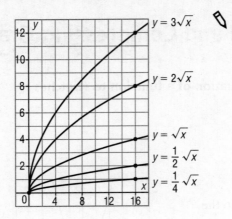

$y = 3\sqrt{x}$

$y = 2\sqrt{x}$

$y = \sqrt{x}$

$y = \frac{1}{2}\sqrt{x}$

$y = \frac{1}{4}\sqrt{x}$

Graphs of the form $y = \sqrt{bx}$

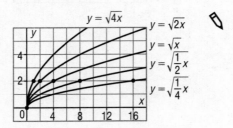

$y = \sqrt{4x}$

$y = \sqrt{2x}$

$y = \sqrt{x}$

$y = \sqrt{\frac{1}{2}x}$

$y = \sqrt{\frac{1}{4}x}$

Graphs of the form $y = a\sqrt{bx}$

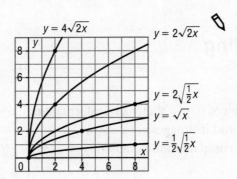

$y = 4\sqrt{2x}$

$y = 2\sqrt{2x}$

$y = 2\sqrt{\frac{1}{2}x}$

$y = \sqrt{x}$

$y = \frac{1}{2}\sqrt{\frac{1}{2}x}$

Consider the graph of $y = x^3$.

If y is replaced with $2y$, the equation becomes $2y = x^3$, or $y = \frac{1}{2}x^3$.

If y is replaced with $\frac{1}{2}y$, the equation becomes $\frac{1}{2}y = x^3$, or $y = 2x^3$.

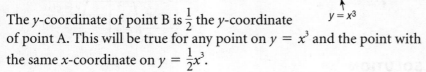

Look at the points where the graphs intersect the vertical line $x = 2$: A(2, 8), B(2, 4), C(2, 16)

The y-coordinate of point B is $\frac{1}{2}$ the y-coordinate of point A. This will be true for any point on $y = x^3$ and the point with the same x-coordinate on $y = \frac{1}{2}x^3$.

So, the graph of $y = \frac{1}{2}x^3$ is the image of the graph of $y = x^3$ after a vertical compression by a factor of $\frac{1}{2}$.

The y-coordinate of point C is 2 times the y-coordinate of point A. This will be true for any point on $y = x^3$ and the point with the same x-coordinate on $y = 2x^3$.

So, the graph of $y = 2x^3$ is the image of the graph of $y = x^3$ after a vertical stretch by a factor of 2.

Consider the graph of $y = x^3$.

If y is replaced with $-\frac{1}{2}y$, the equation becomes $-\frac{1}{2}y = x^3$, or $y = -2x^3$.

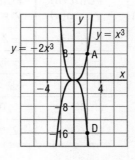

The y-coordinate of point D(2, −16) is −2 times the y-coordinate of point A(2, 8). This will be true for any point on $y = x^3$ and the point with the same x-coordinate on $y = -2x^3$.

So, the graph of $y = -2x^3$ is the image of the graph of $y = x^3$ after a vertical stretch by a factor of 2 and a reflection in the x-axis.

Vertical Stretches, Compressions, and Reflections

The graph of $y = af(x)$ is the image of the graph of $y = f(x)$ after a vertical stretch, compression, or reflection. Point (x, y) on $y = f(x)$ corresponds to point (x, ay) on $y = af(x)$.

- When $0 < |a| < 1$, there is a vertical compression by a factor of $|a|$.
- When $|a| > 1$, there is a vertical stretch by a factor of $|a|$.
- When $a < 0$, there is a reflection in the x-axis as well as the stretch or compression.

1. Here is the graph of $y = f(x)$. Sketch the graph of $y = -\frac{1}{4}f(x)$.

State the domain and range of each function.

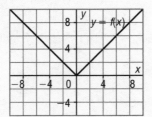

Here is the graph of $y = g(x)$. Sketch the graph of $y = -3g(x)$. State the domain and range of each function.

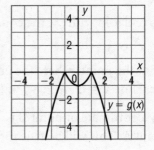

SOLUTION

Compare $y = ag(x)$ to $y = -3g(x)$:

$a = -3$

So, the graph of $y = g(x)$ is vertically stretched by a factor of 3, then reflected in the x-axis.

Use: (x, y) on $y = g(x)$ corresponds to $(x, -3y)$ on $y = -3g(x)$.

Choose the intercepts and some lattice points on $y = g(x)$.

Point on $y = g(x)$	Point on $y = -3g(x)$
$(-2, -3)$	$(-2, 9)$
$(-1, 0)$	$(-1, 0)$
$(0, -1)$	$(0, 3)$
$(1, 0)$	$(1, 0)$
$(2, -3)$	$(2, 9)$

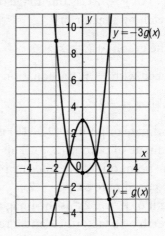

Plot the points, then draw a smooth curve through them.

Both functions have domain: $x \in \mathbb{R}$

The range of $y = g(x)$ is: $y \leq 0$

The range of $y = -3g(x)$ is: $y \geq 0$

THINK FURTHER

In *Example 1*, the graph of $y = g(x)$ has equation $y = -|-x^2 + 1|$. What is the explicit equation for $y = -3g(x)$?

Consider the graph of $y = x^3$.
If x is replaced with $2x$, the equation becomes $y = (2x)^3$.

If x is replaced with $\frac{1}{4}x$, the equation becomes $y = \left(\frac{1}{4}x\right)^3$.

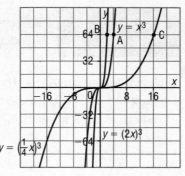

Look at the points where the graphs intersect the horizontal line $y = 64$:
A(4, 64), B(2, 64), C(16, 64)
The x-coordinate of point B is $\frac{1}{2}$ the x-coordinate of point A.

This will be true for any point on $y = x^3$ and the point with the same y-coordinate on $y = (2x)^3$. So, the graph of $y = (2x)^3$ is the image of the graph of $y = x^3$ after a horizontal compression by a factor of $\frac{1}{2}$.

The x-coordinate of point C is 4 times the x-coordinate of point A.
This will be true for any point on $y = x^3$ and the point with the same y-coordinate on $y = \left(\frac{1}{4}x\right)^3$. So, the graph of $y = \left(\frac{1}{4}x\right)^3$ is the image of the graph of $y = x^3$ after a horizontal stretch by a factor of 4.

Consider the graph of $y = x^3$.

If x is replaced with $-\frac{1}{4}x$, the equation becomes $y = \left(-\frac{1}{4}x\right)^3$.

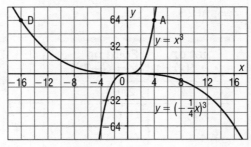

The x-coordinate of point D(−16, 64) is −4 times the x-coordinate of point A(4, 64).
This will be true for any point on $y = x^3$ and the point with the same y-coordinate on $y = \left(-\frac{1}{4}x\right)^3$. So, the graph of $y = \left(-\frac{1}{4}x\right)^3$ is the image of the graph of $y = x^3$ after a horizontal stretch by a factor of 4 and a reflection in the y-axis.

Horizontal Stretches, Compressions, and Reflections

The graph of $y = f(bx)$ is the image of the graph of $y = f(x)$ after a horizontal stretch, compression, or reflection. Point (x, y) on $y = f(x)$ corresponds to point $\left(\frac{x}{b}, y\right)$ on $y = f(bx)$.

- When $0 < |b| < 1$, there is a horizontal stretch by a factor of $\frac{1}{|b|}$.

- When $|b| > 1$, there is a horizontal compression by a factor of $\frac{1}{|b|}$.

- When $b < 0$, there is a reflection in the y-axis as well as the stretch or compression.

2. Here is the graph of $y = g(x)$. Sketch the graph of $y = g(0.5x)$. State the domain and range of each function.

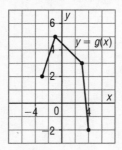

Here is the graph of $y = f(x)$. Sketch the graph of $y = f(-3x)$. State the domain and range of each function.

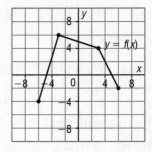

SOLUTION

Compare $y = f(bx)$ to $y = f(-3x)$: $b = -3$

So, the graph of $y = f(x)$ is horizontally compressed by a factor of $\frac{1}{3}$, then reflected in the y-axis.

Use: (x, y) on $y = f(x)$ corresponds to $\left(\dfrac{x}{-3}, y\right)$ on $y = f(-3x)$.

The graph consists of line segments. Choose the endpoints of the line segments.

Point on $y = f(x)$	Point on $y = f(-3x)$
$(-6, -4)$	$(2, -4)$
$(-3, 6)$	$(1, 6)$
$(3, 4)$	$(-1, 4)$
$(6, -2)$	$(-2, -2)$

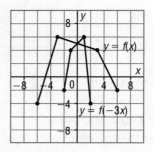

Plot the points, then join them in order with line segments.

The domain of $y = f(x)$ is: $-6 \leq x \leq 6$

The domain of $y = f(-3x)$ is: $-2 \leq x \leq 2$

Both functions have range: $-4 \leq y \leq 6$

Combining Transformations

Stretches, compressions, and reflections may be combined.

The point (x, y) on $y = f(x)$ corresponds to the point $\left(\dfrac{x}{b}, ay\right)$ on $y = af(bx)$.

Example 3 — **Sketching the Graph of a Function after a Combination of Transformations**

Check Your Understanding

Here is the graph of $y = h(x)$.

Sketch the graph of $y = -\dfrac{1}{2}h(2x)$.

State the domain and range of each function.

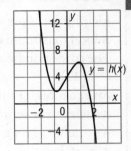

3. Here is the graph of $y = f(x)$. Sketch the graph of $y = 4f(-0.5x)$. State the domain and range of each function.

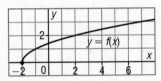

SOLUTION

Compare $y = ah(bx)$ to $y = -\dfrac{1}{2}h(2x)$:

$a = -\dfrac{1}{2}$ and $b = 2$

So, the graph of $y = h(x)$ is vertically compressed by a factor of $\dfrac{1}{2}$, horizontally compressed by a factor of $\dfrac{1}{2}$, then reflected in the x-axis.

Use: (x, y) on $y = h(x)$ corresponds to $\left(\dfrac{x}{2}, -\dfrac{1}{2}y\right)$ on $y = -\dfrac{1}{2}h(2x)$.
Choose lattice points on $y = h(x)$.

Point on $y = h(x)$	Point on $y = -0.5h(2x)$
$(-2, 12)$	$(-1, -6)$
$(-1, 2)$	$(-0.5, -1)$
$(0, 4)$	$(0, -2)$
$(1, 6)$	$(0.5, -3)$
$(2, -4)$	$(1, 2)$

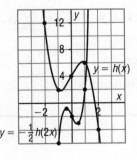

Plot the points, then join them with a smooth curve.
Both functions have domain: $x \in \mathbb{R}$
Both functions have range: $y \in \mathbb{R}$

---

4. The graphs of $y = f(x)$ and its image after a vertical and/or horizontal compression are shown. Write an equation of the image graph in terms of the function f.

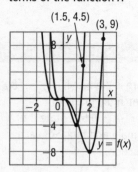

(1.5, 4.5) (3, 9)

The graphs of $y = f(x)$ and its image after a vertical and/or horizontal stretch are shown. Write an equation of the image graph in terms of the function f.

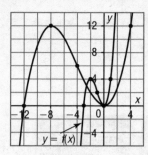

SOLUTION

Identify corresponding points on $y = f(x)$ and its image.

A local maximum of $y = f(x)$ has coordinates $(-2, 4)$.

The corresponding local maximum of its image has coordinates $(-8, 12)$.

An equation for the image graph after a vertical and/or horizontal stretch can be written in the form $y = af(bx)$.

A point (x, y) on $y = f(x)$ corresponds to the point $\left(\dfrac{x}{b}, ay\right)$ on $y = af(bx)$.

So, the image of $(-2, 4)$ is $\left(\dfrac{-2}{b}, a(4)\right)$, which is $(-8, 12)$.

Equate the x-coordinates:
$$-8 = \frac{-2}{b}$$
$$b = \frac{1}{4}, \text{ or } 0.25$$

Equate the y-coordinates:
$$12 = a(4)$$
$$a = 3$$

So, an equation is: $y = 3f\left(\dfrac{1}{4}x\right)$

Verify with a different pair of corresponding points.

$(1, 4)$ lies on $y = f(x)$ so $\left(\dfrac{1}{0.25}, 3(4)\right)$, or $(4, 12)$ should lie on

$y = 3f\left(\dfrac{1}{4}x\right)$, which it does.

So, the equation $y = 3f\left(\dfrac{1}{4}x\right)$ is likely correct.

Discuss the Ideas

1. How is the image of a graph after a translation different from the image of the graph after a stretch?

2. Why does the graph of $y = 2f(x)$ illustrate a stretch of the graph of $y = f(x)$, while the graph of $y = f(2x)$ illustrates a compression of the graph of $y = f(x)$?

Exercises

A

3. Here is the graph of $y = g(x)$. On the same grid, sketch the graph of each function.

a) $y = \frac{1}{3}g(x)$

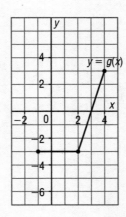

b) $y = -2g(x)$

4. Here is the graph of $y = f(x)$. On the same grid, sketch the graph of each function.

   a) $y = f(4x)$

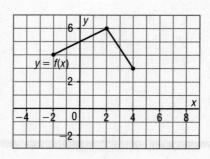

   b) $y = f\left(\frac{1}{2}x\right)$

5. The graph of $y = f(x)$ is transformed as described below. Write an equation of the image graph in terms of the function f.

   a) a vertical stretch by a factor of 4

   b) a horizontal compression by a factor of $\frac{1}{3}$ and a reflection in the y-axis

   c) a vertical compression by a factor of $\frac{1}{5}$ and a reflection in the x-axis

B

6. The graph of $y = |x|$ is transformed, and the equation of its image is $y = |2x|$. Student A says the graph of $y = |x|$ was horizontally compressed by a factor of $\frac{1}{2}$. Student B says the graph of $y = |x|$ was vertically stretched by a factor of 2. Who is correct? Explain.

7. The point A(36, 6) lies on the graph of $y = \sqrt{x}$. What are the coordinates of its image A′ on the graph of $y = -\frac{1}{2}\sqrt{3x}$? How do you know?

8. Here is the graph of $y = g(x)$. On the same grid, sketch the graph of each function. State the domain and range of each function.

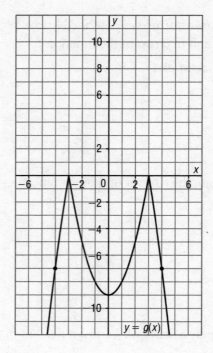

$y = g(x)$

a) $y = g\left(\frac{3}{4}x\right)$

b) $y = -\frac{1}{2}g(x)$

9. On each grid, sketch the graph of each given function then state its domain and range.

a) i) $y = (-2x)^3$

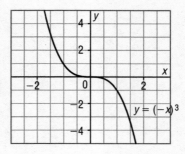

ii) $y = \frac{1}{2}(-2x)^3$

b) i) $y = 2\sqrt{3x}$

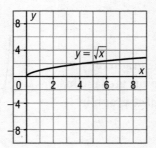

ii) $y = -3\sqrt{3x}$

10. The function $f(x) = (x - 10)(x + 8)$ has zeros at 10 and –8.

What are the zeros of the function $y = 4f\left(\frac{1}{3}x\right)$?

11. Use transformations to describe how the graph of the second function compares to the graph of the first function.

a) $y = 3x + 4$ $y = -\frac{1}{2}(3(5x) + 4)$

b) $y = x^3 - 6x$ $y = \frac{1}{4}\left[\left(-\frac{1}{2}x\right)^3 - 6\left(-\frac{1}{2}x\right)\right]$

12. The graph of $y = g(x)$ is a transformation image of the graph of $y = f(x)$. Corresponding points are labelled. Write an equation of the image graph in terms of the function f.

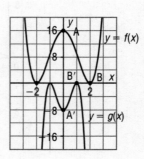

13. The graph of $y = h(x)$ is a transformation image of the graph of $y = \sqrt{x}$. Corresponding points are labelled. Write an equation of the image graph in terms of x.

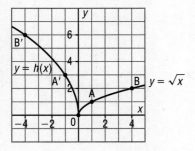

14. a) Determine the equation of the function $y = \sqrt{x}$ after each transformation.

   i) a horizontal compression by a factor of $\frac{1}{9}$

   ii) a vertical stretch by a factor of 3

b) What do you notice about the equations in part a? Explain.

c) Write the equation of a different function whose image would be the same after two different stretches or compressions. Justify your answer.

15. a) Write the equation of a quartic or quintic polynomial function.

b) Sketch its graph.

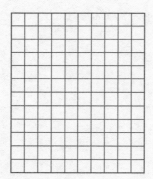

c) Choose a vertical and a horizontal stretch or compression. Sketch the final image after these transformations on the grid in part b.

d) Write an equation of the final image.

16. On the same grid:

a) Sketch the graph of $y = \dfrac{1}{x^2} + 2$.

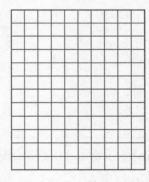

b) Sketch the final image after a vertical stretch by a factor of 2, a reflection in the *x*-axis, and a horizontal compression by a factor of $\frac{1}{2}$.

c) How does the final image relate to the graph of $y = \frac{1}{x^2}$? Are the asymptotes the same? Explain.

Multiple-Choice Questions

1. The graph of $y = g(x)$ is transformed, and the equation of the image graph is $y = -3g\left(\frac{1}{4}x\right)$. Which statement describes how the graph of $y = g(x)$ may have been transformed?

A. Vertically stretched by a factor of 3, reflected in the *y*-axis, then horizontally stretched by a factor of 4

B. Horizontally stretched by a factor of 3, reflected in the *x*-axis, then vertically stretched by a factor of $\frac{1}{4}$

C. Vertically stretched by a factor of 3, reflected in the *x*-axis, then horizontally stretched by a factor of 4

D. Vertically stretched by a factor of 3, reflected in the *y*-axis, then horizontally compressed by a factor of $\frac{1}{4}$

2. After a transformation, the image of point (x, y) on the graph of $y = f(x)$ is $(2x, 3y)$. What is the equation of the transformation image?

    A. $y = 3f(2x)$ **B.** $y = 3f\left(\dfrac{1}{2}x\right)$

    C. $y = \dfrac{1}{2}f(3x)$ **D.** $y = 2f\left(\dfrac{1}{3}x\right)$

Study Note

How does the graph of a function $y = af(bx)$ relate to the graph of the function $y = f(x)$?

ANSWERS

Check Your Understanding

1. both functions have domain: $x \in \mathbb{R}$; range of $y = f(x)$: $y \geq 0$; range of $y = -\dfrac{1}{4}f(x)$: $y \leq 0$ **2.** domain of $y = g(x)$: $-3 \leq x \leq 4$; domain of $y = g(0.5x)$: $-6 \leq x \leq 8$; both functions have range: $-2 \leq y \leq 5$

3. domain of $y = f(x)$ is: $x \geq -2$; domain of $y = 4f(-0.5x)$ is: $x \leq 4$; both functions have range: $y \geq 0$ **4.** $y = \dfrac{1}{2}f(2x)$

Exercises

5. a) $y = 4f(x)$ **b)** $y = f(-3x)$ **c)** $y = -\dfrac{1}{5}f(x)$ **7.** A'$(12, -3)$

8. a) both functions have domain $x \in \mathbb{R}$ and range $y \leq 0$
b) both functions have domain $x \in \mathbb{R}$; range of $y = g(x)$: $y \leq 0$; range of $y = -\dfrac{1}{2}g(x)$: $y \geq 0$ **9. a) i), ii)** both functions have domain $x \in \mathbb{R}$ and range $y \in \mathbb{R}$
b) i) domain: $x \geq 0$; range: $y \geq 0$ **ii)** domain: $x \geq 0$; range: $y \leq 0$

10. $30, -24$ **12.** $y = -\dfrac{1}{2}f(2x)$ **13.** $y = 3\sqrt{-x}$ **14. a) i)** $y = 3\sqrt{x}$ **ii)** $y = 3\sqrt{x}$

Multiple Choice

1. C   **2.** B

Additional Workspace

Self-Assess

Can you ...	Try *Checkpoint* question	For review, see
sketch the graph of $y - k = f(x - h)$, given the values of h and k and the graph of $y = f(x)$?	2	Page 166 in Lesson 3.1 (Example 2)
write the equation of a function whose graph is a vertical and/or horizontal translation of the graph of $y = f(x)$?	3	Page 166 in Lesson 3.1 (Example 2)
sketch the reflection of the graph of $y = f(x)$ in the x-axis or the y-axis, given the graph of $y = f(x)$?	5	Page 180 in Lesson 3.2 (Example 1)
sketch the graphs of $y = -f(x)$ and $y = f(-x)$, given the graph of $y = f(x)$?	5	Page 181 in Lesson 3.2 (Example 2)
write the equation of a function, given its graph which is a reflection of the graph of $y = f(x)$ in the x-axis or the y-axis?	6	Page 182 in Lesson 3.2 (Example 3)
sketch the graph of $y = af(bx)$ for given values of a and b, given the graph of $y = f(x)$?	8	Page 199 in Lesson 3.3 (Example 3)
write the equation of a function, given its graph which is a vertical and/or horizontal stretch or compression of the graph of $y = f(x)$?	9	Page 200 in Lesson 3.3 (Example 4)

Assess Your Understanding

3.1

1. **Multiple Choice** The graph of $y = -3x^3 + 4$ is translated 4 units right and 5 units down. What is an equation of the translation image?

   A. $y = -3(x + 4)^3 + 9$ **B.** $y = -3(x - 4)^3 + 9$

   C. $y = -3(x + 4)^3 - 1$ **D.** $y = -3(x - 4)^3 - 1$

2. Here is the graph of $y = g(x)$. On the same grid, sketch the graph of each function below. State the domain and range of each function.

a) $y - 3 = g(x)$

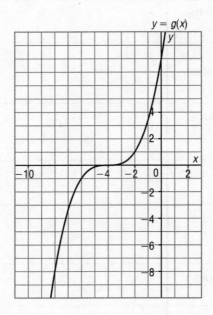

b) $y = g(x + 2)$

c) $y + 1 = g(x - 3)$

3. The graph of $y = f(x)$ was translated to create each graph below.
Write an equation of each graph in terms of the function f.

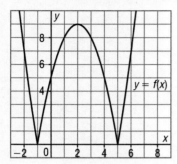

a)

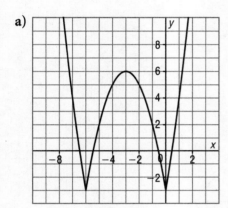

b)

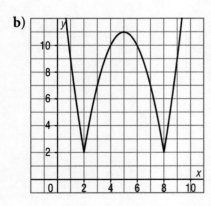

3.2

4. Multiple Choice The graph of $y = f(x)$ was
reflected in the x-axis. Which graph below
is its reflection image?

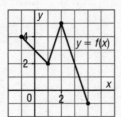

A.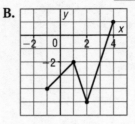

B.

C.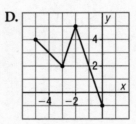

D.

5. Here is the graph of $y = k(x)$. On the same
grid, sketch and label the graph of each
function below, then state its domain and
range.

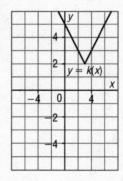

a) $y = -k(x)$

b) $y = k(-x)$

6. The graph of $y = -x^3 + 3x^2 - x + 3$ was reflected in the y-axis and its image is shown. What is an equation of the image?

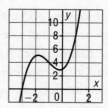

7. Multiple Choice The point $(-6, 2)$ lies on the graph of $y = f(x)$. After vertical and horizontal stretches or compressions of the graph, the equation of the image is $y = 3f(2x)$. Which point is the image of $(-6, 2)$?

A. $(-3, 6)$ **B.** $(-12, 6)$ **C.** $(-2, 4)$ **D.** $(-18, 1)$

8. Here is the graph of $y = h(x)$. On the same grid, sketch the graph of each function below, then state its domain and range.

a) $y = \frac{1}{3}h(-2x)$

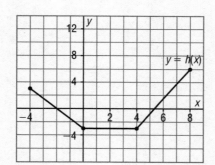

b) $y = 2h(4x)$

9. The graph of $y = g(x)$ is the image of the graph of $y = f(x)$ after a vertical and/or horizontal stretch and/or reflection. Corresponding points are labelled. Write an equation of the image graph in terms of the function f.

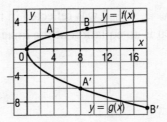

3.4 Combining Transformations of Functions

FOCUS Apply translations and stretches to the graphs and equations of functions.

Get Started

Two different transformation images of the graph of $y = \sqrt{x}$ are shown.
Write an equation for each transformation image.

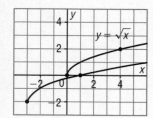
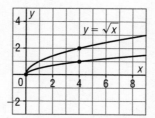

Construct Understanding

On the same grid, sketch the graph of each function below then describe it as a transformation image of the preceding graph.

- $y = |x|$
- $y = |2x|$
- $y = \frac{1}{4}|2x|$
- $y = \frac{1}{4}|2(x + 3)|$
- $y = \frac{1}{4}|2(x + 3)| + 4$

Describe how the graph of $y = \frac{1}{4}|2(x + 3)| + 4$ is related to the graph of $y = |x|$.

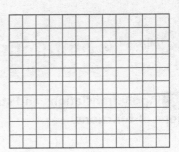

Here is the graph of $y = x^3$ and its images after a translation of 2 units down, followed by a vertical stretch by a factor of 3.

Here is the graph of $y = x^3$ and its images after a vertical stretch by a factor of 3, followed by a translation of 2 units down.

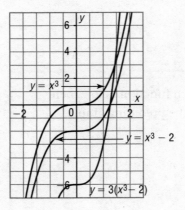

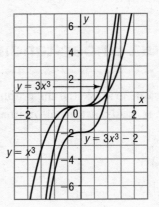

The same transformations are applied, but the image graphs are different. When two or more transformations are applied to a graph, the order in which the transformations are applied may make a difference; as shown above.

Here is the graph of $y = f(x)$. Sketch and label its image after a horizontal compression by a factor of $\frac{1}{2}$, then a translation of 3 units left.

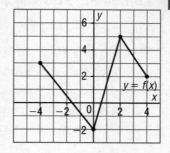

1. Here is the graph of $y = g(x)$.

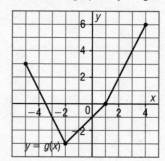

Sketch and label its image after a vertical compression by a factor of $\frac{1}{3}$, then a translation of 2 units up.

SOLUTION

Perform the horizontal compression by a factor of $\frac{1}{2}$ first.

The point (x, y) on $y = f(x)$ corresponds to the point $\left(\frac{x}{2}, y\right)$ on the image graph $y = f(2x)$.

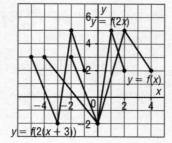

Point on $y = f(x)$	Point on $y = f(2x)$
$(-4, 3)$	$(-2, 3)$
$(0, -2)$	$(0, -2)$
$(2, 5)$	$(1, 5)$
$(4, 2)$	$(2, 2)$

Plot the points, then join them in order with line segments to form the graph of $y = f(2x)$. Then translate this graph 3 units left to form the graph of $y = f(2(x + 3))$.

The results from Lessons 3.1 to 3.3 can be combined.

Combining Stretches, Compressions, and Translations

The graph of $y - k = af(b(x - h))$ is the image of the graph of $y = f(x)$ after these transformations:

- a horizontal stretch or compression by a factor of $\frac{1}{|b|}$;
- a reflection in the y-axis if $b < 0$;
- a vertical stretch or compression by a factor of $|a|$;
- a reflection in the x-axis if $a < 0$

Followed by:

- a horizontal translation of h units
- a vertical translation of k units

Point (x, y) on the graph of $y = f(x)$ corresponds to the point $\left(\frac{x}{b} + h, ay + k \right)$ on the graph of $y - k = af(b(x - h))$; this is the *general transformation*.

When graphing from an equation, to ensure the correct transformation image is sketched, apply the transformations in this order:

- stretches or compressions
- reflections
- translations

THINK FURTHER

How do the expressions in $\left(\frac{x}{b} + h, ay + k \right)$ account for the order in which the transformations should be performed?

Example 2

Example 2 | **Using the General Transformation to Sketch the Graph of a Function**

Here is the graph of $y = f(x)$. Sketch the graph of $y - 6 = f(4(x + 2))$. State the domain and range of each function.

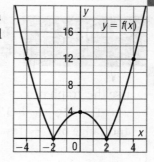

2. Here is the graph of $y = f(x)$. Sketch the graph of

$y + 4 = f\left(\frac{1}{2}(x + 1)\right)$. State the domain and range of each function.

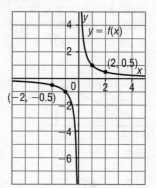

SOLUTION

Compare: $y - k = af(b(x - h))$ to
$$y - 6 = f(4(x + 2))$$
$k = 6, a = 1, b = 4,$ and $h = -2$

So, the graph of $y = f(x)$ is horizontally compressed by a factor of $\frac{1}{4}$, then translated 2 units left and 6 units up. Use the general transformation: (x, y) corresponds to $\left(\frac{x}{b} + h, ay + k\right)$

The point (x, y) on $y = f(x)$ corresponds to the point $\left(\frac{x}{4} - 2, y + 6\right)$ on $y - 6 = f(4(x + 2))$.

Choose some lattice points on $y = f(x)$, including the intercepts.

Point on $y = f(x)$	Point on $y - 6 = f(4(x + 2))$
(x, y)	$\left(\frac{x}{4} - 2, y + 6\right)$
$(-4, 12)$	$(-3, 18)$
$(-2, 0)$	$(-2.5, 6)$
$(0, 4)$	$(-2, 10)$
$(2, 0)$	$(-1.5, 6)$
$(4, 12)$	$(-1, 18)$

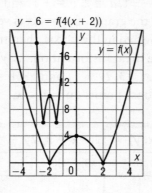

Plot the points, then draw a smooth curve through them.
The domain of $y = f(x)$ is: $x \in \mathbb{R}$
The range of $y = f(x)$ is: $y \geq 0$
The domain of $y - 6 = f(4(x + 2))$ is: $x \in \mathbb{R}$
The range of $y - 6 = f(4(x + 2))$ is: $y \geq 6$

In Chapter 2, you studied the graph of $y = \sqrt{x}$.
Example 3 illustrates 4 transformations of this function.

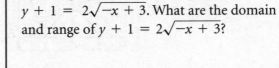

Example 3 — Transforming the Graph of a Radical Function

Check Your Understanding

3. Use the graph of $y = \sqrt{x}$ to graph $y - 2 = -\sqrt{3x + 3}$. What are the domain and range of $y - 2 = -\sqrt{3x + 3}$?

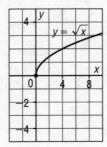

Use the graph of $y = \sqrt{x}$ to graph $y + 1 = 2\sqrt{-x + 3}$. What are the domain and range of $y + 1 = 2\sqrt{-x + 3}$?

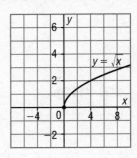

SOLUTION

$y + 1 = 2\sqrt{-x + 3}$

To write the equation in the form $y - k = a\sqrt{b(x - h)}$, remove a common factor of –1 in the radicand.

$y + 1 = 2\sqrt{-1(x - 3)}$

Compare: $y - k = a\sqrt{b(x - h)}$ to $y + 1 = 2\sqrt{-1(x - 3)}$

$k = -1, a = 2, b = -1,$ and $h = 3$

So, the graph of $y = \sqrt{x}$ is vertically stretched by a factor of 2, reflected in the y-axis, then translated 3 units right and 1 unit down.

Use the transformation: (x, y) on $y = \sqrt{x}$ corresponds to $(-x + 3, 2y - 1)$ on $y + 1 = 2\sqrt{-x + 3}$.

Choose points on $y = \sqrt{x}$.

(x, y)	$(-x + 3, 2y - 1)$
$(0, 0)$	$(3, -1)$
$(1, 1)$	$(2, 1)$
$(4, 2)$	$(-1, 3)$
$(9, 3)$	$(-6, 5)$

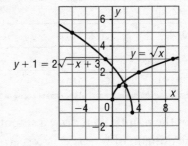

Plot the points, then draw a smooth curve through them.

Domain of $y + 1 = 2\sqrt{-x + 3}$: $x \leq 3$

Range of $y + 1 = 2\sqrt{-x + 3}$: $y \geq -1$

| Example 4 | **Writing the Equation of a Function after Transformations** |

The graph of $y = g(x)$ is the image of the graph of $y = f(x)$ after a combination of transformations. Corresponding points are labelled. Write then verify an equation for the image graph in terms of the function f.

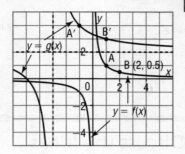

4. The graph of $y = g(x)$ is the image of the graph of $y = f(x)$ after a combination of transformations. Corresponding points are labelled. Write then verify an equation for the image graph in terms of the function f.

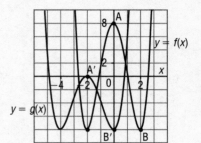

SOLUTION

Write the equation for the image graph in the form $y - k = af(b(x - h))$.
To identify the transformations, use A(1, 1) and B(2, 0.5).
The horizontal distance between A and B is: $|2 - 1| = 1$
The vertical distance between A and B is: $|0.5 - 1| = 0.5$
Use A$'(-1, 4)$ and B$'(1, 3)$:
The horizontal distance between A$'$ and B$'$ is: $|1 - (-1)| = 2$
The vertical distance between A$'$ and B$'$ is: $|3 - 4| = 1$
The horizontal distance doubles, so the graph of $y = f(x)$ is horizontally stretched by a factor of 2.
The vertical distance doubles, so the graph of $y = f(x)$ is vertically stretched by a factor of 2.
So, $a = 2$ and $b = \frac{1}{2}$, or 0.5
To determine the coordinates of A(1, 1) after these stretches, substitute:
$x = 1$, $y = 1$, $a = 2$, and $b = 0.5$ in $\left(\frac{x}{b}, ay\right)$ to get $\left(\frac{1}{0.5}, 2\right)$, or (2, 2).

Determine the translation that would move (2, 2) to A$'(-1, 4)$.
A translation of 3 units left and 2 units up is required, so $h = -3$ and $k = 2$.
An equation for the image graph in terms of $f(x)$ is:
$y - 2 = 2f(0.5(x + 3))$
Check:
Each point (x, y) on $y = f(x)$ corresponds to the point $(2x - 3, 2y + 2)$ on $y - 2 = 2f(0.5(x + 3))$.
So, the image of B(2, 0.5) is: $(2(2) - 3, 2(0.5) + 2)$, or B$'(1, 3)$
Since B$'$ lies on $y = g(x)$, the equation is likely correct.

THINK FURTHER

In *Example 4*, how could you use the asymptotes of the graphs to determine the translation?

Discuss the Ideas

1. To graph $y - k = af(b(x - h))$, which transformations are applied to the graph of $y = f(x)$ when a, b, k, or h is negative?

2. Functions of the form $y - k = a\sqrt{b(x - h)}$ form a *family of functions*. Why do you think $y = \sqrt{x}$ is considered the original or *parent function* in this family?

Exercises

A

3. The graph of $y = g(x)$ is the image of the graph of $y = f(x)$ after a single transformation. Identify the transformation.

a)

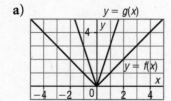

b)

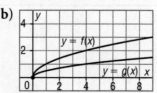

4. Describe how the graph of each function below is related to the graph of $y = f(x)$.

   a) $y + 5 = -2f(x)$

   b) $y = f(3(x - 4))$

   c) $y = \frac{1}{2}f(x + 7)$

   d) $y - 2 = f\left(\frac{1}{3}x\right)$

5. The graph of $y = f(x)$ is transformed as described below. Write the equation of the image graph in terms of the function f.

   a) a horizontal compression by a factor of $\frac{1}{4}$, a reflection in the y-axis, and a translation of 3 units left

   b) a vertical compression by a factor of $\frac{1}{2}$, a reflection in the y-axis, and a translation of 7 units up

   c) a horizontal stretch by a factor of 5, a vertical compression by a factor of $\frac{1}{3}$, and a translation of 6 units left and 3 units up

B

6. Here is the graph of $y = f(x)$. On the same grid, sketch and label its image after a vertical stretch by a factor of 3, and a translation of 4 units left and 2 units down.

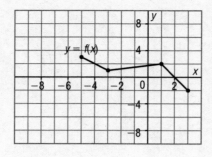

7. Here is the graph of $y = f(x)$. On the same grid, sketch the graph of each function below then state its domain and range.

a) $y - 3 = -\frac{1}{2}f(2(x + 1))$

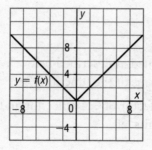

b) $y + 1 = 3f(-(x - 4))$

8. On each grid, graph $y = \sqrt{x}$, apply transformations to sketch the given function, then state its domain and range.

   a) $y = -\sqrt{x + 2}$

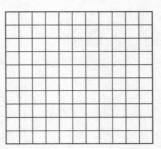

   b) $y + 5 = -2\sqrt{3(x - 1)}$

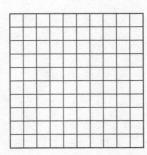

9. The graph of $y = g(x)$ is the image of the graph of $y = f(x)$ after a combination of transformations. Corresponding points are labelled. Write an equation of each image graph in terms of the function f.

a)

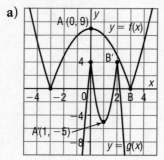

b)

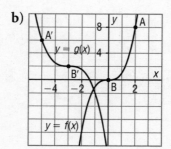

10. For each pair of functions below, describe the graph of the second function as a transformation image of the graph of the first function.

a) $y = |x|$ $y + 6 = -2|3(x - 4)|$

b) $y = \frac{1}{x}$ $y - 3 = 2\left(\frac{5}{x + 1}\right)$

c) $y = x^4$ $y + 1 = \frac{1}{4}[-2(x + 3)]^4$

11. A transformation image of the graph of $y = f(x)$ is represented by the equation $y - 1 = -2f\left(\frac{x + 5}{3}\right)$. The point $(7, 5)$ lies on the image graph. What are the coordinates of the corresponding point on the graph of $y = f(x)$?

12. This graph is the image of the graph of $y = |x|$ after a combination of transformations. Write an equation of the image.

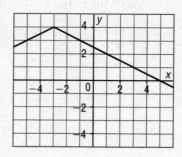

Multiple-Choice Questions

1. The graph of $y = f(x)$ is horizontally compressed by a factor of $\frac{1}{2}$, then translated 2 units right. Which equation represents the transformation image?

A. $y = f(2x + 4)$ **B.** $y = f(2x - 4)$

C. $y = f\left(\dfrac{x - 2}{2}\right)$ **D.** $y = f\left(\dfrac{x}{2} - 2\right)$

2. The image of the graph of $y = f(x)$ after a combination of transformations is shown. Which equation represents the image graph?

A. $y - 3 = \frac{1}{2}f(x - 1)$

B. $y - 3 = f(2(x - 1))$

C. $y + 3 = 2f(x - 1)$

D. $y + 3 = f\left(\frac{1}{2}(x - 1)\right)$

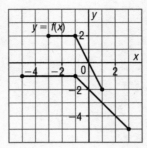

Study Note

When you are given the graph of a function and its transformation image, how do you identify the types of transformations that were used?

ANSWERS

Check Your Understanding

2. $y = f(x)$: domain: $x \neq 0$; range: $y \neq 0$; $y + 4 = f\left(\frac{1}{2}(x + 1)\right)$: domain: $x \neq -1$;

range: $y \neq -4$ **3.** domain: $x \geq -1$; range: $y \leq 2$ **4.** $y + 4 = 0.5f(x + 2)$

Exercises

5. a) $y = f(-4(x + 3))$ **b)** $y - 7 = \frac{1}{2}f(-x)$ **c)** $y - 3 = \frac{1}{3}f\left(\frac{1}{5}(x + 6)\right)$

7. a) domain: $x \in \mathbb{R}$, range: $y \leq 3$ **b)** domain: $x \in \mathbb{R}$, range: $y \geq -1$

8. a) domain: $x \geq -2$, range: $y \leq 0$ **b)** domain: $x \geq 1$, range: $y \leq -5$

9. a) $y - 4 = -f(3(x - 1))$ **b)** $y - 2 = \frac{1}{2}f(-(x + 3))$

11. $(4, -2)$ **12.** $y - 4 = -\frac{1}{2}|x + 3|$

Multiple Choice

1. B   **2.** D

3.5 Inverse Relations

FOCUS Graph inverse relations and determine equations.

Get Started

Solve each equation for x.

- $y = 3x - 4$

- $y = \dfrac{3x - 5}{2}$

- $y = 3x^2 - 5$

- $y = 2(x - 3)^2 + 4$

Construct Understanding

State the domain and range of each function below.
On each grid, reflect the graph in the line $y = x$.
Describe your strategy.
State the domain and range of the reflection image.
What is the relationship between the coordinates of pairs of
corresponding points?
Use this relationship to describe a possible rule for reflecting a
graph in the line $y = x$.

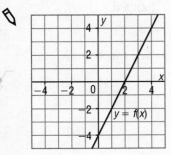

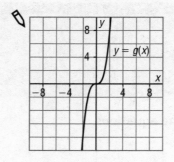

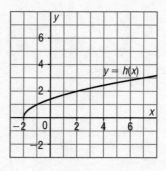

Here are the graphs of $y = 2x + 4$ and $y = \frac{1}{2}x - 2$.

The graph of $y = \frac{1}{2}x - 2$ is the image of the graph of $y = 2x + 4$ after a reflection in the line $y = x$.

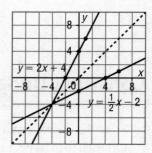

A point, such as $(-4, -4)$, which lies on the graphs of $y = f(x)$ and $y = x$ is an *invariant point*. This point also lies on the graph of the inverse.

Point on $y = 2x + 4$	Point on $y = \frac{1}{2}x - 2$
(1, 6)	(6, 1)
(0, 4)	(4, 0)
(−2, 0)	(0, −2)

The coordinates of corresponding points are interchanged.

$y = \frac{1}{2}x - 2$ is the *inverse* of the function $y = 2x + 4$.

The equation of the inverse, $y = \frac{1}{2}x - 2$, can be solved for x and written as $x = 2y + 4$, or $x = f(y)$.

Reflecting in the Line $y = x$

For a function $y = f(x)$, the graph of $x = f(y)$ is the image of the graph of $y = f(x)$ after a reflection in the line $y = x$.
$y = f(x)$ and $x = f(y)$ are inverses of each other.
A point (x, y) on $y = f(x)$ corresponds to the point (y, x) on $x = f(y)$.

When the inverse is also a function, the notation $f^{-1}(x)$ is used to denote the **inverse function**. We say, "f *inverse of x*."
For example, when $f(x) = 2x + 4$, then $f^{-1}(x) = \frac{1}{2}x - 2$

Example 1 | **Sketching the Inverse of a Function Given Its Graph**

Here is the graph of $y = f(x)$.

a) Sketch the graph of its inverse on the same grid.
b) Is the inverse a function? Explain.
c) State the domain and range of the function and its inverse.

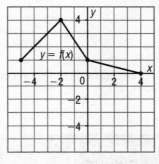

Check Your Understanding

1. Here is the graph of $y = g(x)$.

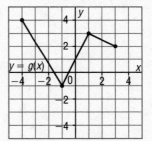

SOLUTION

a) Sketch the line $y = x$. Reflect points in this line.

Point on $y = f(x)$	Point on $x = f(y)$
(x, y)	(y, x)
$(-5, 1)$	$(1, -5)$
$(-2, 4)$	$(4, -2)$
$(0, 1)$	$(1, 0)$
$(4, 0)$	$(0, 4)$

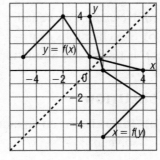

a) Sketch the graph of its inverse on the same grid.
b) Is the inverse a function? Explain.
c) State the domain and range of the function and its inverse.

Plot the points, then join them with line segments.

b) Both points $(1, 0)$ and $(1, -5)$ lie on the graph of the inverse. So, the inverse is not a function because its graph does not pass the vertical line test.

c) The domain of $y = f(x)$ is: $-5 \leq x \leq 4$
The range of $y = f(x)$ is: $0 \leq y \leq 4$
The domain of $x = f(y)$ is: $0 \leq x \leq 4$
The range of $x = f(y)$ is: $-5 \leq y \leq 4$

The results from *Example 1* show a relationship between the domains and ranges of a function and its inverse.

Domain and Range of a Function and Its Inverse

The domain of $y = f(x)$ is the range of $x = f(y)$, and the range of $y = f(x)$ is the domain of $x = f(y)$.

To determine an equation of the inverse of a function, interchange x and y in the equation of the function, then solve the resulting equation for y.

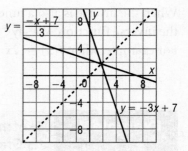

To determine the equation of the inverse of $y = -3x + 7$:

$y = -3x + 7$ Interchange x and y.

$x = -3y + 7$ Solve for y.

$3y = -x + 7$

$y = \dfrac{-x + 7}{3}$

So, the equation of the inverse of $y = -3x + 7$ is $y = \dfrac{-x + 7}{3}$.

Example 2	Determining the Equation and Sketching the Graph of the Inverse of a Function

a) Determine an equation of the inverse of $y = x^2 + 3$.
b) Sketch graphs of $y = x^2 + 3$ and its inverse.
c) Is the inverse a function? Explain.

SOLUTION

a) To determine an equation of the inverse, interchange x and y then solve for y.

$y = x^2 + 3$

$x = y^2 + 3$

$y^2 = x - 3$

$y = \pm\sqrt{x - 3}$

An equation of the inverse is: $y = \pm\sqrt{x - 3}$

b) The graph of $y = x^2 + 3$ is the image of the graph of $y = x^2$ after a translation of 3 units up. Sketch the graph of $y = x^2 + 3$, then reflect some points in the line $y = x$ by interchanging their coordinates. Join the points with a smooth curve.

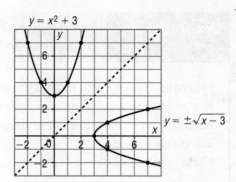

$y = x^2 + 3$

$y = \pm\sqrt{x - 3}$

c) Since the graph of the inverse does not pass the vertical line test, the inverse is not a function.

In *Example 2*, notice that the distance between a point on the graph of $y = f(x)$ and the line $y = x$ is the same as the distance between the corresponding point on the graph of $x = f(y)$ and the line $y = x$. This characteristic can be used to determine whether the graph of the inverse has been drawn correctly, or to determine whether two functions are inverses of each other.

If corresponding points are equidistant from the line $y = x$, then the midpoint of the line segment joining the points lies on the line $y = x$.

For example, in *Example 2*, to determine the midpoint of the line segment that joins corresponding points $(0, 3)$ and $(3, 0)$:

$$\text{Midpoint} = \left(\frac{0 + 3}{2}, \frac{3 + 0}{2}\right)$$

$$= \left(\frac{3}{2}, \frac{3}{2}\right)$$

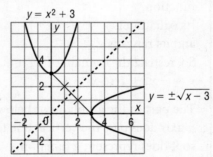

$y = x^2 + 3$

$y = \pm\sqrt{x - 3}$

Since this point lies on the line $y = x$, $(0, 3)$ and $(3, 0)$ are equidistant from the line. So, the graphs are likely inverses of each other.

Examples 1 and *2* illustrate that the inverse of a function may not be a function. The domain of $f(x)$ can be restricted to ensure that its inverse is a function.

THINK FURTHER

When is the inverse of a function also a function?

Example 3   Determining Restrictions on the Domain of a Function

Check Your Understanding

3. Determine two ways to restrict the domain of $y = (x - 1)^2 + 3$ so that its inverse is a function. Write the equation of the inverse each time. Use a graph to illustrate each way.

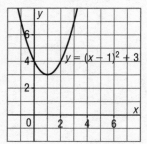

Determine two ways to restrict the domain of $y = -x^2 + 5$ so that its inverse is a function. Write the equation of the inverse each time.
Use a graph to illustrate each way.

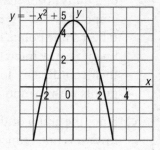

SOLUTION

Sketch the graph of the inverse.
Determine an equation of the inverse:

$x = -y^2 + 5$

$y^2 = -x + 5$

$y = \pm\sqrt{-x + 5}$

The graph of the inverse does not pass the vertical line test, so it is not a function.

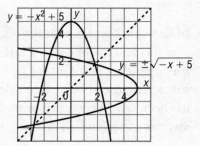

The part of the graph on or above the x-axis does pass the vertical line test, so it does represent a function.
Its equation is $y = \sqrt{-x + 5}$ and its range is $y \geq 0$.
So, restrict the domain of $y = -x^2 + 5$ to $x \geq 0$.

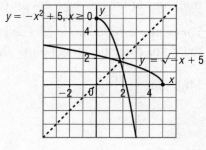

The part of the graph on or below the x-axis does pass the vertical line test, so it does represent a function.
Its equation is $y = -\sqrt{-x + 5}$ and its range is $y \leq 0$.
So, another way is to restrict the domain of $y = -x^2 + 5$ to $x \leq 0$.

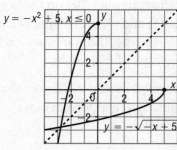

THINK FURTHER

In *Example 3*, are there other ways to restrict the domain so the inverse is a function? Explain.

Example 4 | **Determining Whether Two Functions Are Inverses of Each Other**

a) Determine algebraically whether the functions in each pair are inverses of each other.

   i) $y = 7x - 3$ and $y = \dfrac{x + 3}{7}$

   ii) $y = (x - 2)^2 + 1$, $x \leq 2$ and $y = \sqrt{x - 1} + 2$

b) Verify the answers to part a graphically.

SOLUTION

a) **i)** Determine an equation of the inverse of $y = 7x - 3$.
Interchange x and y, then solve for y.

$$x = 7y - 3$$
$$x + 3 = 7y$$
$$y = \frac{x + 3}{7}$$

An equation of the inverse is: $y = \dfrac{x + 3}{7}$

Since this matches the given equation, $y = 7x - 3$ and $y = \dfrac{x + 3}{7}$ are inverses of each other.

ii) Determine an equation of the inverse of $y = (x - 2)^2 + 1$, $x \leq 2$. Interchange x and y, then solve for y.

$$x = (y - 2)^2 + 1$$
$$x - 1 = (y - 2)^2$$
$$\pm\sqrt{x - 1} = y - 2$$
$$y = \pm\sqrt{x - 1} + 2$$

Since the domain of $y = (x - 2)^2 + 1$ is $x \leq 2$, then the range of its inverse is $y \leq 2$.

So, an equation of the inverse is: $y = -\sqrt{x - 1} + 2$

Since this equation is not equivalent to the given equation, $y = \sqrt{x - 1} + 2$, the given functions are not inverses of each other.

b) **i)** Graph $y = 7x - 3$, $y = \dfrac{x + 3}{7}$, and $y = x$ on the same grid.

The graphs appear to be reflections of each other in the line $y = x$.

To verify, determine the midpoint of the line segment that joins corresponding points $(4, 1)$ and $(1, 4)$:

4. a) Determine algebraically whether the functions in each pair are inverses of each other.

   i) $y = 3x - 6$ and $y = \dfrac{x - 6}{3}$

   ii) $y = -x^2 + 3$, $x \geq 0$ and $y = \sqrt{3 - x}$

b) Verify the answers to part a graphically.

Midpoint $= \left(\dfrac{4 + 1}{2}, \dfrac{1 + 4}{2} \right)$, or $\left(\dfrac{5}{2}, \dfrac{5}{2} \right)$

Since this point lies on the line $y = x$, $(4, 1)$ and $(1, 4)$ are equidistant from the line. So, the graphs are likely inverses of each other.

ii) Graph $y = (x - 2)^2 + 1$,
$x \leq 2$; $y = \sqrt{x - 1} + 2$;
and $y = x$ on the same grid.
$y = (x - 2)^2 + 1, x \leq 2$,
is part of the image of
$y = x^2$ after a translation
of 2 units right and 1 unit
up. $y = \sqrt{x - 1} + 2$ is
the image of $y = \sqrt{x}$ after
a translation of 1 unit right and 2 units up.
Since the graphs are not reflections of each other in the line
$y = x$, the functions are not inverses of each other.

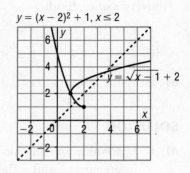

Discuss the Ideas

1. Is the inverse of a linear function always a function? Is the inverse of a quadratic function with domain $x \in \mathbb{R}$ always a function? Explain.

2. What is the relationship between the domains and ranges of a function and its inverse? Explain.

3. What different strategies can you use to sketch the inverse of a function?

Exercises

A

4. For each graph below, sketch its image after a reflection in the line
$y = x$.

a)

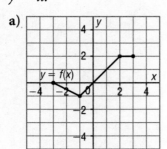

b)

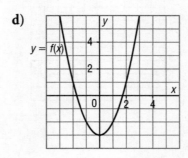

c)

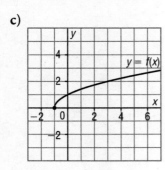

d)

5. Determine an equation of the inverse of each function.

a) $y = 2x + 9$

b) $y = x^2 + 5$

c) $y = \dfrac{5x - 3}{4}$

d) $y = 2x^2 - 3$

6. For each function below:

    i) Determine an equation of its inverse.

    ii) Sketch the graphs of the function and its inverse.

    iii) Is the inverse a function? Explain.

    a) $y = 4x - 1$ **b)** $y = -x^2 + 3$

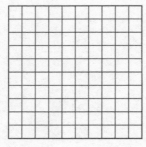 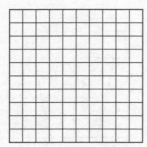

7. Determine whether the functions in each pair are inverses of each other. Justify your answer.

    a) $y = x^2 + 7, x \geq 0$ and $y = \sqrt{x - 7}$

    b) $y = 5x - 3$ and $y = \dfrac{3 - x}{5}$

c) $y = (x + 4)^2 - 2, x \geq -4$ and $y = -\sqrt{x + 2} + 4$

d) $y = \frac{1}{2}x - 6$ and $y = 2x + 12$

8. Determine whether the functions in each pair are inverses of each other. Justify your answer.

a)

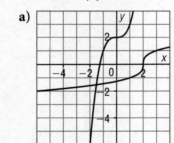

b)

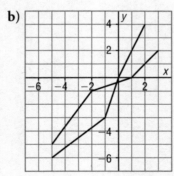

9. Sketch the graph of the inverse of each relation. Is the inverse a function? Justify your answer.

a)

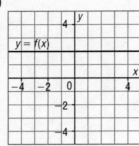

b)

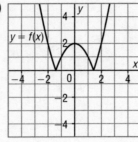

10. Determine two ways to restrict the domain of each function below so its inverse is a function. Write the equation of the inverse each time. Use a graph to illustrate each way.

a) $y = 2(x + 1)^2 - 2$

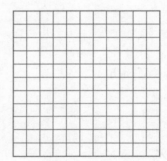

b) $y = -3(x - 2)^2 + 4$

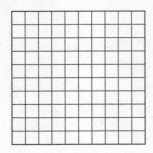

11. The point A$(5, -6)$ lies on the graph of $y = f(x)$. What are the coordinates of its image A$'$ on the graph of $y = f^{-1}(x - 3)$?

12. a) Graph the function $y = (x - 3)^2 + 4, x \geq 3$.

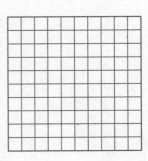

b) What is the range of the function?

c) Determine the equation of its inverse. Sketch its graph.

d) What are the domain and range of the inverse?

13. Determine the coordinates of two points that lie on the graphs of both $y = x^2 + 2x - 6$ and its inverse. Explain the strategy you used.

14. A graph was reflected in the line $y = x$. Its reflection image is shown. Determine an equation of the original graph in terms of x and y.

a)

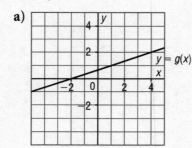

b)

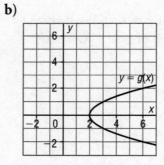

15. Determine the equations of two functions such that the graphs of each function and its inverse coincide.

16. The graphs of $y = \dfrac{x + 5}{x + k}$ and its inverse coincide. Determine the value of k.

Multiple-Choice Questions

1. Which equation represents the inverse of $y = \frac{1}{4}x - \frac{3}{2}$?

    A. $y = 4x + 6$ **B.** $y = 4x - 6$

    C. $y = 4x - \frac{2}{3}$ **D.** $y = 4x + \frac{2}{3}$

2. Which restrictions on the graph of $y = f(x)$ will make the graph of its inverse a function?

    I. $x \geq 2$

    II. $x \leq -2$

    III. $1 \leq x \leq 2$

    IV. $-1 \leq x \leq 1$

    A. I and II   **B.** I, II, and III

    C. IV   **D.** all of the above

Study Note

How can you determine whether two functions are inverses of each other?

ANSWERS

Check Your Understanding

1. b) no **c)** $y = g(x)$; domain: $-4 \leq x \leq 3$; range: $-1 \leq y \leq 4$; $x = g(y)$: domain: $-1 \leq x \leq 4$; range: $-4 \leq y \leq 3$ **2. a)** $y = \pm\sqrt{-x + 4}$ **c)** no

3. restrict domain to $x \geq 1$: $y = \sqrt{x - 3} + 1$; restrict domain to $x \leq 1$: $y = -\sqrt{x - 3} + 1$ **4. a) i)** no **ii)** yes

Exercises

5. a) $y = \dfrac{x - 9}{2}$ **b)** $y = \pm\sqrt{x - 5}$ **c)** $y = \dfrac{4x + 3}{5}$ **d)** $y = \pm\sqrt{\dfrac{x + 3}{2}}$

6. a) i) $y = \dfrac{x + 1}{4}$ **iii)** yes **b) i)** $y = \pm\sqrt{-x + 3}$ **iii)** no **7. a)** yes **b)** no

c) no **d)** yes **8. a)** yes **b)** no **9. a)** no **b)** no

10. a) $x \geq -1$, $y = \sqrt{\dfrac{x + 2}{2}} - 1$; $x \leq -1$, $y = -\sqrt{\dfrac{x + 2}{2}} - 1$

b) $x \geq 2$, $y = \sqrt{\dfrac{4 - x}{3}} + 2$; $x \leq 2$, $y = -\sqrt{\dfrac{4 - x}{3}} + 2$ **11.** $(-3, 5)$

12. b) $y \geq 4$ **c)** $y = \sqrt{x - 4} + 3$ **d)** domain: $x \geq 4$; range: $y \geq 3$

13. $(2, 2)$ and $(-3, -3)$ **14. a)** $y = 3x - 2$ **b)** $y = x^2 + 2$ **16.** $k = -1$

Multiple Choice

1. A **2.** B

Additional Workspace

Concept Summary

Big Ideas	Applying the Big Ideas
• The graphs of functions can be translated, reflected, stretched, or compressed.	This means that: • The graphs of a function and its image after a translation or reflection are congruent. • The graphs of a function and its image after a stretch or compression are not congruent.

• When a function is written in the form $y - k = af(b(x - h))$, its graph is a transformation image of the graph of $y = f(x)$, and the transformations can be identified.	• The combinations of transformations are applied in this order:
	  – stretches or compressions
	  – reflections
	  – translations
	• The point (x, y) on the graph of $y = f(x)$ corresponds to the point $\left(\dfrac{x}{b} + h, ay + k\right)$ on the graph of $y - k = af(b(x - h))$.

• The graphs of a relation and its inverse are reflections of each other in the line $y = x$.	• The point (x, y) on the graph of $y = f(x)$ corresponds to the point (y, x) on the graph of $x = f(y)$. • The domain of $y = f(x)$ is the range of $x = f(y)$, and the range of $y = f(x)$ is the domain of $x = f(y)$. • The inverse of a function may not be a function.

Chapter Study Notes

• The graph of $y - k = af(b(x - h))$ is a transformation image of the graph of $y = f(x)$. From this equation, what do you know about how the graph of $y = f(x)$ was transformed?

• By looking at the graph of a function, how can you tell whether its inverse is a function?

Skills Summary

Skill	Description	Example
Write the equation of a function after a vertical and/or horizontal translation. **(3.1)**	The equation has the form $y - k = f(x - h)$. The horizontal translation is the value of h, and the vertical translation is the value of k. Determine the values of h and k, then substitute them in the equation.	Determine an equation of the image of the graph of $y = f(x)$ after a translation of 4 units left and 7 units up. Horizontal translation: 4 units left $h = -4$ Vertical translation: 7 units up $k = 7$ So, an equation of the image is: $y - 7 = f(x + 4)$
Sketch the graph of a function after a reflection in the x-axis and/or y-axis. **(3.2)**	When the graph of a function is reflected in the x-axis, a point (x, y) on $y = f(x)$ corresponds to the point $(x, -y)$ on the graph of $y = -f(x)$. When the graph of a function is reflected in the y-axis, a point (x, y) on $y = f(x)$ corresponds to the point $(-x, y)$ on the graph of $y = f(-x)$.	The graph of $y = f(x)$ is shown below. Sketch the image graph after a reflection in the x-axis. <table><tr><th>Point on $y = f(x)$</th><th>Point on $y = -f(x)$</th></tr><tr><td>(x, y)</td><td>$(x, -y)$</td></tr><tr><td>$(-1, 0)$</td><td>$(-1, 0)$</td></tr><tr><td>$(0, 1)$</td><td>$(0, -1)$</td></tr><tr><td>$(3, 2)$</td><td>$(3, -2)$</td></tr><tr><td>$(8, 3)$</td><td>$(8, -3)$</td></tr></table>
Sketch the graph of a function after a vertical and/or horizontal stretch or compression. **(3.3)**	Compare the equation of the function to $y = af(bx)$ to determine the values of a and b. A point (x, y) on the graph of $y = f(x)$ corresponds to the point $\left(\frac{x}{b}, ay\right)$ on the transformation image.	The graph of $y = f(x)$ is shown below. Sketch the graph of $y = 2f(2x)$. Compare to $y = af(bx)$: $a = 2$ and $b = 2$ <table><tr><th>Point on $y = f(x)$</th><th>Point on $y = 2f(2x)$</th></tr><tr><td>(x, y)</td><td>$(0.5x, 2y)$</td></tr><tr><td>$(0, 0)$</td><td>$(0, 0)$</td></tr><tr><td>$(-2, 4)$</td><td>$(-1, 8)$</td></tr><tr><td>$(2, 4)$</td><td>$(1, 8)$</td></tr></table>

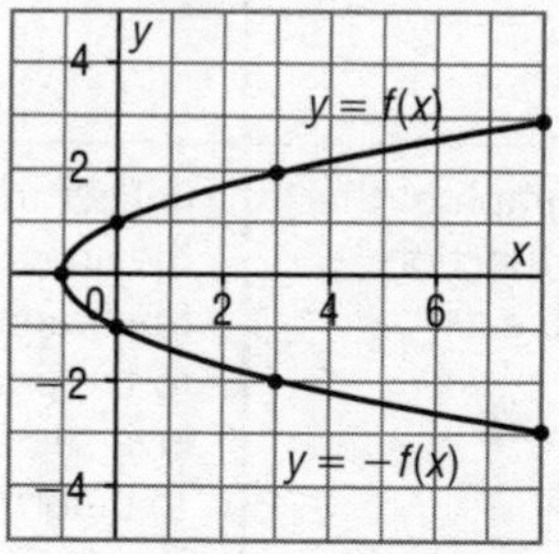

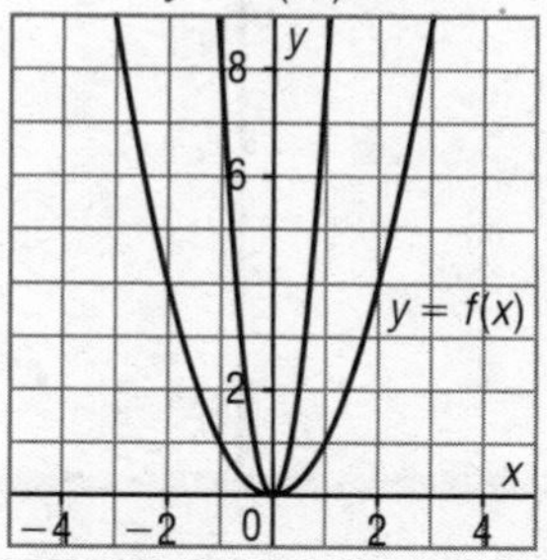

Skill	Description	Example
Sketch the graph of a function after a combination of transformations. **(3.4)**	Compare the equation of the function to $y - k = af(b(x - h))$ to determine the values of a, b, h, and k. A point (x, y) on the graph of $y = f(x)$ corresponds to the point $\left(\dfrac{x}{b} + h,\ ay + k\right)$ on the graph of the transformation image.	The graph of $y = f(x)$ is shown below. Sketch the graph of $y - 1 = -2f(x + 1)$. Compare to $y - k = af(b(x - h))$: $k = 1$, $a = -2$, $b = 1$, $h = -1$

Point on $y = f(x)$	Point on $y - 1 = -2f(x + 1)$
(x, y)	$(x - 1, -2y + 1)$
$(-2, 2)$	$(-3, -3)$
$(0, 0)$	$(-1, 1)$
$(2, 2)$	$(1, -3)$

Skill	Description	Example
Sketch the graph of the inverse of a function and determine its equation. **(3.5)**	Reflect the graph of the function in the line $y = x$. Each point (x, y) on the graph of the function corresponds to the point (y, x) on the graph of its inverse. To determine an equation of the inverse, interchange x and y, then solve for y.	Sketch the graph of the inverse of $y = 2x - 3$, then determine its equation.

Point on $y = 2x - 3$	Point on its inverse
(x, y)	(y, x)
$(-1, -5)$	$(-5, -1)$
$(0, -3)$	$(-3, 0)$
$(1, -1)$	$(-1, 1)$

Interchange x and y, then solve for y.

$$x = 2y - 3$$
$$x + 3 = 2y$$
$$\frac{x + 3}{2} = y$$

An equation of the inverse is: $y = \dfrac{x + 3}{2}$

REVIEW

1. Here is the graph of $y = f(x)$. Sketch the graph of each function below. Write the domain and range of each translation image.

a) $y - 2 = f(x)$

b) $y = f(x - 3)$

c) $y + 3 = f(x + 4)$

2. The graph of the function $y = x^3 - 2$ is translated 3 units left and 4 units up. Write the equation of the translation image.

3. Here is the graph of $y = g(x)$. On the same grid, sketch the graph of each function below. Write the domain and range of each reflection image.

a) $y = -g(x)$

b) $y = g(-x)$

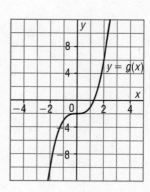

4. The graph of $f(x) = (x - 2)^3 - 4$ was reflected in the x-axis and its image is shown. What is an equation of the image?

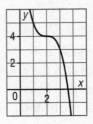

5. Here is the graph of $y = h(x)$. Sketch the graph of each function below. Write the domain and range of each transformation image.

a) $y = h(3x)$ **b)** $y = \frac{1}{2}h(x)$

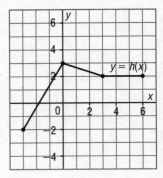

c) $y = 2h(-3x)$

6. The graph of $y = g(x)$ is the image of the graph of $y = f(x)$ after a transformation. Corresponding points are labelled. Write an equation of the image graph in terms of the function f.

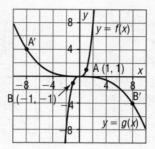

3.4

7. Here is the graph of $y = f(x)$. On the same grid, sketch the graph of $y - 4 = 3f(2(x - 5))$. Write the domain and range of the transformation image.

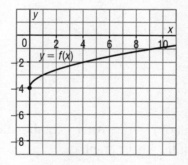

8. The graph of $y = g(x)$ is the image of the graph of $y = f(x)$ after a combination of transformations. Corresponding points are labelled. Write an equation of the image graph in terms of the function f.

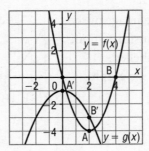

9. The point $(2, 2)$ lies on the graph of $y = \frac{1}{4}x^3$. After a combination of transformations, the equation of the image graph is $y + 6 = 5\left(\frac{1}{4}(2(x - 3))^3\right)$. What are the coordinates of the point that is the image of $(2, 2)$?

3.5

10. Determine an equation of the inverse of each function, then sketch graphs of the function and its inverse.

   a) $y = -\frac{2}{5}x + 3$

   b) $y = (x - 3)^2 + 7$

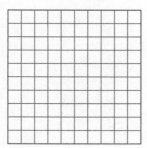

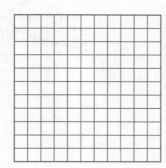

11. Restrict the domain of the function $y = f(x)$ so its inverse is a function.

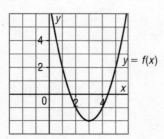

12. A graph was reflected in the line $y = x$. Its reflection image $y = g(x)$ is shown. Determine an equation of the original graph in terms of x and y.

a)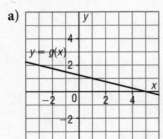

b)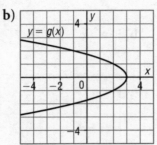

1. **Multiple Choice** The graph of $y + 2 = -3f\left(\frac{1}{2}(x + 5)\right)$ is the image of the graph of $y = f(x)$ after several transformations. Which statement about how the graph of $y = f(x)$ was transformed is false?

   A. The graph was reflected in the x-axis.

   B. The graph was horizontally stretched by a factor of 2.

   C. The graph was translated 2 units down.

   D. The graph was reflected in the y-axis.

2. **Multiple Choice** Which statement about a function and its inverse is not always true?

   A. The inverse of a function is a function.

   B. The domain of a function is the range of its inverse, and the range of a function is the domain of its inverse.

   C. The graph of the inverse of a function can be sketched by reflecting the graph of the function in the line $y = x$.

   D. Each point (x, y) on the graph of a function corresponds to the point (y, x) on the graph of its inverse.

3. Write an equation of the function $y = \sqrt{x - 3}$ after each transformation below.

   a) a translation of 2 units right and 5 units down

   b) a reflection in the x-axis

   c) a reflection in the y-axis

d) a vertical stretch by a factor of 2 and a horizontal compression by a factor of $\frac{1}{3}$

4. Here is the graph of $y = f(x)$. On the same grid, use transformations to sketch the graph of $y - 5 = -3f(2x)$. Describe the transformations.

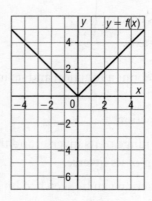

5. Here is the graph of $y = \sqrt{x}$.

a) Use this graph to sketch a graph of $y - 1 = -2\sqrt{\frac{1}{2}(x - 4)}$.

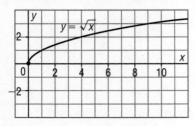

b) Write the domain and range of the function in part a.

6. a) Determine an equation of the inverse of $y = (x - 4)^2 + 5$.

b) Sketch the graph of the inverse. Is the inverse a function? Explain.

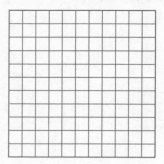

c) If your answer to part b is yes, explain how you know. If your answer to part b is no, determine a possible restriction on the domain of $y = (x - 4)^2 + 5$ so its inverse is a function, then write the equation of the inverse function.

ANSWERS

1. D   2. A   3. a) $y + 5 = \sqrt{x - 5}$ b) $y = -\sqrt{x - 3}$ c) $y = \sqrt{-x - 3}$
d) $y = 2\sqrt{3x - 3}$ 5. b) domain: $x \geq 4$; range: $y \leq 1$ 6. a) $y = \pm\sqrt{x - 5} + 4$
b) no

4

Combining Functions

BUILDING ON

- domain and range of functions

- sketching graphs of functions

- function notation

BIG IDEAS

- A new function can be created by adding, subtracting, multiplying, or dividing other functions on appropriate domains.

- A composite function is the result of applying two functions in succession.

LEADING TO

- the study of functions in calculus

VOCABULARY

composite function

4.1 Combining Functions Graphically

FOCUS Sketch the graphs of functions that are the sum, difference, product, or quotient of two functions.

Get Started

What are the domain and the range of each function?

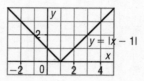 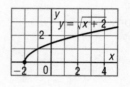 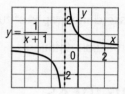

Construct Understanding

A. The graph below shows two functions: function A is college enrolment and function B is university enrolment for the past few years. On the same grid, sketch a graph to show the total post-secondary enrolment for these years. Describe your strategy.

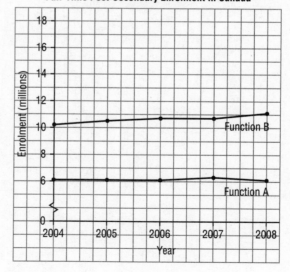

DO NOT COPY. ©P

B. The stopping distance for a car is a function of the speed of the car when the brakes are applied:

Stopping distance = reaction-time distance + braking distance

The graph below shows functions for stopping distance and reaction-time distance against speed. On the same grid, sketch a graph for braking distance against speed. Describe your strategy.

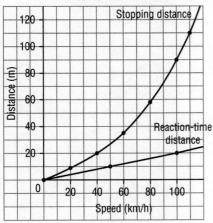

C. The graphs of $y = f(x)$ and $y = g(x)$ are shown. Adapt the strategy you used for Parts A and B to graph the product of these functions:

$y = f(x) \cdot g(x)$

Describe your strategy.

What are the domains of $y = f(x)$, $y = g(x)$, and $y = f(x) \cdot g(x)$?

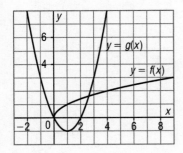

D. The graphs of $y = f(x)$ and $y = g(x)$ are shown. Adapt the strategy you used for Parts A and B to graph the quotient of these functions:

$$y = \frac{f(x)}{g(x)}$$

Describe your strategy.

What are the domains of $y = f(x)$, $y = g(x)$, and $y = \frac{f(x)}{g(x)}$?

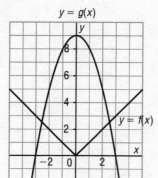

THINK FURTHER

For the graph in Part D, why is $y = \frac{f(x)}{g(x)}$ not a rational function? Explain.

Assess Your Understanding

1. Use the graphs of $y = f(x)$ and $y = g(x)$ on page 269 to sketch the graph of each function below, then identify its domain and range. Estimate the range, where necessary.

a) $y = f(x) + g(x)$

b) $y = f(x) - g(x)$

c) $y = f(x) \cdot g(x)$

d) $y = \frac{f(x)}{g(x)}$

a)

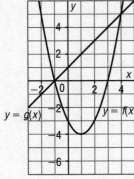

b)

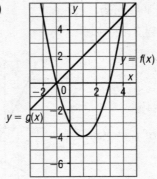

c)

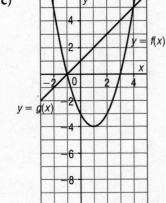

d)

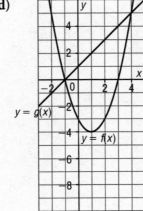

2. Use the graphs of $y = f(x)$ and $y = g(x)$.

    a) State the domain and range of $y = f(x)$.

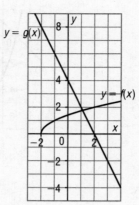

    b) State the domain and range of $y = g(x)$.

    c) Sketch the graph of $y = f(x) \cdot g(x)$.

    d) What is the domain of $y = f(x) \cdot g(x)$? How is it related to the domains of $y = f(x)$ and $y = g(x)$?

3. Use the graphs of $y = f(x)$ and $y = g(x)$.

a) What are the domain and range of
   $y = f(x)$?

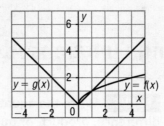

b) What are the domain and range of $y = g(x)$?

c) Consider the function $h(x) = f(x) + g(x)$. Without graphing, determine the domain and the range of this function and justify your answer.

d) Use the graphs in parts a and b to sketch the graph of $h(x)$. Use the graph to verify the domain and range.

FOCUS Write the equations of functions that are the sum, difference, product, or quotient of other functions, then determine their domains and ranges.

Get Started

Given $f(x) = 3 - 4x + 5x^2$, determine each value:

$f(0)$ $\qquad\qquad$ $f(2)$ $\qquad\qquad$ $f(-1)$

Construct Understanding

For the graphs below, how is the function $h(x)$ a combination of the functions $f(x)$ and $g(x)$? Use algebra to verify the answer.

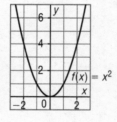

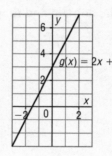

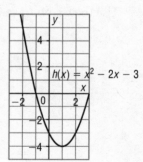

Given two functions $f(x)$ and $g(x)$, another function can be defined by adding, subtracting, or multiplying $f(x)$ and $g(x)$.

Consider coordinates of corresponding points.

- *Adding functions*

  The sum of functions $f(x)$ and $g(x)$ is $f(x) + g(x)$; this may also be written as $(f + g)(x)$.

  For $h(x) = f(x) + g(x)$, to determine the value of $h(2)$, add $f(2)$ and $g(2)$.

  From the graph, $f(2) + g(2) = 2 - 1$
  $$= 1$$
  $$= h(2)$$

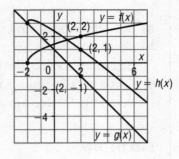

  The domain of $f(x)$ is: $x \geq -2$
  The domain of $g(x)$ is: $x \in \mathbb{R}$
  The domain of $h(x)$ is: $x \geq -2$

- *Subtracting functions*

  The difference of functions $f(x)$ and $g(x)$ is $f(x) - g(x)$; this may also be written as $(f - g)(x)$.

  For $d(x) = f(x) - g(x)$, to determine the value of $d(2)$, subtract $g(2)$ from $f(2)$.

  From the graph, $f(2) - g(2) = 2 - (-1)$
  $$= 3$$
  $$= d(2)$$

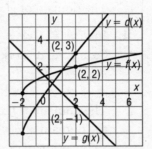

  The domain of $f(x)$ is: $x \geq -2$
  The domain of $g(x)$ is: $x \in \mathbb{R}$
  The domain of $d(x)$ is: $x \geq -2$

- *Multiplying functions*

  The product of functions $f(x)$ and $g(x)$ is $f(x) \cdot g(x)$; this may also be written as $(f \cdot g)(x)$.

  For $p(x) = f(x) \cdot g(x)$, to determine the value of $p(2)$, multiply $f(2)$ and $g(2)$.

  From the graph, $f(2) \cdot g(2) = (2)(-1)$
  $$= -2$$
  $$= p(2)$$

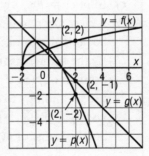

  The domain of $f(x)$ is: $x \geq -2$
  The domain of $g(x)$ is: $x \in \mathbb{R}$
  The domain of $p(x)$ is: $x \geq -2$

The graphs above illustrate that when two functions, $f(x)$ and $g(x)$, are added, subtracted, or multiplied, the domain of the new function is the set of values of x that are common to the domains of $f(x)$ and $g(x)$.

1. Use $f(x) = x + 2$ and $g(x) = |x|$.

a) State the domain and range of $f(x)$ and of $g(x)$.

b) Given $h(x) = f(x) + g(x)$, write an explicit equation for $h(x)$, then determine its domain and range.

c) Given $p(x) = f(x) \cdot g(x)$, write an explicit equation for $p(x)$, then determine its domain and range.

Use $f(x) = \sqrt{x}$ and $g(x) = x - 3$.

a) State the domain and range of $f(x)$ and of $g(x)$.

b) Given $d(x) = f(x) - g(x)$, write an explicit equation for $d(x)$, then determine its domain and range.

c) Given $p(x) = f(x) \cdot g(x)$, write an explicit equation for $p(x)$, then determine its domain and range.

SOLUTION

a) $f(x) = \sqrt{x}$

The domain of $f(x)$ is $x \geq 0$ and the range is $y \geq 0$.

$g(x) = x - 3$

The domain of $g(x)$ is $x \in \mathbb{R}$ and the range is $y \in \mathbb{R}$.

b) In $d(x) = f(x) - g(x)$, substitute: $f(x) = \sqrt{x}$ and $g(x) = x - 3$

So, an equation is:

$d(x) = \sqrt{x} - (x - 3)$, or

$d(x) = \sqrt{x} - x + 3$

The domain of $f(x)$ is $x \geq 0$ and the domain of $g(x)$ is $x \in \mathbb{R}$, so the domain of $d(x)$ is $x \geq 0$.

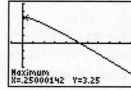

For the range, use technology to graph $d(x) = \sqrt{x} - x + 3$

Use [2nd] [TRACE] [4] to determine the maximum value: $y = 3.25$

So, the range of $d(x)$ is: $y \leq 3.25$

c) In $p(x) = f(x) \cdot g(x)$, substitute:

$f(x) = \sqrt{x}$ and $g(x) = x - 3$

So, an equation is: $p(x) = \sqrt{x}\,(x - 3)$

By the same reasoning as in part b, the domain of $p(x)$ is $x \geq 0$. For the range, use technology to graph $p(x) = \sqrt{x}\,(x - 3)$

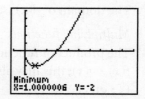

Use [2nd] [TRACE] [3] to determine the minimum value: $y = -2$

So, the range of $p(x)$ is: $y \geq -2$

Given two functions $f(x)$ and $g(x)$, another function can be defined by dividing $f(x)$ and $g(x)$.

The quotient of functions $f(x)$ and $g(x)$ is $f(x) \div g(x)$; this may also be written as $(f \div g)(x)$.

Given $q(x) = \dfrac{f(x)}{g(x)}$, consider coordinates of corresponding points.

To determine the value of $q(2)$, divide $f(2)$ by $g(2)$.

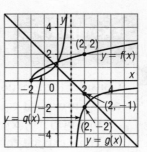

From the graph, $\dfrac{f(2)}{g(2)} = \dfrac{2}{-1}$

$\qquad\qquad\qquad = -2$

$\qquad\qquad\qquad = q(2)$

The domain of $f(x)$ is: $x \geq -2$; the domain of $g(x)$ is: $x \in \mathbb{R}$

The domain of $q(x)$ is: $x \geq -2, x \neq 1$

The graph above illustrates that the domain of the function $y = \dfrac{f(x)}{g(x)}$ is restricted to those values of x for which $g(x) \neq 0$, and for which $f(x)$ and $g(x)$ are defined.

Example 2 | **Writing the Equation of a Function that Is a Quotient of Functions**

Check Your Understanding

Use $f(x) = \sqrt{x}$ and $g(x) = (x - 3)^2$.

a) State the domain and range of $f(x)$ and of $g(x)$.

b) Given $q(x) = \dfrac{f(x)}{g(x)}$, write an explicit equation for $q(x)$, then determine its domain and range.

2. Use $f(x) = \sqrt{x}$ and $g(x) = x - 2$.

a) State the domain and range of $f(x)$ and of $g(x)$.

b) Given $q(x) = \dfrac{f(x)}{g(x)}$, write an explicit equation for $q(x)$, then determine its domain and range.

SOLUTION

a) $f(x) = \sqrt{x}$

The domain of $f(x)$ is $x \geq 0$ and the range is $y \geq 0$.

$g(x) = (x - 3)^2$

$g(x)$ is a quadratic function whose graph opens up and has vertex $(3, 0)$; the domain is $x \in \mathbb{R}$ and the range is $y \geq 0$.

b) $q(x) = \dfrac{f(x)}{g(x)}$

Substitute: $f(x) = \sqrt{x}$ and

$g(x) = (x - 3)^2$

$q(x) = \dfrac{\sqrt{x}}{(x - 3)^2}$

Both $f(x)$ and $g(x)$ are defined for $x \geq 0$, and $g(x) = 0$ when $x = 3$.

So, the domain of $q(x)$ is: $x \geq 0, x \neq 3$

For the range, use technology to graph: $q(x) = \dfrac{\sqrt{x}}{(x - 3)^2}$

Use TRACE or 2nd GRAPH for TABLE to determine that the range of $q(x)$ is: $y \geq 0$

Example 3 | Writing a Function as the Sum or Difference of Functions

3. Consider the function:
$h(x) = 4 + 5x + 2x^3$

a) Write explicit equations for four functions $f(x)$, $g(x)$, $n(x)$, and $m(x)$ so that
$h(x) = f(x) + g(x) + n(x) + m(x)$.

b) Write explicit equations for two functions $f(x)$ and $g(x)$ so that $h(x) = f(x) - g(x)$.

Consider the function: $h(x) = x^2 - 2x + 3$

a) Write explicit equations for three functions $f(x)$, $g(x)$, and $n(x)$ so that $h(x) = f(x) + g(x) + n(x)$.

b) Write explicit equations for two functions $f(x)$ and $g(x)$ so that $h(x) = f(x) - g(x)$.

SOLUTION

a) $h(x) = x^2 - 2x + 3$
One possible sum is: $h(x) = x^2 + (-2x) + 3$
So, $f(x) = x^2$, $g(x) = -2x$, and $n(x) = 3$

b) $h(x) = x^2 - 2x + 3$
One possible difference is: $h(x) = x^2 - (2x - 3)$
So, $f(x) = x^2$ and $g(x) = 2x - 3$

The results of *Example 3* can be verified using graphing technology.
For part a:

On a TI-83 Plus calculator, enter
$Y_1 = x^2$, $Y_2 = -2x$, $Y_3 = 3$,
$Y_4 = x^2 - 2x + 3$, and
$Y_5 = Y_1 + Y_2 + Y_3$
The graphs of functions Y_4 and Y_5
should coincide.

To enter $Y_5 = Y_1 + Y_2 + Y_3$,
place the cursor next to $Y_5 =$,
then press: VARS ▶ 1 1 + VARS
▶ 1 2 + VARS ▶ 1 3

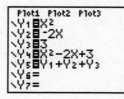
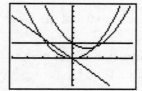

THINK FURTHER

In *Example 3b*, what are other possible equations for $f(x)$ and $g(x)$?

a) Given $p(x) = x^2 - 2x - 8$, write explicit equations for two functions $f(x)$ and $g(x)$ so that $p(x) = f(x) \cdot g(x)$.

b) Given $q(x) = x - 4$, write explicit equations for two functions $f(x)$ and $g(x)$ so that $q(x) = \dfrac{f(x)}{g(x)}$.

SOLUTION

a) Factor: $p(x) = x^2 - 2x - 8$
$$p(x) = (x - 4)(x + 2)$$
So, $f(x) = x - 4$ and $g(x) = x + 2$

b) The domain of $q(x) = x - 4$ is $x \in \mathbb{R}$.

So, the domains of $f(x)$ and $g(x)$ must also be $x \in \mathbb{R}$, and $g(x)$ must never equal 0. Choose a function $g(x)$ that is never equal to 0 and has domain $x \in \mathbb{R}$, such as $g(x) = x^2 + 2$.

Multiply $g(x)$ by $(x - 4)$ to get:

$$f(x) = (x^2 + 2)(x - 4)$$
$$= x^3 - 4x^2 + 2x - 8$$

So, $q(x) = \dfrac{x^3 - 4x^2 + 2x - 8}{x^2 + 2}$

4. a) Given $p(x) = x^2 - 9$, write explicit equations for two functions $f(x)$ and $g(x)$ so that $p(x) = f(x) \cdot g(x)$.

b) Given $q(x) = x + 1$, write explicit equations for two functions $f(x)$ and $g(x)$ so that $q(x) = \dfrac{f(x)}{g(x)}$.

Discuss the Ideas

1. Two functions $f(x)$ and $g(x)$ are combined to form the function $h(x)$. When is the domain of $h(x)$ not the values of x that are common to the domains of $f(x)$ and $g(x)$?

2. When a function $q(x)$ is written as $\dfrac{f(x)}{g(x)}$, why must $q(x)$ and $\dfrac{f(x)}{g(x)}$ have the same domain?

Exercises

A

3. Given $f(x) = x^3$ and $g(x) = x^2 + 1$, write an explicit equation for each combination.

    a) $h(x) = f(x) + g(x)$ **b)** $d(x) = f(x) - g(x)$

    c) $p(x) = f(x) \cdot g(x)$ **d)** $q(x) = \dfrac{f(x)}{g(x)}$

4. For each function $h(x)$ below, write explicit equations for $f(x)$ and $g(x)$ so that:

    i) $h(x)$ is the sum $f(x) + g(x)$
    ii) $h(x)$ is the difference $f(x) - g(x)$

    a) $h(x) = x^2 + 3x - 4$ **b)** $h(x) = x^3 - x^2 + 8$

B

5. Use $f(x) = 2x - 4$ and $g(x) = -x + 2$.

    a) Write an explicit equation for $h(x)$.

        i) $h(x) = f(x) + g(x)$ **ii)** $h(x) = g(x) + f(x)$

        iii) $h(x) = f(x) - g(x)$ **iv)** $h(x) = g(x) - f(x)$

        v) $h(x) = f(x) \cdot g(x)$ **vi)** $h(x) = g(x) \cdot f(x)$

b) For part a, compare the answers to parts i and ii; parts iii and iv; and parts v and vi. Explain the results.

6. Given that $f(x) = x^2 - 4$, $g(x) = 2x - 1$, and $h(x) = 3 - x^3$, write an explicit equation for $k(x)$, then state its domain.

    a) $k(x) = f(x) + g(x) + h(x)$ **b)** $k(x) = f(x) - g(x) + h(x)$

    c) $k(x) = f(x) + g(x) \cdot h(x)$ **d)** $k(x) = g(x) \cdot f(x) - h(x)$

7. Use the function $k(x) = x^2 - 3x - 28$.

    a) Write explicit equations for three functions $f(x)$, $g(x)$, and $h(x)$ so that $k(x) = f(x) + g(x) + h(x)$.

    b) Write explicit equations for two functions $f(x)$ and $g(x)$ so that $k(x) = f(x) \cdot g(x)$.

8. For each function $h(x)$ below, write explicit equations for $f(x)$ and $g(x)$ so that:

  i) $h(x)$ is the sum $f(x) + g(x)$
  ii) $h(x)$ is the difference $f(x) - g(x)$
  iii) $h(x)$ is the product $f(x) \cdot g(x)$
  iv) $h(x)$ is the quotient $\dfrac{f(x)}{g(x)}$

  a) $h(x) = x^2$ **b)** $h(x) = \sqrt{x}$

9. Use $f(x) = |x - 4|$ and $g(x) = x^2$.

  a) State the domain and range of $f(x)$ and of $g(x)$.

  b) Given $h(x) = f(x) + g(x)$, write an explicit equation for $h(x)$, then determine its domain and range.

c) Given $d(x) = f(x) - g(x)$, write an explicit equation for $d(x)$, then determine its domain and range.

10. Use $f(x) = x^3 - x$ and $g(x) = \dfrac{1}{x + 3}$.

   a) State the domain and range of $f(x)$ and of $g(x)$.

   b) Given $h(x) = f(x) + g(x)$, write an explicit equation for $h(x)$, then determine its domain and range.

   c) Given $p(x) = f(x) \cdot g(x)$, write an explicit equation for $p(x)$, then determine its domain and range.

11. Use $f(x) = \sqrt{x + 2}$ and $g(x) = |x - 2|$.

   a) State the domain and range of $f(x)$ and of $g(x)$.

   b) Given $p(x) = f(x) \cdot g(x)$, write an explicit equation for $p(x)$, then determine its domain and range.

c) Given $q(x) = \dfrac{f(x)}{g(x)}$, write an explicit equation for $q(x)$, then determine its domain and range.

12. a) When asked to write $f(x) = x^2$ as the quotient of two functions, a student wrote $f(x) = \dfrac{x^3}{x}$. Is this correct? Justify your answer.

b) If your answer to part a is no, write $f(x) = x^2$ as a quotient of two functions.

13. Consider the functions: $f(x) = (x + 3)^2$ and $g(x) = \dfrac{x - 2}{x + 3}$

Given $p(x) = f(x) \cdot g(x)$, write an explicit equation for $p(x)$, then determine its domain and range.

14. Consider the function $g(x) = 4$ and any function $f(x)$. Predict how the graph of each function below will be a transformation image of $y = f(x)$. Use graphing technology to check.

a) $y = f(x) + g(x)$ **b)** $y = f(x) - g(x)$

c) $y = f(x) \cdot g(x)$ **d)** $y = \dfrac{f(x)}{g(x)}$

15. When each function $h(x)$ below is evaluated at $x = a$, its value is 0. What do you know about the values of $f(a)$ and $g(a)$?

a) $h(x) = f(x) + g(x)$ **b)** $h(x) = f(x) - g(x)$

c) $h(x) = f(x) \cdot g(x)$ **d)** $h(x) = \dfrac{f(x)}{g(x)}$

16. Given $f(x) = \sqrt{x}$ and $g(x) = \sqrt{2 - x}$, determine an explicit equation for each function, then state its domain.

a) $h(x) = f(x) + g(x)$ **b)** $d(x) = f(x) - g(x)$

c) $p(x) = f(x) \cdot g(x)$ **d)** $q(x) = \dfrac{f(x)}{g(x)}$

C

17. Consider the function: $f(x) = \dfrac{x^2 - 3x + 4}{x - 1}$

a) Determine the domain and the approximate range of $f(x)$.

b) Determine explicit equations for $g(x)$, $h(x)$, and $k(x)$ so that

$$f(x) = g(x) + \frac{h(x)}{k(x)}.$$

18. Is it possible to combine $f(x) = \sqrt{x}$ with a second function $g(x)$ to get a new function whose domain is all real numbers? Justify your answer.

Multiple-Choice Questions

1. Given the functions $f(x) = 3x - 2$ and $g(x) = x^2 + x - 1$, which function is $h(x) = g(x) - f(x)$?

   A. $h(x) = x^2 - 2x - 3$ **B.** $h(x) = x^2 - 2x + 1$

   C. $h(x) = x^2 + 4x - 3$ **D.** $h(x) = -x^2 + 2x - 1$

2. Given $f(x) = x - 3$ and $g(x) = (x + 4)^2$, what is the domain of

$h(x) = \dfrac{f(x)}{g(x)}$?

   A. $x \in \mathbb{R}$ **B.** $x \neq -4$ **C.** $x \neq 3$ **D.** $x \neq -4, x \neq 3$

Study Note

Use examples to explain how to determine the domains and ranges of functions formed by adding, subtracting, multiplying, or dividing two functions.

ANSWERS

Check Your Understanding

1. a) For $f(x)$, domain: $x \in \mathbb{R}$; range: $y \in \mathbb{R}$; for $g(x)$, domain: $x \in \mathbb{R}$; range: $y \geq 0$

b) $h(x) = x + 2 + |x|$; domain: $x \in \mathbb{R}$; range: $y \geq 2$

c) $p(x) = (x + 2) \cdot |x|$; domain: $x \in \mathbb{R}$; range: $y \in \mathbb{R}$

2. a) For $f(x)$, domain: $x \geq 0$; range: $y \geq 0$; for $g(x)$, domain: $x \in \mathbb{R}$; range: $y \in \mathbb{R}$

b) $q(x) = \dfrac{\sqrt{x}}{x - 2}$; domain: $x \geq 0, x \neq 2$; range: $y \in \mathbb{R}$

Exercises

3. a) $h(x) = x^3 + x^2 + 1$ **b)** $d(x) = x^3 - x^2 - 1$ **c)** $p(x) = x^3(x^2 + 1)$

d) $q(x) = \dfrac{x^3}{x^2 + 1}$ **5. a) i)** $h(x) = x - 2$ **ii)** $h(x) = x - 2$ **iii)** $h(x) = 3x - 6$

iv) $h(x) = -3x + 6$ **v)** $h(x) = -2x^2 + 8x - 8$ **vi)** $h(x) = -2x^2 + 8x - 8$

6. a) $k(x) = -x^3 + x^2 + 2x - 2; x \in \mathbb{R}$ **b)** $k(x) = -x^3 + x^2 - 2x; x \in \mathbb{R}$

c) $k(x) = -2x^4 + x^3 + x^2 + 6x - 7; x \in \mathbb{R}$ **d)** $k(x) = 3x^3 - x^2 - 8x + 1; x \in \mathbb{R}$

9. a) For $f(x)$ and $g(x)$, domain: $x \in \mathbb{R}$; range: $y \geq 0$

b) $h(x) = |x - 4| + x^2$; domain: $x \in \mathbb{R}$; range: $y \geq 3.75$

c) $d(x) = |x - 4| - x^2$; domain: $x \in \mathbb{R}$; range: $y \leq 4.25$

10. a) For $f(x)$, domain: $x \in \mathbb{R}$; range: $y \in \mathbb{R}$; for $g(x)$, domain: $x \neq -3$; range: $y \neq 0$

b) $h(x) = x^3 - x + \dfrac{1}{x + 3}$; domain: $x \neq -3$; approximate range: $y \leq -34.5$ or

$y \geq -14.2$ **c)** $p(x) = \dfrac{x^3 - x}{x + 3}$; domain: $x \neq -3$; range: $y \in \mathbb{R}$

11. a) For $f(x)$, domain: $x \geq -2$; range; $y \geq 0$; for $g(x)$, domain: $x \in \mathbb{R}$; range: $y \geq 0$

b) $p(x) = \sqrt{x + 2} \cdot |x - 2|$; domain: $x \geq -2$; range: $y \geq 0$

c) $q(x) = \dfrac{\sqrt{x + 2}}{|x - 2|}$; domain: $x \geq -2, x \neq 2$; range: $y \geq 0$ **12. a)** incorrect

13. $p(x) = x^2 + x - 6, x \neq -3$; domain: $x \neq -3$; range: $y \geq -6.25$

14. a) translated 4 units up **b)** translated 4 units down

c) stretched vertically by a factor of 4 **d)** compressed vertically by a factor of $\frac{1}{4}$

15. a) $f(a) = -g(a)$ **b)** $f(a) = g(a)$ **c)** $f(a) = 0$, or $g(a) = 0$, or both

d) $f(a) = 0, g(a) \neq 0$ **16. a)** $h(x) = \sqrt{x} + \sqrt{2 - x}; 0 \leq x \leq 2$

b) $d(x) = \sqrt{x} - \sqrt{2 - x}; 0 \leq x \leq 2$ **c)** $p(x) = \sqrt{x} \cdot \sqrt{2 - x}; 0 \leq x \leq 2$

d) $q(x) = \dfrac{\sqrt{x}}{\sqrt{2 - x}}; 0 \leq x < 2$

17. a) domain: $x \neq 1$; approximate range: $y \leq -3.8$ or $y \geq 1.8$ **18.** no

Multiple Choice

1. B **2.** B

Self-Assess

Can you. . .	Try *Checkpoint* question	For review, see
sketch the graph of a function that is the sum or difference of two functions, given their graphs?	2	Page 268 in Lesson 4.1
sketch the graph of a function that is the product or quotient of two functions, given their graphs?	2	Page 269 in Lesson 4.1
write the equation of a function that is the sum, difference, or product of two or more functions, given their equations?	5	Page 274 in Lesson 4.2 (Example 1)
write the equation of a function that is the quotient of two or more functions, given their equations?	5	Page 275 in Lesson 4.2 (Example 2)
determine the domain and range of a function that is the sum, difference, or product of two functions?	5	Page 274 in Lesson 4.2 (Example 1)
determine the domain and range of a function that is the quotient of two functions?	5	Page 275 in Lesson 4.2 (Example 2)
write a function as the sum or difference of two or more functions?	4	Page 276 in Lesson 4.2 (Example 3)
write a function as the product or quotient of two or more functions?	4	Page 277 in Lesson 4.2 (Example 4)

Assess Your Understanding

4.1

1. **Multiple Choice** Given the graphs of $y = f(x)$ and $y = g(x)$, which graph below represents $y = \dfrac{f(x)}{g(x)}$?

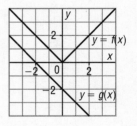

A.

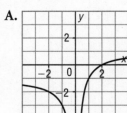

B.

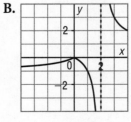

C.

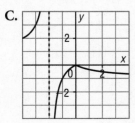

D.

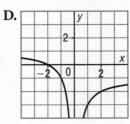

2. Use the graphs of $y = f(x)$ and $y = g(x)$ to sketch the graph of each given function. Identify its domain and range; approximate the range where necessary.

a) $y = f(x) + g(x)$

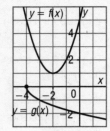

b) $y = f(x) - g(x)$

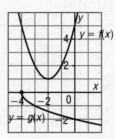

c) $y = f(x) \cdot g(x)$

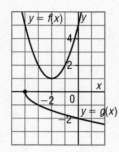

d) $y = \dfrac{f(x)}{g(x)}$

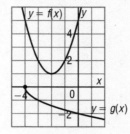

4.2

3. Multiple Choice Given $f(x) = x - 2$ and $g(x) = \sqrt{x}$, what is the domain of $h(x) = f(x) \cdot g(x)$?

A. $x \in \mathbb{R}$ **B.** $x \neq 2$ **C.** $x > 2$ **D.** $x \geq 0$

4. Use $f(x) = x^2 + x - 20$.

  a) Write explicit equations for two functions $g(x)$ and $k(x)$ so that $f(x) = g(x) \cdot k(x)$.

  b) Write explicit equations for three functions $g(x)$, $h(x)$, and $k(x)$ so that $f(x) = g(x) - h(x) - k(x)$.

c) Write explicit equations for two functions $g(x)$ and $k(x)$ so that

$$f(x) = \frac{g(x)}{k(x)}.$$

5. Use $f(x) = 3x^2 - 1, g(x) = \frac{1}{x + 2}$, and $h(x) = \sqrt{x - 5}$.

   i) Write an explicit equation for each function below.

   ii) State the domain and range of each function; approximate the range where necessary.

a) $h(x) = f(x) + g(x)$ **b)** $d(x) = g(x) - h(x)$

c) $p(x) = f(x) \cdot g(x)$ **d)** $q(x) = \frac{h(x)}{g(x)}$

ANSWERS

1. C   2. a) domain: $x \geq -4$; approximate range: $y \geq -0.4$

b) domain: $x \geq -4$; approximate range: $y \geq 2.4$

c) domain: $x \geq -4$; range: $y \leq 0$

d) domain: $x > -4$; approximate range: $y \leq -0.7$ **3.** D

5. a) i) $h(x) = 3x^2 - 1 + \frac{1}{x + 2}$ ii) domain: $x \neq -2$; range: $y \in \mathbb{R}$

b) i) $d(x) = \frac{1}{x + 2} - \sqrt{x - 5}$ ii) domain: $x \geq 5$; range: $y \leq \frac{1}{7}$

c) i) $p(x) = \frac{3x^2 - 1}{x + 2}$ ii) domain: $x \neq -2$; approximate range: $y \geq -0.5$ or $y \leq -23.5$

d) i) $q(x) = (x + 2)\sqrt{x - 5}$ ii) domain: $x \geq 5$; range: $y \geq 0$

4.3 Introduction to Composite Functions

Determine the value of a composition of functions at a point and determine the equation of a composite function.

Get Started

Here are two function machines. The output of machine A is the input for machine B.

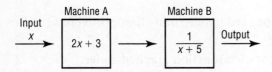

What is the output from machine B for each input in machine A?

- $x = 3$

- $x = 0$

- $x = -2$

Construct Understanding

When a drop of liquid falls on a flat surface, it forms a circle whose radius, r centimetres, is a function of time, t seconds, since the drop landed. The area of the circle, A square centimetres, is a function of the radius, r centimetres.

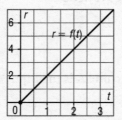 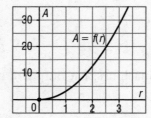

How can the graphs above be used to determine the approximate area of the circle after 1.5 s?

Write an explicit equation for each function graphed above.

What is an explicit equation for A as a function of t?

Use the equation to determine the area of the circle after 1.5 s, to the nearest tenth of a square centimetre.

For a vehicle, the cost of gasoline, c dollars, is a function of the amount used, v litres.

This can be written as the function: $c(v)$

The amount of fuel used, v, is a function of the distance driven, d kilometres.

This can be written as the function: $v(d)$

Since c is a function of v and v is a function of d, c can be written as a function of d: $c(v(d))$

The function $c(v(d))$ represents the cost of gasoline as a function of the distance driven.

This is an example of a **composite function**; $c(v(d))$ is the composition of functions c and v; it is the function that results when function c is applied to function v.

Composition of Functions

Given f and g are two functions of x, the composition of f and g is:
$f(g(x))$, or $f \circ g(x)$
Both expressions are read as: "f of g at x."

The definition above illustrates that functions may simply be described by single letters, such as f and g.

Consider the two functions partially described by the arrow diagrams below.

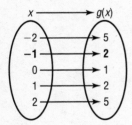 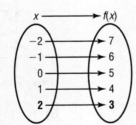

To determine $f(g(-1))$, start with the "inside" function g and determine $g(-1)$.

From the first arrow diagram, $g(-1) = 2$

So, $f(g(-1)) = f(2)$

From the second arrow diagram, $f(2) = 3$

So, $f(g(-1)) = 3$

The composition on page 293 can be illustrated graphically. Here are the graphs of $y = f(x)$, $y = g(x)$, and $y = x$, for $x \in \mathbb{R}$. To determine $f(g(-1))$:

- Draw a vertical line through $x = -1$ to intersect the graph of $y = g(x)$; the point of intersection is $(-1, 2)$.
- From the point $(-1, 2)$, draw a horizontal line to intersect the graph of $y = x$; the point of intersection is $(2, 2)$. The y-value of $g(x)$ is the x-value of $f(x)$.
- From the point $(2, 2)$, draw a vertical line to intersect the graph of $y = f(x)$; the point of intersection is $(2, 3)$. So, $f(g(-1)) = 3$

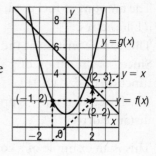

This is called a *web graph*.

Check Your Understanding

1. Use the functions in *Example 1* to determine each value.
   a) $g(f(2))$ **b)** $g(g(2))$

Example 1	Determining the Value of a Composite Function Using Tables of Values

The tables below define two functions. Use these tables to determine each value below.

x	f(x)
−2	8
−1	3
0	0
1	−1
2	0

x	g(x)
−2	3
−1	2
0	1
1	0
2	−1

a) $f(g(-1))$ **b)** $f(f(1))$

SOLUTION

a) $f(g(-1))$

First determine: $g(-1) = 2$
Then, $f(g(-1)) = f(2)$
$\qquad\qquad = 0$

b) $f(f(1))$

First determine: $f(1) = -1$
Then, $f(f(1)) = f(-1)$
$\qquad\qquad = 3$

THINK FURTHER
....

In *Example 1*, why can the value of $f(f(-2))$ not be determined with any certainty?

Example 2 **Determining the Value of a Composite Function Graphically**

Given the graphs of $y = f(x)$ and $y = g(x)$, determine each value below.

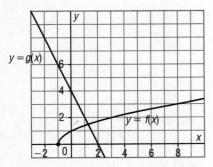

a) $f(g(-2))$ **b)** $g(f(3))$

2. Use the graph in *Example 2* to determine each value.

     a) $f(g(2))$ **b)** $g(f(-1))$

SOLUTION

On the graph, draw the line $y = x$.

a) $f(g(-2))$
Draw the line $x = -2$, which intersects the graph of $y = g(x)$ at P. From P, draw a horizontal line, which intersects the graph of $y = x$ at Q. From Q, draw a vertical line, which intersects the graph of $y = f(x)$ at R(8, 3). So, $f(g(-2)) = 3$

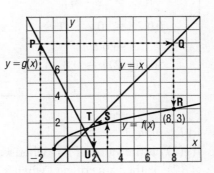

b) $g(f(3))$
Draw the line $x = 3$, which intersects the graph of $y = f(x)$ at S. From S, draw a horizontal line, which intersects the graph of $y = x$ at T. From T, draw a vertical line, which intersects the graph of $y = g(x)$ at U(2, 0). So, $g(f(3)) = 0$

THINK FURTHER

In *Example 2a*, why is it possible to determine $f(g(-2))$ when the function f is not defined for $x = -2$?

Example 3 | Determining the Value of a Composite Function Algebraically

3. Given the functions
$f(x) = x^2 + 3x$ and
$g(x) = -2x + 1$, determine
each value.

a) $f(g(9))$ **b)** $g(f(9))$

Given the functions $f(x) = |x - 1|$ and $g(x) = \dfrac{1}{x^2 + 1}$, determine each value.

a) $f(g(2))$ **b)** $g(f(2))$

SOLUTION

a) $f(g(2))$
To determine $g(2)$,
substitute $x = 2$ in
$$g(x) = \frac{1}{x^2 + 1}$$
$$g(2) = \frac{1}{2^2 + 1}$$
$$= 0.2$$
So, $f(g(2)) = f(0.2)$
Substitute $x = 0.2$ in
$$f(x) = |x - 1|$$
$$f(0.2) = |0.2 - 1|$$
$$= 0.8$$
So, $f(g(2)) = 0.8$

b) $g(f(2))$
To determine $f(2)$,
substitute $x = 2$ in
$$f(x) = |x - 1|$$
$$f(2) = |2 - 1|$$
$$= 1$$
So, $g(f(2)) = g(1)$
Substitute $x = 1$ in
$$g(x) = \frac{1}{x^2 + 1}$$
$$g(1) = \frac{1}{1^2 + 1}$$
$$= 0.5$$
So, $g(f(2)) = 0.5$

In *Example 3*:
$f(g(2))$ is the value of $f(x)$ when $x = g(2)$.
$g(f(2))$ is the value of $g(x)$ when $x = f(2)$.
This example illustrates that, in general, $f(g(a)) \neq g(f(a))$, where $a \in \mathbb{R}$.

For two functions, such as $f(x) = 3x - 4$ and $g(x) = x^2 + 5x$, a composite function, $h(x)$, is formed by replacing x in $f(x)$ with $g(x)$.
That is, $h(x) = f(g(x))$
Begin with:

$f(x) = 3x - 4$ Replace x with $g(x)$.
$f(g(x)) = 3(g(x)) - 4$ On the right side, replace $g(x)$ with $x^2 + 5x$.
$f(g(x)) = 3(x^2 + 5x) - 4$ Simplify.
So, $h(x) = 3x^2 + 15x - 4$

Consider the function: $f(x) = 2x + 3$, or $y = 2x + 3$
The inverse function is:

$x = 2y + 3$ Solve for y.
$2y = x - 3$
$y = \dfrac{x - 3}{2}$

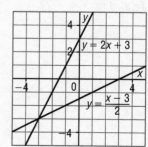

Let the inverse function be $g(x)$.

Then, $g(x) = \dfrac{x - 3}{2}$

So, $f(g(x)) = 2\left(\dfrac{x - 3}{2}\right) + 3$ And, $g(f(x)) = \dfrac{(2x + 3) - 3}{2}$

         $= x$ $= x$

In *Example 3*, it was shown that, in general, $f(g(x))$ and $g(f(x))$ are usually different. The example above illustrates that if two functions $f(x)$ and $g(x)$ are inverses of each other, then $f(g(x)) = g(f(x)) = x$ for all values of x in the domains of both functions.

Example 4   Writing the Equation of a Composite Function

Check Your Understanding

Given $f(x) = x^2 + 3x$ and $g(x) = 3x - 5$, determine an explicit equation for each composite function, then state its domain and range.

a) $f(g(x))$ **b)** $g(f(x))$ **c)** $f(f(x))$

4. Given $f(x) = 2x^2 + 1$ and $g(x) = 2x + 7$, determine an explicit equation for each composite function, then state its domain and range.

a) $f(g(x))$ **b)** $g(f(x))$
c) $g(g(x))$

SOLUTION

Use $f(x) = x^2 + 3x$ and $g(x) = 3x - 5$.
Use graphing technology to determine the range.

a) $f(g(x)) = f(3x - 5)$
In $f(x) = x^2 + 3x$, replace x with $3x - 5$.
$f(g(x)) = (3x - 5)^2 + 3(3x - 5)$
$f(g(x)) = 9x^2 - 30x + 25 + 9x - 15$
$f(g(x)) = 9x^2 - 21x + 10$
This is a quadratic function. Its domain is: $x \in \mathbb{R}$
From the graph, the range is: $y \geq -2.25$

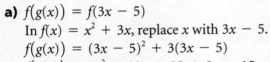

b) $g(f(x)) = g(x^2 + 3x)$
In $g(x) = 3x - 5$, replace x with $x^2 + 3x$.
$g(f(x)) = 3(x^2 + 3x) - 5$
$g(f(x)) = 3x^2 + 9x - 5$
This is a quadratic function.
Its domain is: $x \in \mathbb{R}$
From the graph, the range is: $y \geq -11.75$

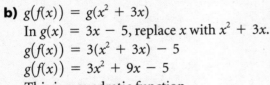

c) $f(f(x)) = f(x^2 + 3x)$
In $f(x) = x^2 + 3x$, replace x with $x^2 + 3x$.
$f(f(x)) = (x^2 + 3x)^2 + 3(x^2 + 3x)$
$f(f(x)) = x^4 + 6x^3 + 9x^2 + 3x^2 + 9x$
$f(f(x)) = x^4 + 6x^3 + 12x^2 + 9x$
This is a quartic function. Its domain is: $x \in \mathbb{R}$
From the graph, the minimum points have the same y-coordinate, and the range is: $y \geq -2.25$

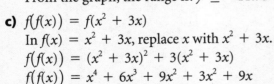

Discuss the Ideas

1. What is a composite function?

2. Suppose you are given the equation of a composite function $f(g(x))$. How do you determine the value of $f(g(a))$, where a is a real number?

3. Why is it important to evaluate a composite function in the correct order?

Exercises

A

4. Use these tables to determine each value below.

x	f(x)
−2	4
−1	2
0	0
1	−2
2	−4

x	g(x)
−4	−3
−2	1
0	5
2	9
4	13

a) $f(g(-2))$

b) $g(f(-2))$

c) $f(f(-1))$

d) $g(f(0))$

15. Given the graphs of $y = f(x)$ and $y = g(x)$

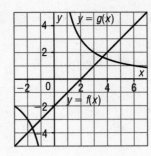

a) Determine the value of a for which
$f(g(a)) = -1$.

b) Determine the value of a for which $g(f(a)) = 2$.

C

16. Given the functions $f(x) = x^2 - 2x$ and $g(x) = 3x + 2$, write an explicit expression for each value.

a) $g(f(a))$ b) $f(g(a))$

c) $f(g(a - 1))$ d) $f(g(1 - a))$

17. Given the functions $f(x) = x^2 - 2x + 2$, $g(x) = 5x - 2$, and $h(x) = \sqrt{x + 3}$

a) Determine the value of a for which $g(h(a)) = 13$.

b) Determine the values of a for which $f(g(a)) = 5$.

c) Why are there two values of a for part b but only one value for part a?

Multiple-Choice Questions

1. For the functions $f(x)$ and $g(x)$, what is the value of $f(g(3))$?

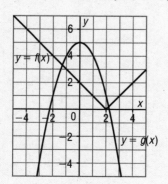

A. -4 **B.** 2   **C.** 4   **D.** 6

2. For the functions $f(x) = -3x + 5$ and $g(x) = x^2 + x - 1$, which expression has the greatest value?

A. $f(g(1))$ **B.** $g(f(4))$ **C.** $f(g(-2))$ **D.** $g(f(3))$

Study Note

Choose two polynomial functions $f(x)$ and $g(x)$.
Show how to write explicit equations for the composite functions $f(g(x))$ and $g(f(x))$, then determine each domain and range.

ANSWERS

Check Your Understanding

1. a) 1   **b)** 2   **2. a)** 1   **b)** 4   **3. a)** 238   **b)** -215
4. a) $f(g(x)) = 8x^2 + 56x + 99$; domain: $x \in \mathbb{R}$; range: $y \geq 1$
b) $g(f(x)) = 4x^2 + 9$; domain: $x \in \mathbb{R}$; range: $y \geq 9$
c) $g(g(x)) = 4x + 21$; domain: $x \in \mathbb{R}$; range: $y \in \mathbb{R}$

Exercises

4. a) -2 **b)** 13   **c)** -4 **d)** 5   **5. a)** -2 **b)** 5   **c)** 1   **d)** -6 **6. a)** 1   **b)** 45
c) -4 **d)** 22   **7. a)** -2 **b)** -3 **8. a)** 1   **b)** -0.5 **9. a)** 5   **b)** 6   **c)** $14 - 8\sqrt{2}$
d) 2   **10. a)** $f(g(x)) = -8x^2 + 12x - 3$; domain: $x \in \mathbb{R}$; range: $y \leq 1.5$
b) $g(f(x)) = -32x^2 + 60x - 27$; domain: $x \in \mathbb{R}$; range: $y \leq 1.125$
c) $g(g(x)) = -8x^4 + 24x^3 - 24x^2 + 9x$; domain: $x \in \mathbb{R}$; range: $y \leq 1.125$
d) $f(f(x)) = 16x - 15$; domain: $x \in \mathbb{R}$; range: $y \in \mathbb{R}$
11. a) $f(g(x)) = (3x + 1)^3 - 5$; domain: $x \in \mathbb{R}$; range: $y \in \mathbb{R}$
b) $g(f(x)) = 3x^3 - 14$; domain: $x \in \mathbb{R}$; range: $y \in \mathbb{R}$
c) $f(f(x)) = (x^3 - 5)^3 - 5$; domain: $x \in \mathbb{R}$; range: $y \in \mathbb{R}$
d) $g(g(x)) = 9x + 4$; domain: $x \in \mathbb{R}$; range: $y \in \mathbb{R}$ **12.** no
13. a) $f(g(2)) = 2; g(f(2)) = 2$ **b)** $f(g(1)) = 1; g(f(1)) = 1$
c) The functions are inverses.   **14. a)** The functions are inverses.
b) The functions are not inverses.   **15. a)** 6   **b)** 5   **16. a)** $3a^2 - 6a + 2$
b) $9a^2 + 6a$ **c)** $9a^2 - 12a + 3$ **d)** $15 - 24a + 9a^2$ **17. a)** 6   **b)** 0.2, 1

Multiple Choice

1. D   **2.** B

4.4 Determining Restrictions on Composite Functions

4.4

FOCUS Sketch graphs and determine equations of composite functions, then identify restrictions.

Get Started

Solve each quadratic inequality:

$$x^2 + 9 \leq 25 \qquad\qquad x^2 + x - 6 > 0$$

Construct Understanding

Graph $f(x) = \sqrt{3 - x}$ and $g(x) = x^2 - 1$ on the grid on page 308.

- Identify the domain and range of $f(x)$.
- Identify the domain and range of $g(x)$.

Complete the table on page 308, then graph $y = f(g(x))$ on the same grid.

- What are the domain and range of $f(g(x))$?
- How is the domain of $f(g(x))$ related to the domains or ranges of $f(x)$ and $g(x)$?

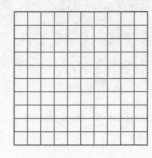

x	g(x)	f(g(x))
−3		
−2		
−1		
0		
1		
2		
3		

Given the equations of two functions, a composition of the two functions can be graphed by plotting points.

Check Your Understanding

1. Use the functions
$f(x) = x + 1$ and
$g(x) = 4 - x^2$.
- State the domain and range of each function.
- Sketch a graph of each composite function below.
- State the domain and range of the composite function.

a) $y = f(g(x))$ **b)** $y = f(f(x))$

Example 1 · Graphing a Composition of a Linear Function and a Quadratic Function

Use the functions $f(x) = 2x - 1$ and $g(x) = x^2 - 2$.
- State the domain and range of each function.
- Sketch a graph of each composite function below.
- State the domain and estimate the range of the composite function.

a) $y = g(f(x))$ **b)** $y = g(g(x))$

SOLUTION

The function $f(x) = 2x - 1$ is linear; its domain is $x \in \mathbb{R}$ and its range is $y \in \mathbb{R}$.
The function $g(x) = x^2 - 2$ is quadratic. Its graph opens up and has vertex $(0, -2)$; the domain is $x \in \mathbb{R}$ and the range is $y \geq -2$.

a) Identify the coordinates of points $(x, f(x))$ that satisfy the equation $f(x) = 2x - 1$, by substituting values of x in this equation. Then substitute each value of $f(x)$ for x in $g(x) = x^2 - 2$.

x	f(x)	g(f(x))
−2	−5	23
−1	−3	7
0	−1	−1
1	1	−1
2	3	7
3	5	23

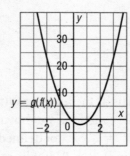

Graph the points with coordinates $(x, g(f(x)))$.
Draw a smooth curve through the points for the graph of
$y = g(f(x))$. From the graph, the domain is $x \in \mathbb{R}$.
The line $x = 0.5$ is the axis of symmetry, so the minimum point
has x-coordinate 0.5.
Determine: $g(f(0.5))$
$f(0.5) = 2(0.5) - 1$, or 0
And $g(f(0.5)) = g(0)$, or −2
So, the range is $y \geq -2$.

b) Identify the coordinates of points $(x, g(x))$ that satisfy the equation $g(x) = x^2 - 2$.
Then, substitute each value of $g(x)$ for x in $g(x) = x^2 - 2$.

x	g(x)	g(g(x))
−2	2	2
−1.5	0.25	≐ −2
−1	−1	−1
0	−2	2
1	−1	−1
1.5	0.25	≐ −2
2	2	2

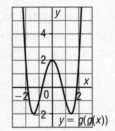

Graph the points with coordinates $(x, g(g(x)))$.
Draw a smooth curve through the points for the graph of
$y = g(g(x))$. From the graph, the domain is $x \in \mathbb{R}$ and the
approximate range is $y \geq -2$.

THINK FURTHER

In *Example 1*, what other strategy could you use to sketch graphs of the composite functions?

The graphs of the functions $f(x) = \sqrt{x}$, $g(x) = x + 3$, and two composite functions are shown below.

Since $f(x) = \sqrt{x}$ is not defined for negative values of x, its domain is $x \geq 0$, and its range is $y \geq 0$.

Since $g(x) = x + 3$ is defined for all real values of x, its domain is $x \in \mathbb{R}$, and its range is $y \in \mathbb{R}$.

Graph of $f\big(g(x)\big)$

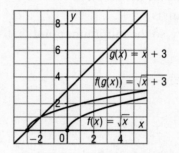

Graph of $g\big(f(x)\big)$

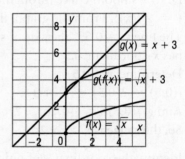

For the composite function $f\big(g(x)\big)$, the function f is applied to the range of g.

The domain of f is restricted to $x \geq 0$, so $f\big(g(x)\big)$ is defined when $g(x) \geq 0$; that is, for $x \geq -3$.

For the composite function $g\big(f(x)\big)$, the function g is applied to the range of f. The domain of f is restricted to $x \geq 0$, so $g\big(f(x)\big)$ is defined for $x \geq 0$.

In general, $f\big(g(x)\big)$ is only defined for $x = a$ when:

- a is in the domain of g, and

- $g(a)$, which is an element of the range of g, is in the domain of f.

THINK FURTHER

When f and g are polynomial functions, why are there no restrictions on the domain of $f(g(x))$?

Given the functions $f(x) = \dfrac{1}{x-2}$ and $g(x) = x^2 - x$, determine an explicit equation for each composite function below, then state its domain.

a) $g(f(x))$ **b)** $f(g(x))$

2. Given the functions

$f(x) = \dfrac{1}{x+3}$ and

$g(x) = x^2 - 4x$, determine an explicit equation for each composite function below, then state its domain.

a) $g(f(x))$ **b)** $f(g(x))$

SOLUTION

a) For $g(f(x))$:

In $g(x) = x^2 - x$, replace x with $\dfrac{1}{x-2}$.

$$g(f(x)) = \left(\dfrac{1}{x-2}\right)^2 - \left(\dfrac{1}{x-2}\right)$$

The domain of $f(x) = \dfrac{1}{x-2}$ is $x \neq 2$.

The domain of $g(x) = x^2 - x$ is $x \in \mathbb{R}$.

So, the domain of $g(f(x))$ is $x \neq 2$.

b) For $f(g(x))$:

In $f(x) = \dfrac{1}{x-2}$, replace x with $x^2 - x$.

$$f(g(x)) = \dfrac{1}{x^2 - x - 2}$$

The domain of $g(x) = x^2 - x$ is $x \in \mathbb{R}$.

The domain of $f(x) = \dfrac{1}{x-2}$ is $x \neq 2$.

So, $g(x)$ cannot equal 2; that is,

$x^2 - x \neq 2$

$x^2 - x - 2 \neq 0$

$(x+1)(x-2) \neq 0$

So, $x \neq -1$ and $x \neq 2$

So, the domain of $f(g(x))$ is $x \neq -1$ and $x \neq 2$.

The results of *Example 2* can be verified by using graphing technology.

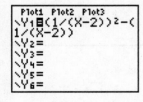

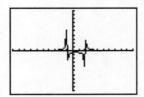

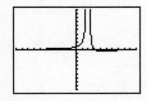

3. Given the functions $f(x) = \sqrt{x}$ and $g(x) = x^2 - 4$, determine an explicit equation for each composite function below, then state its domain.

a) $g(f(x))$ **b)** $f(g(x))$

Given the functions $f(x) = \sqrt{x}$ and $g(x) = -x^2 + 2x$, determine an explicit equation for each composite function below, then state its domain.

a) $g(f(x))$ **b)** $f(g(x))$

SOLUTION

a) For $g(f(x))$:

In $g(x) = -x^2 + 2x$, replace x with $\sqrt{x}$.

$g(f(x)) = -(\sqrt{x})^2 + 2\sqrt{x}$

$g(f(x)) = -x + 2\sqrt{x}$

The domain of $f(x) = \sqrt{x}$ is $x \geq 0$.

The domain of $g(x) = -x^2 + 2x$ is $x \in \mathbb{R}$.

So, the domain of $g(f(x)) = -x + 2\sqrt{x}$ is $x \geq 0$.

b) For $f(g(x))$:

In $f(x) = \sqrt{x}$, replace x with $-x^2 + 2x$.

$f(g(x)) = \sqrt{-x^2 + 2x}$

The domain of $g(x) = -x^2 + 2x$ is $x \in \mathbb{R}$.

The domain of $f(x) = \sqrt{x}$ is $x \geq 0$.

So, $g(x)$ cannot be negative; that is,

$-x^2 + 2x \geq 0$

$x^2 - 2x \leq 0$

Solve the corresponding quadratic equation.

$x^2 - 2x = 0$

$x(x - 2) = 0$

$x = 0 \text{ or } x = 2$

Choose a value of $x < 0$, such as $x = -1$.

Use mental math to substitute $x = -1$ in $x^2 - 2x \leq 0$.

L.S. = 3   R.S. = 0

So, the interval $x < 0$ is not the correct interval.

That means that $0 \leq x \leq 2$ is the correct interval.

So, the domain of $f(g(x)) = \sqrt{-x^2 + 2x}$ is $0 \leq x \leq 2$.

The results of *Example 3* can be verified by using graphing technology.

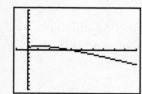

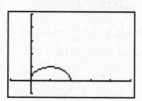

Two functions that form a composite function may be determined by working backward.

Consider the quadratic function: $h(x) = 2(x - 3)^2 + 1$

To write $h(x)$ as a composite function $f(g(x))$, first identify a function of x contained within $h(x)$.

The binomial $(x - 3)$ is a function of x, and can be written as:

$g(x) = x - 3$

Then $h(x) = 2(g(x))^2 + 1$

Replace $g(x)$ with x to get: $f(x) = 2x^2 + 1$

So, $f(x) = 2x^2 + 1$ and $g(x) = x - 3$ form the composite function $f(g(x)) = 2(x - 3)^2 + 1$.

The function $f(g(x)) = 2(x - 3)^2 + 1$ can be considered as a composite function in a different way.

Consider $g(x) = (x - 3)^2$, then $f(g(x)) = 2g(x) + 1$

Replace $g(x)$ with x to get: $f(x) = 2x + 1$

So, $f(x) = 2x + 1$ and $g(x) = (x - 3)^2$ form the composite function $f(g(x)) = 2(x - 3)^2 + 1$.

Example 4	Writing a Function as a Composition of Two Functions

For each function, determine possible functions f and g so that $y = f(g(x))$.

a) $y = \dfrac{1}{x^2}$

b) $y = (3x^2 + 1)^4$

SOLUTION

a) Let $f(g(x)) = \dfrac{1}{x^2}$

Replace x^2 with x.

Then, $g(x) = x^2$ and $f(x) = \dfrac{1}{x}$

b) Let $f(g(x)) = (3x^2 + 1)^4$

Replace $3x^2 + 1$ with x.

Then, $g(x) = 3x^2 + 1$ and $f(x) = x^4$

Check Your Understanding

4. For each function, determine possible functions f and g so that $y = f(g(x))$.

a) $y = (x - 2)^3$

b) $y = \sqrt{3 + x}$

A composition of functions may involve more than two functions. In *Example 4b*, the function $y = (3x^2 + 1)^4$ can be written as $y = f(g(h(x)))$, where $h(x) = x^2$, $g(x) = 3x + 1$, and $f(x) = x^4$.

Discuss the Ideas

1. How is determining the domain of a composite function different from determining the domain of the combination of two functions?

2. Can every quadratic function be written as the composition of a linear function and a quadratic function? Justify your response.

Exercises

A

3. For each function below, determine possible functions f and g so that $y = f(g(x))$.

   a) $y = (x + 4)^2$

   b) $y = \sqrt{x + 5}$

   c) $y = \dfrac{1}{x - 2}$

   d) $y = (6 - x)^3$

4. Given $f(x) = x + 3$ and $g(x) = x^2 + 1$, sketch the graph of each composite function below then state its domain and range.

a) $y = f(f(x))$

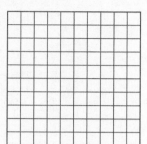

b) $y = f(g(x))$

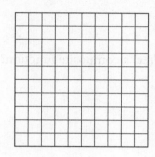

c) $y = g(f(x))$

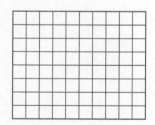

d) $y = g(g(x))$

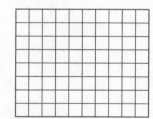

5. Consider the function $h(x) = (x - 1)(x + 5)$.

    a) Why is it incorrect to write $h(x) = f(g(x))$, where $f(x) = x - 1$ and $g(x) = x + 5$?

    b) For what functions $f(x)$ and $g(x)$ is $h(x)$ a composite function?

6. For each pair of functions below:

    i) Determine an explicit equation for the indicated composite function.

    ii) State the domain of the composite function, and explain any restrictions on the variable.

    a) $f(x) = \sqrt{x + 1}$ and $g(x) = x^2 - x - 6$; $g(f(x))$

    b) $f(x) = \sqrt{x - 1}$ and $g(x) = \dfrac{1}{x + 3}$; $g(f(x))$

c) $f(x) = \sqrt{x + 3}$ and $g(x) = 2x - 1$; $f(g(x))$

d) $f(x) = \dfrac{1}{x - 1}$ and $g(x) = x^2 + 2x$; $f(f(x))$

7. For each function below
   i) Determine possible functions f and g so that $y = f(g(x))$.
   ii) Determine possible functions f, g, and h so that $y = f(g(h(x)))$.

a) $y = x^2 - 6x + 5$ **b)** $y = -3x^2 - 30x - 40$

c) $y = \sqrt{(x - 2)^2 + 3}$ **d)** $y = \sqrt{x^2 + 4x + 3}$

8. Create composite functions using either or both functions in each pair of functions below. In each case, how many different composite functions could you create? Justify your answer.

a) $f(x) = |x|$ and $g(x) = \frac{1}{x}$

b) $f(x) = \sqrt{x}$ and $g(x) = |x|$

c) $f(x) = x^3$ and $g(x) = \frac{1}{x}$

9. Given the function $y = \dfrac{x}{\sqrt{x-3}}$, determine possible functions:

a) f and g so that $y = \dfrac{f(x)}{g(x)}$

b) f, g, and h so that $y = \dfrac{f(x)}{g(h(x))}$

c) f and g so that $y = f(g(x))$

10. Given the functions $f(x) = \sqrt{x}$, $g(x) = x^2 - x + 6$, and $k(x) = \dfrac{2}{x}$, write an explicit equation for each combination.

a) $h(x) = f(g(x)) + k(x)$

b) $h(x) = g(f(x)) - f(g(x))$

c) $h(x) = k(g(x)) + k(f(x))$

d) $h(x) = f(g(x)) \cdot k(x)$

11. Given the function $y = (x^2 - 9)\sqrt{x + 2}$, determine possible functions in each case:

a) functions f and g so that $y = f(x) \cdot g(x)$

b) functions f, g, and h so that $y = f(x) \cdot g(h(x))$

c) functions f, g, h, and k so that $y = f(x) \cdot k(x) \cdot g(h(x))$

12. Is there a function $f(x)$ such that each relationship is true? Justify your answer.

a) $f(f(x)) = f(x)$

b) $f(f(x)) = f(x) + f(x)$

C

13. Given $f(x) = \dfrac{1}{x - 2}$, $g(x)$ is a quadratic function, and $h(x) = f(g(x))$, determine an explicit equation for $g(x)$ for each situation below. Explain your strategies.

a) The domain of $h(x)$ is $x \in \mathbb{R}$.

b) The domain of $h(x)$ is $x \neq a$ and $x \neq b$, where a and b are real numbers.

c) The domain of $h(x)$ is $x \neq c$, where c is a real number.

14. Use $f(x) = \dfrac{1 - x}{1 + x}$.

a) Determine an explicit equation for $f(f(x))$, then state the domain of the function.

b) What is the inverse of $f(x)$? Explain.

Multiple-Choice Questions

1. The function $h(x) = f(g(x))$ is the composite of $f(x) = \sqrt{x}$ and $g(x) = x - 6$. What is the domain of $h(x)$?

A. $x \geq 0$ **B.** $x \geq 6$ **C.** $x \geq -6$ **D.** $x \neq 6$

2. Given the functions $f(x) = \sqrt{x + 1}$ and $g(x) = \dfrac{1}{x - 1}$, which expression is equal to $f(g(x))$?

A. $\dfrac{1}{\sqrt{x}}$ **B.** $\dfrac{1}{\sqrt{x + 1} - 1}$ **C.** $\sqrt{\dfrac{x}{x + 1}}$ **D.** $\sqrt{\dfrac{x}{x - 1}}$

Study Note

Use two functions different from those in this lesson. Explain how to determine an equation of a composite function and its domain.

ANSWERS

Check Your Understanding

1. For $f(x)$, domain: $x \in \mathbb{R}$; range: $y \in \mathbb{R}$; for $g(x)$, domain: $x \in \mathbb{R}$; range: $y \leq 4$

a) For $y = f(g(x))$, domain: $x \in \mathbb{R}$; range: $y \leq 5$

b) For $y = f(f(x))$, domain: $x \in \mathbb{R}$; range: $y \in \mathbb{R}$

2. a) $g(f(x)) = \left(\dfrac{1}{x+3}\right)^2 - \left(\dfrac{4}{x+3}\right), x \neq -3$

b) $f(g(x)) = \dfrac{1}{x^2 - 4x + 3}, x \neq 1$ and $x \neq 3$

3. a) $g(f(x)) = x - 4, x \geq 0$ **b)** $f(g(x)) = \sqrt{x^2 - 4}, x \leq -2$ or $x \geq 2$

Exercises

4. a) domain: $x \in \mathbb{R}$; range: $y \in \mathbb{R}$ **b)** domain: $x \in \mathbb{R}$; range: $y \geq 4$

c) domain: $x \in \mathbb{R}$; range: $y \geq 1$ **d)** domain: $x \in \mathbb{R}$; range: $y \geq 2$

6. a) i) $g(f(x)) = x - 5 - \sqrt{x+1}$ **ii)** $x \geq -1$

b) i) $g(f(x)) = \dfrac{1}{\sqrt{x-1} + 3}$ **ii)** $x \geq 1$ **c) i)** $f(g(x)) = \sqrt{2x+2}$ **ii)** $x \geq -1$

d) i) $f(f(x)) = \dfrac{x-1}{2-x}, x \neq 1$ **ii)** $x \neq 1$ and $x \neq 2$

8. a) 3   **b)** 4   **c)** 3   **10. a)** $h(x) = \sqrt{x^2 - x + 6} + \dfrac{2}{x}, x \neq 0$

b) $h(x) = x - \sqrt{x} + 6 - \sqrt{x^2 - x + 6}, x \geq 0$

c) $h(x) = \dfrac{2}{x^2 - x + 6} + \dfrac{2}{\sqrt{x}}, x > 0$ **d)** $h(x) = \sqrt{x^2 - x + 6} \cdot \left(\dfrac{2}{x}\right), x \neq 0$

12. a) $f(x) = x$ **b)** $f(x) = 2x$ **14. a)** $f(f(x)) = x, x \neq -1$ **b)** $f^{-1}(x) = \dfrac{1-x}{1+x}$

Multiple Choice

1. B   **2.** D

Concept Summary

Big Ideas	Applying the Big Ideas
A new function can be created by adding, subtracting, multiplying, or dividing other functions on appropriate domains.	This means that: • The domain of a function that is formed by adding, subtracting, or multiplying two functions is the set of values of x that are common to the domains of the original functions. However, if a new function is formed by dividing two functions, any value of x that makes the divisor 0 is non-permissible. • If the graphs of the original functions are given, the indicated operation is performed on the y-values generated by these functions to get the graph of the new function.
A composite function is the result of applying two functions in succession.	• The domain of a composite function $f(g(x))$ is the set of values of x for which g is defined and for which $g(x)$ is in the domain of f.

Chapter Study Notes

• Describe a strategy to sketch the graph of a function that is the difference of two functions whose graphs are given. How do you determine the domain of the new function?

• What is a composite function? What do you have to consider when you determine the equation of a composite function and its domain?

Skills Summary

Skill	Description	Example
Sketch a graph that is the sum, difference, product, or quotient of two functions whose graphs are given. **(4.1)**	Identify points on the given graphs with the same x-coordinate, perform the indicated operation on the corresponding y-coordinates to determine the y-coordinate of the point on the graph of the new function. Repeat the process for several other pairs of points, then join the points.	Graph $y = f(x) \cdot g(x)$, given the graphs of $y = f(x)$ and $y = g(x)$. Multiply the y-coordinates of corresponding points. For the graphs below: When $x = -1$, $y = 0 \cdot 5$, or 0 When $x = 0$, $y = 1 \cdot 4$, or 4 When $x = 1$, $y = 2 \cdot 3$, or 6 When $x = 2$, $y = 3 \cdot 2$, or 6 When $x = 3$, $y = 4 \cdot 1$, or 4 When $x = 4$, $y = 5 \cdot 0$, or 0
Write the equation of a function that is the sum, difference, product, or quotient of two functions whose equations are given, then determine the domain and range. **(4.2)**	Perform the indicated operation on the given equations. The domain of the new function is the set of values of x that are common to the domains of the original functions and do not make the denominator of a quotient 0.	Given $f(x) = x + 3$ and $g(x) = x - 2$, determine $h(x) = \dfrac{f(x)}{g(x)}$. $h(x) = \dfrac{x + 3}{x - 2}$ The domains of both $f(x)$ and $g(x)$ are $x \in \mathbb{R}$. So, the domain of $h(x)$ is $x \neq 2$.
Determine the value of a composite function, given the equations of the functions that form the composite function. **(4.3)**	To determine the value of the function $f(g(x))$ at $x = a$, first determine $g(a)$, then substitute this value for x in $f(x)$.	Given $f(x) = 3x - 1$ and $g(x) = x^2 + 3$, determine $f(g(2))$. First determine $g(2)$: $g(2) = 2^2 + 3$, or 7 Then substitute $x = 7$ in $f(x)$: $f(7) = 3(7) - 1$, or 20 So, $f(g(2)) = 20$

Given the equations of two functions, determine the equation of a composite function and determine the domain. **(4.3)**	For the functions f and g, the composite function $f(g(x))$ is formed by substituting $g(x)$ for x in $f(x)$.	Given $f(x) = \sqrt{x + 1}$ and $g(x) = 2x$, write an equation for $f(g(x))$. Substitute $2x$ for x in $\sqrt{x + 1}$: $f(g(x)) = \sqrt{2x + 1}$ $g(x)$ is defined for $x \in \mathbb{R}$. $f(x)$ is defined for $x \geq -1$. So, $2x \geq -1$ $x \geq -0.5$ The domain of $f(g(x))$ is $x \geq -0.5$.
Given the equations of two functions, sketch the graph of a composite function. **(4.4)**	To determine the coordinates of points on the graph of $y = f(g(x))$, substitute values of x in $g(x)$, then substitute the corresponding values of $g(x)$ in $f(x)$.	Given $f(x) = x^2 + 3$ and $g(x) = x - 1$, graph $y = f(g(x))$. To determine points on the graph of $y = f(g(x))$: $x = -1, g(-1) = -2; f(-2) = 7$ $x = 0, g(0) = -1; f(-1) = 4$ $x = 1, g(1) = 0; f(0) = 3$ $x = 2, g(2) = 1; f(1) = 4$ $x = 3, g(3) = 2; f(2) = 7$ Plot the points $(x, f(g(x)))$.

4.1

1. Use the graphs of $y = f(x)$ and $y = g(x)$ to sketch the graph of each function below, then identify its domain and range. Estimate the range if necessary.

a) $y = f(x) + g(x)$

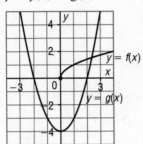

b) $y = f(x) - g(x)$

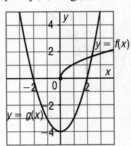

2. Use the graphs of $y = f(x)$ and $y = g(x)$ to sketch the graph of each function below.

a) $y = f(x) \cdot g(x)$

b) $y = \dfrac{f(x)}{g(x)}$

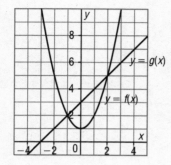

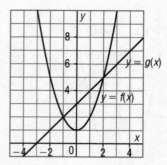

3. Given $f(x) = 3x - 4$ and $g(x) = |2 - 4x|$, write an explicit equation for each function below then determine its domain and range.

a) $h(x) = f(x) + g(x)$

b) $d(x) = f(x) - g(x)$

c) $p(x) = f(x) \cdot g(x)$

d) $q(x) = \dfrac{f(x)}{g(x)}$

4. Given the function $h(x) = 3x^2 - 7x + 4$, write explicit equations for:

a) two functions $f(x)$ and $g(x)$ so that $h(x) = f(x) \cdot g(x)$

b) three functions $f(x)$, $g(x)$, and $k(x)$ so that
$h(x) = f(x) + g(x) + k(x)$

c) three functions $f(x)$, $g(x)$, and $k(x)$ so that
$h(x) = f(x) - g(x) - k(x)$

d) two functions $f(x)$ and $g(x)$ so that $h(x) = \dfrac{f(x)}{g(x)}$

5. Given the graphs of $y = f(x)$ and
$y = g(x)$, determine each value below.

a) $f(g(2))$

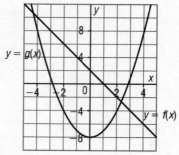

b) $g(f(2))$

c) $f(f(1))$

d) $g(g(-2))$

6. Given the functions $f(x) = -2x + 3$, $g(x) = x^2 - 3x$, and
$h(x) = \sqrt{x - 4}$, determine each value.

a) $f(g(1))$ b) $h(f(-3))$

c) $f(g(h(9)))$ d) $h(g(f(-0.5)))$

7. Given $f(x) = 2x^2 - x$ and $g(x) = x + 4$, determine an explicit equation for each composite function then state its domain and range.

a) $f(g(x))$

b) $g(f(x))$

c) $g(g(x))$

d) $f(f(x))$

8. Use composition of functions to determine whether $f(x) = \frac{1}{2}x - 3$ and $g(x) = 2x + 6$ are inverse functions.

4.4

9. Determine possible functions f and g so that $f(g(x)) = 2x^2 + 10x - 6$. Do this in two ways.

10. Given the functions $f(x) = x^2 - 3x$ and $g(x) = -2x + 1$, sketch a graph of each composite function below. Why are there no restrictions on x?

a) $y = g(g(x))$

b) $y = g(f(x))$

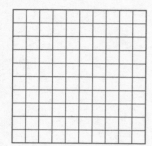
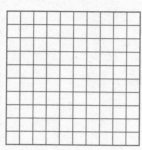

11. Given the functions $f(x) = \sqrt{3 + x}$, $g(x) = 1 - 2x^2$, and $k(x) = \dfrac{1}{x - 3}$, write an explicit equation for each combination.

a) $h(x) = f(g(x)) - k(x)$

b) $h(x) = g(f(x)) - f(g(x))$

c) $h(x) = k(g(x)) + k(f(x))$ **d)** $h(x) = g(g(x)) \cdot k(x)$

12. Given the functions $f(x) = \sqrt{x}$ and $g(x) = x^2 - 3x - 18$, determine an explicit equation for each composite function then state its domain.

a) $f(g(x))$

b) $g(f(x))$

13. For each function below

      i) Determine possible functions f and g so that $y = f(g(x))$.

      ii) Determine possible functions f, g, and h so that $y = f(g(h(x)))$.

    a) $y = -3\sqrt{x + 4}$ **b)** $y = (2 - 5x)^3$

ANSWERS

1. a) domain: $x \geq 0$; range: $y \geq 4$ **b)** domain: $x \geq 0$; approximate range: $y \leq 4.5$

3. a) $h(x) = 3x - 4 + |2 - 4x|$; domain: $x \in \mathbb{R}$; range: $y \geq -2.5$

b) $d(x) = 3x - 4 - |2 - 4x|$; domain: $x \in \mathbb{R}$; range: $y \leq -2.5$

c) $p(x) = (3x - 4) \cdot |2 - 4x|$; domain: $x \in \mathbb{R}$; range: $y \in \mathbb{R}$

d) $q(x) = \dfrac{3x - 4}{|2 - 4x|}$; domain: $x \neq 0.5$; range: $y < 0.75$ **5. a)** 10   **b)** -4 **c)** 2

d) 8   **6. a)** 7   **b)** $\sqrt{5}$ **c)** $-7 + 6\sqrt{5}$ **d)** 0   **7. a)** $f(g(x)) = 2x^2 + 15x + 28$;

domain: $x \in \mathbb{R}$; range: $y \geq -0.125$ **b)** $g(f(x)) = 2x^2 - x + 4$; domain: $x \in \mathbb{R}$;

range: $y \geq 3.875$ **c)** $g(g(x)) = x + 8$; domain: $x \in \mathbb{R}$; range: $y \in \mathbb{R}$

d) $f(f(x)) = 8x^4 - 8x^3 + x$; domain: $x \in \mathbb{R}$; range: $y \geq -0.125$ **8.** The functions

are inverses.   **11. a)** $h(x) = \sqrt{4 - 2x^2} - \dfrac{1}{x - 3}$, $-\sqrt{2} \leq x \leq \sqrt{2}$

b) $h(x) = -5 - 2x - \sqrt{4 - 2x^2}$, $-\sqrt{2} \leq x \leq \sqrt{2}$

c) $h(x) = \dfrac{1}{-2x^2 - 2} + \dfrac{1}{\sqrt{3 + x} - 3}$, $x \geq -3, x \neq 6$ **d)** $h(x) = (-1 + 8x^2 - 8x^4)\left(\dfrac{1}{x - 3}\right)$,

$x \neq 3$ **12. a)** $f(g(x)) = \sqrt{x^2 - 3x - 18}$; domain: $x \leq -3$ or $x \geq 6$

b) $g(f(x)) = x - 3\sqrt{x} - 18$; domain: $x \geq 0$

1. **Multiple Choice** Given $f(x) = \sqrt{x}$ and $g(x) = 3x - 6$, which function is a composition of f and g?

   A. $y = \sqrt{x} + 3x - 6$ **B.** $y = 3\sqrt{x} - 6$

   C. $y = \dfrac{\sqrt{x}}{3x - 6}$ **D.** $y = \sqrt{x} - 3x + 6$

2. **Multiple Choice** For $f(x) = 3x - 5$ and $g(x) = 4x^2 - 7$, which value is greatest?

   A. $f(g(1))$ **B.** $g(f(1))$ **C.** $f(f(1))$ **D.** $g(g(1))$

3. Use the graphs of $y = f(x)$ and $y = h(x)$ to graph $y = f(x) + h(x)$.

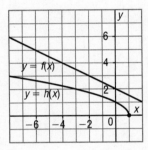

Use these functions for questions 4 to 9:

$f(x) = 2 - 0.5x$ $g(x) = x^2 + 5x$ $h(x) = \sqrt{1 - x}$ $k(x) = \dfrac{1}{4 - x}$

4. Write an explicit equation for each combination of functions, then determine the domain and range of the function. Approximate the range where necessary.

   a) $y = g(x) \cdot f(x)$

   b) $y = \dfrac{f(x)}{h(x)}$

5. Write explicit equations in each case.

   a) two functions $a(x)$ and $b(x)$ so that $g(x) = a(x) \cdot b(x)$

   b) three functions $a(x), b(x),$ and $c(x)$ so that $f(x) = a(x) + b(x) + c(x)$

   c) i) two functions $a(x)$ and $b(x)$ so that $k(x) = a(b(x))$

   ii) three functions $a(x), b(x),$ and $c(x)$ so that $k(x) = a\big(b(c(x))\big)$

6. Determine each value.

    a) $f(g(2))$ **b)** $g(h(-4)$

7. Determine an explicit equation for each composite function and explain any restrictions on x.

    a) $g(h(x))$ **b)** $h(f(x))$

8. Sketch a graph of the composite function $y = k(f(x))$, then state the domain of the composite function.

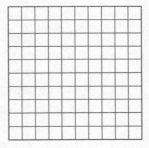

9. Write an explicit equation for each combination.

    a) $y = k(x) + h(g(x))$

    b) $y = f(f(x)) - g(g(x))$

ANSWERS

1. B   **2.** D   **4. a)** $y = -0.5x^3 - 0.5x^2 + 10x$; domain: $x \in \mathbb{R}$; range: $y \in \mathbb{R}$

b) $y = \dfrac{2 - 0.5x}{\sqrt{1 - x}}$; domain: $x \leq 1$; approximate range: $y \geq 1.7$

6. a) -5 **b)** $5 + 5\sqrt{5}$ **7. a)** $g(h(x)) = 1 - x + 5\sqrt{1 - x}$; $x \leq 1$

b) $h(f(x)) = \sqrt{-1 + 0.5x}$; $x \geq 2$ **8.** domain: $x \neq -4$

9. a) $y = \dfrac{1}{4 - x} + \sqrt{1 - x^2 - 5x}$ **b)** $y = 1 - 24.75x - x^4 - 10x^3 - 30x^2$

5 Exponential and Logarithmic Functions

BUILDING ON

- transformations of functions
- inverse functions
- exponent laws
- geometric sequences

BIG IDEAS

- An exponential function can be described by the equation $y = a^x$, $a > 0$.
- A logarithmic function is the inverse of an exponential function.
- Functions involving exponents and logarithms can be used to model financial and physical situations.

LEADING TO

- descriptions of natural growth
- differential equations

NEW VOCABULARY

exponential function	logarithmic function
exponential equation	common logarithm
compound interest	laws of logarithms
exponential growth	logarithmic equation
exponential decay	Richter scale
logarithm	

5.1 Graphing Exponential Functions

FOCUS Investigate the graphs of exponential functions.

Get Started

Evaluate each power.

$$5^3 \qquad\qquad 2^{-3} \qquad\qquad 4^0 \qquad\qquad \left(\frac{1}{3}\right)^{-2}$$

Construct Understanding

A. Complete the table of values for the function $y = 2^x$.
Graph the function.
Describe the graph; include characteristics such as intercepts, equations of the asymptotes, domain, and range.

x	y = 2^x
−3	
−2	
−1	
0	
1	
2	
3	

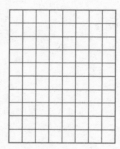

B. Repeat Part A for the function $y = \left(\dfrac{1}{2}\right)^x$.

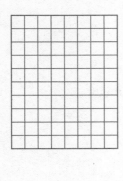

x	$y = \left(\dfrac{1}{2}\right)^x$
−3	
−2	
−1	
0	
1	
2	
3	

C. How are the functions in Parts A and B alike? How are they different?

Assess Your Understanding

1. Use graphing technology. Graph each function below, then complete the table.

Function	x-intercept	y-intercept	Equation of asymptote	Domain	Range
$y = 4^x$					
$y = \left(\dfrac{5}{3}\right)^x$					
$y = \left(\dfrac{1}{3}\right)^x$					
$y = \left(\dfrac{2}{5}\right)^x$					

2. The functions in *Construct Understanding* and question 1 are **exponential functions**. Why do you think this name is appropriate?

3. The graphs of three functions are shown. Which graphs might represent exponential functions? How do you know?

a)

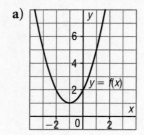

b)

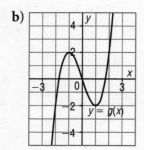

c)

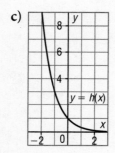

4. Could each table of values describe an exponential function? Justify your answer.

a)

x	y
−2	0.01
−1	0.1
0	1
1	10
2	100

b)

x	y
−2	25
−1	5
0	1
1	0.2
2	0.04

c)

x	y
−2	9
−1	4
0	1
1	0
2	1

ANSWERS

3. graph c   **4. a)** yes   **b)** yes   **c)** no

5.2 Analyzing Exponential Functions

FOCUS Sketch the graph of an exponential function and describe its characteristics.

Get Started

Suppose a colony of bacteria doubles in size every hour. Initially, there were 100 bacteria. How many bacteria would there be after each time?

- 3 h later

- 5 h later

- 12 h later

Construct Understanding

Use graphing technology. Graph each set of functions below on the same screen. For each set, how do the graphs change as the base of the power changes?

Which point do all 6 graphs have in common?

How are the graphs in set A different from the graphs in set B?

Set A: $y = 1.1^x$ $y = 3^x$ $y = 10^x$
Set B: $y = 0.9^x$ $y = 0.5^x$ $y = 0.1^x$

Exponential Function

An exponential function is any function of x that can be written in the form $y = a^x$, where a is a positive constant.

Graph of $y = a^x$, $a > 1$

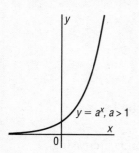

Graph of $y = a^x$, $0 < a < 1$

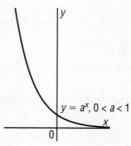

When $a > 1$, as x increases y increases.
The function is increasing.

When $0 < a < 1$, as x increases y decreases and approaches 0.
The function is decreasing.

An exponential function, $y = a^x$, $a > 0$, $a \neq 1$, has these characteristics:

- The graph has y-intercept 1.
- The graph approaches the x-axis, but never reaches it. The function has a horizontal asymptote with equation $y = 0$.
- The graph does not have an x-intercept.
- The domain of the function is $x \in \mathbb{R}$.
- The range of the function is $y > 0$.

THINK FURTHER

Is it possible for the graph of an exponential function $y = a^x$, $a > 0$, to have a y-intercept other than 1?

THINK FURTHER

Describe the graph of the exponential function when $a = 1$.

Example 1 | **Sketching the Graph of an Exponential Function and Identifying Its Characteristics**

a) Graph $y = 3^x$.
b) Determine:
 i) the effect on y when x increases by 1
 ii) whether the function is increasing or decreasing
 iii) the intercepts
 iv) the equations of any asymptotes
 v) the domain of the function
 vi) the range of the function

Check Your Understanding

1. a) Graph $y = \left(\dfrac{1}{3}\right)^x$.

 b) Determine:
  i) the effect on y when x increases by 1
  ii) whether the function is increasing or decreasing
  iii) the intercepts
  iv) the equations of any asymptotes
  v) the domain of the function
  vi) the range of the function

SOLUTION

a) Create a table of values.

x	$y = 3^x$
-2	$\frac{1}{9}$
-1	$\frac{1}{3}$
0	1
1	3
2	9

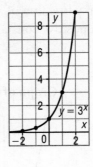

b) **i)** From the table of values, when x increases by 1, y is multiplied by 3.

ii) Since y increases as x increases, the function is increasing.

iii) From the graph, there is no x-intercept. The y-intercept is 1.

iv) The x-axis is a horizontal asymptote; its equation is $y = 0$.

v) The domain of the function is $x \in \mathbb{R}$.

vi) The range of the function is $y > 0$.

THINK FURTHER

How is the exponential function in *Example 1* related to a sequence?

The graph of an exponential function can be stretched, compressed, reflected in an axis, and translated, in that order.

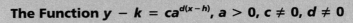

The Function $y - k = ca^{d(x - h)}$, $a > 0$, $c \neq 0$, $d \neq 0$

When the graph of $y = a^x$ is:

- stretched vertically by a factor of $|c|$
- stretched horizontally by a factor of $\frac{1}{|d|}$
- reflected in the x-axis when $c < 0$
- reflected in the y-axis when $d < 0$
- translated k units vertically
- translated h units horizontally

the equation of the image graph is: $y - k = ca^{d(x - h)}$, $a > 0$

The general transformation is: (x, y) corresponds to $\left(\dfrac{x}{d} + h, cy + k \right)$

Example 2   **Transforming the Graph of $y = a^x$**

a) Use the graph of $y = 2^x$ to sketch the graph of $y = 2^{2x} - 4$.

b) For the function $y = 2^{2x} - 4$, determine:

   i) whether the function is increasing or decreasing

   ii) the intercepts

   iii) the equation of the asymptote

   iv) the domain of the function

   v) the range of the function

2. a) Use the graph of $y = 2^x$ to sketch the graph of $y = 3(2^{-x+2})$.

b) From the graph of $y = 3(2^{-x+2})$, determine:

   i) whether the function is increasing or decreasing

   ii) the intercepts

   iii) the equation of the asymptote

   iv) the domain of the function

   v) the range of the function

SOLUTION

a) Write the function as: $y + 4 = 2^{2x}$

Compare $y + 4 = 2^{2x}$ with $y - k = c2^{d(x-h)}$:

$k = -4, c = 1, d = 2$, and $h = 0$

The graph of $y = 2^{2x} - 4$ is the image of the graph of $y = 2^x$ after a horizontal compression by a factor of $\frac{1}{2}$, then a translation of 4 units down.

Use the general transformation: (x, y) corresponds to $\left(\frac{x}{d} + h, cy + k\right)$

The point (x, y) on $y = 2^x$ corresponds to the point $\left(\frac{x}{2}, y - 4\right)$ on $y + 4 = 2^{2x}$.

Choose points (x, y) on $y = 2^x$.

(x, y)	$\left(\frac{x}{2}, y - 4\right)$
$(-2, 0.25)$	$(-1, -3.75)$
$(-1, 0.5)$	$(-0.5, -3.5)$
$(0, 1)$	$(0, -3)$
$(1, 2)$	$(0.5, -2)$
$(2, 4)$	$(1, 0)$

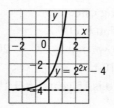

b) From the graph of $y = 2^{2x} - 4$

   i) The function is increasing.

   ii) The graph has y-intercept -3 and x-intercept 1.

   iii) The graph has a horizontal asymptote with equation $y = -4$.

   iv) The domain of the function is $x \in \mathbb{R}$.

   v) The range of the function is $y > -4$.

How are $y = 2^{-x}$ and $y = \left(\frac{1}{2}\right)^x$ related?

In *Example 2*, the y-intercept could be determined from the graph or the table of values. If the y-intercept is not on a lattice point, it can be determined algebraically:

In $y = 2^{2x} - 4$, substitute: $x = 0$

$y = 2^{2(0)} - 4$

$y = 1 - 4$

$y = -3$

Example 3 — Using Transformations of Exponential Functions to Model Real-World Situations

3. For every metre below the surface of water, the light intensity is reduced by 2.5%. The percent, P, of light remaining at a depth d metres can be modelled by the function:

$P = 100(0.975)^d$

a) Graph the function for $0 \le d \le 40$.

b) To the nearest percent, how much light remains at a depth of 10 m?

c) To the nearest metre, what is the depth when only 50% of the light remains?

The growth of the Internet can be measured by the number of computers offering information; these are called *hosts*.

In 1995, there were about 7.4 million hosts.

The number of hosts, n million, at any time t years after 1995 can be modelled by the function: $n = 7.4(1.59)^t$

a) Graph the function for $0 \le t \le 20$.

b) To the nearest million, estimate the number of hosts in 2010.

c) In which year did the number of hosts reach 1000 million, or 1 billion?

SOLUTION

a) Use a graphing calculator.
Input: $Y_1 = 7.4(1.59)^\wedge X$
Set the window so: $0 \le X \le 20$ and
$0 \le Y \le 1100$

b) The year 2010 is 15 years after 1995, so $t = 15$.
Use the graph in part a. Press: [TRACE], then input [1] [5] [ENTER] to display:
$Y = 7765.8426$
So, the number of hosts in 2010 was approximately 7766 million.

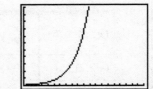

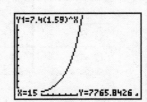

c) Use the graph in part a. Input: $Y_2 = 1000$, then press: [2nd] [TRACE] for CALC, select 5:intersect and follow the prompts to display:
$X = 10.579934$

So, the number of hosts reached 1 billion approximately halfway through 2006.

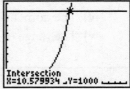

Discuss the Ideas

1. What is the y-intercept of the graph of $y = a^x, a > 0$? Explain how you know.

2. What is the equation of the horizontal asymptote of the graph of $y = a^x, a > 0$? What is the significance of the horizontal asymptote?

Exercises

A

3. Identify each exponential function, then determine whether it is increasing or decreasing.

a) $y = 2x$ **b)** $y = 2^x$

c)
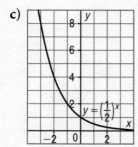

d)
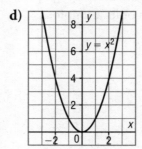

4. Each table of values represents an exponential function. Complete each table. Describe your strategy.

a)

x	y
−2	
−1	4
0	1
1	
2	

b)

x	y
−1	
0	
1	2.5
2	6.25
3	

B

5. a) Write the equations of two exponential functions that are increasing. Explain your strategy. Use a graphing calculator to verify the equations.

b) Write the equations of two exponential functions that are decreasing. Explain your strategy. Use a graphing calculator to verify the equations.

6. Use technology to graph each function below. Sketch the graph, then identify its intercepts and the equation of its asymptote.

a) $y = 3.2^x$ **b)** $y = 0.4^x$

7. Graph each exponential function below. Determine:
  i) whether the function is increasing or decreasing
  ii) the intercepts
  iii) the equation of the asymptote and explain its significance
  iv) the domain of the function
  v) the range of the function

a) $y = 5^x$

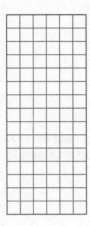

b) $y = \left(\dfrac{1}{4}\right)^x$

8. When a person drinks coffee, tea, cola, or chocolate, the caffeine in these drinks stays in the body for some time. The percent, P, that remains after t hours can be modelled by the function $P = 100(0.87)^t$.

a) Use technology to graph this function for $0 < t < 10$. Sketch the graph.

b) Is the function increasing or decreasing? Include 2 reasons in your solution.

9. Bacteria increase in number by each bacterium splitting in two. Suppose there are 50 bacteria and each bacterium splits in two every 30 min. The number of bacteria, N, after t hours, is modelled by the exponential function $N = 50(2)^{2t}$.

When you input the exponent, insert brackets around 2t.

a) Use technology to graph this function for $0 < t < 5$. Sketch the graph.

b) Is the function increasing or decreasing? Include 2 reasons in your solution.

10. Use transformations to sketch the graph of each function below. Determine:
  i) whether the function is increasing or decreasing
  ii) the intercepts
  iii) the equation of the asymptote
  iv) the domain of the function
  v) the range of the function

a) $y = 2^{2x} + 1$

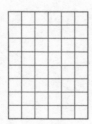

b) $y = -2^{0.5(x + 3)}$

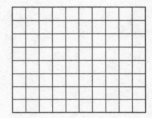

c) $y = 2\left(\dfrac{1}{4}\right)^{-2x}$

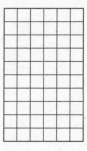

11. Describe two different strategies to graph the function $y = 4(2^x)$.

C

12. The definition of the exponential function $y = a^x$ includes the restriction $a > 0$. Show that if $a < 0$, the function is not defined for all values of x.

13. Use transformations to graph this function:

$$y = -2\left(\frac{1}{4}\right)^{-0.5x+4} - 4$$

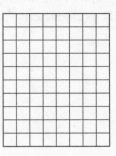

Multiple-Choice Questions

1. Which equation or table of values does not describe an exponential function?

A. $y = 8^x$

B. $y = \left(\frac{3}{7}\right)^x$

C.

x	y
−1	6
0	3
1	0
2	−3

D.

x	y
−2	25
−1	5
0	1
1	0.2

2. What is the range of the function $y = 5(6^{x-4})$?

A. $y \in \mathbb{R}$ **B.** $y > 0$ **C.** $y > 5$ **D.** $y > 4$

Study Note

Choose an exponential function and at least two transformations. Sketch the graph of the function after applying the transformations, then identify its characteristics.

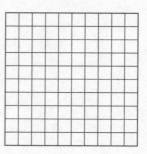

ANSWERS

Check Your Understanding

1. b) i) multiplied by $\frac{1}{3}$ **ii)** decreasing **iii)** no x-intercept; y-intercept: 1
iv) $y = 0$ **v)** $x \in \mathbb{R}$ **vi)** $y > 0$ **2. b) i)** decreasing
ii) y-intercept: 12; no x-intercept **iii)** $y = 0$ **iv)** $x \in \mathbb{R}$ **v)** $y > 0$
3. b) approximately 78% **c)** approximately 27 m

Exercises

3. a) not exponential **b)** exponential; increasing **c)** exponential; decreasing
d) not exponential **6. a), b)** no x-intercept; y-intercept: 1; asymptote: $y = 0$
7. a) i) increasing **ii)** no x-intercept; y-intercept: 1 **iii)** $y = 0$ **iv)** $x \in \mathbb{R}$
v) $y > 0$ **b) i)** decreasing **ii)** no x-intercept; y-intercept: 1 **iii)** $y = 0$
iv) $x \in \mathbb{R}$ **v)** $y > 0$ **8. b)** decreasing **9. b)** increasing
10. a) i) increasing **ii)** no x-intercept; y-intercept: 2 **iii)** $y = 1$ **iv)** $x \in \mathbb{R}$
v) $y > 1$ **b) i)** decreasing **ii)** no x-intercept; y-intercept: approximately -2.8
iii) $y = 0$ **iv)** $x \in \mathbb{R}$ **v)** $y < 0$ **c) i)** increasing **ii)** no x-intercept; y-intercept: 2
iii) $y = 0$ **iv)** $x \in \mathbb{R}$ **v)** $y > 0$

Multiple Choice

1. C **2.** B

FOCUS Solve problems by modelling situations with exponential equations.

Get Started

Solve the equation $2x^2 - x - 3 = 0$ algebraically.
How could you solve it graphically?

Construct Understanding

Solve this equation in two ways: $2^x = 32$
Can you use the same two strategies to solve this equation? $2^x = 12$
Explain your response.
Solve the equation and write the root to the nearest hundredth.

THINK FURTHER

Is it possible for 2^x to be equal to any real number?

An **exponential equation** contains a power with a variable in the exponent. For example, $3^x = 81$ is an exponential equation. One strategy to solve this equation uses the fact that when two powers with the same base are equal, their exponents are also equal.

Since 81 is a power of 3, both sides of the equation can be written as powers of 3.

$3^x = 81$
$3^x = 3^4$
So, $x = 4$

Example 1 | **Solving an Exponential Equation Using Common Bases**

Solve each equation.

a) $2^x = \dfrac{1}{128}$ **b)** $4^x = 8^{x-1}$

SOLUTION

a) $2^x = \dfrac{1}{128}$ Write 128 as a power of 2.

     $2^x = \dfrac{1}{2^7}$ Write the right side with a negative exponent.

     $2^x = 2^{-7}$ Equate the exponents.

     $x = -7$

b) $4^x = 8^{x-1}$

     8 cannot be written as a power of 4; however, both 4 and 8 can be written as powers of 2.

     $(2^2)^x = (2^3)^{x-1}$ Use exponent laws to simplify each side.

     $2^{2x} = 2^{3x-3}$ Equate the exponents.

      $2x = 3x - 3$

       $x = 3$

Check Your Understanding

1. Solve each equation.
   a) $4^x = \dfrac{1}{256}$
   b) $27^x = 9^{2x-1}$

The solutions of the equations in *Example 1* can be verified by substituting the root into each equation.

For example, in part b, for $4^x = 8^{x-1}$, substitute: $x = 3$

L.S. $= 4^x$ R.S. $= 8^{x-1}$

     $= 4^3$ $= 8^{3-1}$

     $= 64$ $= 8^2$

                      $= 64$

Since the left side is equal to the right side, the solution is verified.

Example 2 | Solving an Exponential Equation Involving Radicals

2. Solve each equation.

a) $2^x = 8\sqrt[3]{2}$

b) $(\sqrt{125})^{2x+1} = \sqrt[3]{625}$

Solve each equation.

a) $2^x = 4\sqrt{2}$ b) $(\sqrt{3})^{x-1} = \sqrt[3]{9}$

SOLUTION

a) $2^x = 4\sqrt{2}$ On the right side, write 4 as 2^2 and $\sqrt{2}$ as $2^{\frac{1}{2}}$.

$2^x = 2^2 \cdot 2^{\frac{1}{2}}$ Use the product of powers law.

$2^x = 2^{2+\frac{1}{2}}$

$2^x = 2^{\frac{5}{2}}$

$x = \dfrac{5}{2}$, or 2.5

b) $(\sqrt{3})^{x-1} = \sqrt[3]{9}$ Write both sides as powers of 3.

$\left(3^{\frac{1}{2}}\right)^{x-1} = \sqrt[3]{3^2}$

$\left(3^{\frac{1}{2}}\right)^{x-1} = 3^{\frac{2}{3}}$

$3^{\frac{1}{2}x - \frac{1}{2}} = 3^{\frac{2}{3}}$ Equate the exponents.

$\dfrac{1}{2}x - \dfrac{1}{2} = \dfrac{2}{3}$ Multiply by the common denominator 6.

$6\left(\dfrac{1}{2}x - \dfrac{1}{2}\right) = 6\left(\dfrac{2}{3}\right)$

$3x - 3 = 4$

$3x = 7$

$x = \dfrac{7}{3}$

When money is invested in a savings account, it earns interest. If the interest is reinvested in the account, it also earns interest; this is called **compound interest**.

Consider an investment of $100 in a savings account that pays 2% annual interest, compounded annually. This means that the interest earned is calculated and paid into the account annually (once a year); that is, the *compounding period* is 1 year.

After 1 year, the amount is:

$100 + 2\% \text{ of } \$100 = \$100 + 0.02(\$100)$
$$= \$100(1 + 0.02), \text{ or } \$100(1.02)$$

After 2 years, the amount is:

$100(1.02) + 2\% \text{ of } \$100(1.02) = \$100(1.02)(1 + 0.02)$
$$= \$100(1.02)^2$$

Each subsequent year, the amount increases by a factor of 1.02.

After 3 years, the amount is: $100(1.02)^3$

This pattern continues.

After t years, the amount is: $100(1.02)^t$

For some savings accounts, the interest is added to the account more often.
Consider an investment of $100 in a savings account that pays 2% annual interest, compounded semi-annually.
The interest earned is calculated and paid into the account twice a year; that is, the compounding period is 6 months.
So, the annual interest rate is halved and the number of compounding periods is doubled.
For semi-annual compounding, the amount after t years is: $\$100(1.01)^{2t}$

Consider an investment of $100 in a savings account that pays 2% annual interest, compounded quarterly.
The interest earned is calculated and paid into the account 4 times a year; that is, the compounding period is 3 months.
So, the interest rate is one-quarter of the annual rate and there are 4 compounding periods per year.
For quarterly compounding, the amount after t years is: $\$100(1.005)^{4t}$
This pattern continues.

For monthly compounding, the amount after t years is: $\$100\left(1 + \dfrac{0.02}{12}\right)^{12t}$

This pattern can be generalized for any compounding period and interest rate.

Compound Interest

A principal of A_0 dollars is invested at an annual interest rate of i, with n compounding periods per year. The amount, A dollars, after t years is given by: $A = A_0\left(1 + \dfrac{i}{n}\right)^{nt}$

The *principal* is the initial amount of money that is invested.

In $A = A_0\left(1 + \dfrac{i}{n}\right)^{nt}$, the binomial $1 + \dfrac{i}{n}$ is the *growth factor*.

The equation $A = A_0\left(1 + \dfrac{i}{n}\right)^{nt}$ is an example of **exponential growth**.

Exponential Growth

A function that models exponential growth has the form: $y = ak^{bx}$
where $k^b > 1$, and $a \in \mathbb{R}, b \in \mathbb{R}, k > 0$
k is the *growth factor*.

Check Your Understanding

3. A principal of $1500 is invested at 4% annual interest, compounded quarterly. To the nearest quarter of a year, when will the amount be $2500?

Example 3	Solving a Problem Involving Exponential Growth

A principal of $1000 is invested at 6% annual interest, compounded monthly. To the nearest tenth of a year, when will the amount be $1400?

SOLUTION

Use: $A = A_0\left(1 + \dfrac{i}{n}\right)^{nt}$, where t is the time in years since the principal was invested

Substitute: $A = 1400, A_0 = 1000, i = 0.06, n = 12$

$$1400 = 1000\left(1 + \frac{0.06}{12}\right)^{12t}$$

Since both sides of the equation cannot be written with the same base, use a graphing calculator to graph a related function.

Graph $y = 1000\left(1 + \dfrac{0.06}{12}\right)^{12x} - 1400$, then determine

the approximate zero of the function: 5.6218786

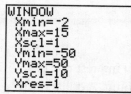 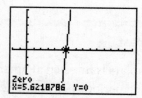

The amount will be $1400 in approximately 5.6 years.

Atmospheric pressure decreases by about 12% for every 1 km increase in altitude. At sea level, atmospheric pressure is approximately 101.3 kilopascals (kPa).

So, at 1 km altitude, the pressure in kilopascals is:
88% of $101.3 = 101.3(0.88)$

At 2 km, the pressure in kilopascals is:
88% of $101.3(0.88) = 101.3(0.88)^2$

At 3 km, the pressure in kilopascals is:
88% of $101.3(0.88)^2 = 101.3(0.88)^3$

This pattern continues.

At an altitude of h kilometres, the pressure, P kilopascals, is modelled by the function: $P = 101.3(0.88)^h$

The function $P = 101.3(0.88)^h$ is an example of **exponential decay**.

Exponential Decay

A function that models exponential decay has the form: $y = ak^{bx}$
where $0 < k^b < 1$, and $a \in \mathbb{R}, b \in \mathbb{R}, k > 0$
k is the *decay factor*.

Example 4	Solving a Problem Involving Exponential Decay

Check Your Understanding

The function $P = 101.3(0.88)^h$ models the atmospheric pressure, P kilopascals, at an altitude of h kilometres. To the nearest kilometre, at what altitude is the atmospheric pressure only 10 kPa?

4. If the cabin pressure in an airplane is less than 70 kPa, passengers can suffer altitude sickness. To the nearest kilometre, at what altitude is the atmospheric pressure 70 kPa?

SOLUTION

Use: $P = 101.3(0.88)^h$ Substitute: $P = 10$
$\qquad 10 = 101.3(0.88)^h$

Use a graphing calculator to graph a related function.
Graph $y = 101.3(0.88)^x - 10$, then determine the approximate zero of the function: 18.113434

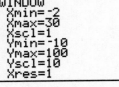
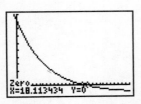

The atmospheric pressure is 10 kPa at approximately 18 km altitude.

Discuss the Ideas

1. What is an exponential equation?

2. How do you identify whether a given function models exponential decay or exponential growth?

5.3 Solving Exponential Equations | **363**

Exercises

A

3. Write each number as a power of 2.

    a) 16   **b)** 128   **c)** $\frac{1}{32}$ **d)** 1

4. Which numbers below can be written as powers of 5? Write each number you identify as a power of 5.

    a) 125   **b)** 10   **c)** $\frac{1}{25}$ **d)** 1

5. Write each number as a power of 3.

    a) $\sqrt[3]{9}$ **b)** $\sqrt{243}$ **c)** $\frac{\sqrt{3}}{3}$ **d)** $27\sqrt{3}$

B

6. Solve each equation.

    a) $2^x = 256$ **b)** $81 = 3^{x+1}$

    c) $3^x = 9^{x-2}$ **d)** $4^{x-1} = 2^{x+3}$

    e) $8^{2x} = 16^{x+3}$ **f)** $9^{x+1} = 243^{x+3}$

7. Use graphing technology to solve each equation. Give the solution to the nearest tenth.

a) $10 = 2^x$

b) $3^x = 100$

c) $3^{x+1} = 50$

d) $30 = 2^{x-1}$

8. Explain why the equation $4^x = -2$ does not have a real solution. Verify, graphically, that there is no solution.

9. Solve each equation.

a) $2^x = 8\sqrt[3]{2}$

b) $81\sqrt{3} = 3^x$

c) $2^{x+1} = 2\sqrt[3]{4}$

d) $9^x = \sqrt{27}$

e) $\sqrt[4]{216} = 36^{x-1}$

f) $(\sqrt{7})^{x+1} = \sqrt[3]{49}$

10. Solve each equation.

a) $\left(\dfrac{1}{4}\right)^3 = 2^x$

b) $5^x = \dfrac{\sqrt[3]{25}}{25}$

c) $\dfrac{\sqrt[3]{49}}{343} = 7^{x+1}$

d) $\left(\dfrac{1}{9}\right)^x = 3\sqrt{27}$

e) $8^{1-x} = \dfrac{\sqrt[3]{16}}{4}$

f) $\left(\dfrac{1}{8}\right)^{x+1} = (\sqrt[3]{16})^x$

11. Use graphing technology to solve each equation. Give the solution to the nearest tenth.

a) $2 = 1.05^x$

b) $2^{-\frac{x}{5}} = 0.4$

c) $2^{x+1} = 3^{x-2}$

d) $3(2^x) = 64$

12. A principal of $600 was invested in a term deposit that pays 5.5% annual interest, compounded semi-annually. To the nearest tenth of a year, when will the amount be $1000?

13. a) To the nearest year, how long will it take an investment of $500 to double at each annual interest rate, compounded annually?

    i) 4%   **ii)** 6%   **iii)** 8%

    iv) 9%   **v)** 12%

b) What pattern is there in the interest rates and times in part a?

14. When light passes through glass, the intensity is reduced by 5%.

a) Determine a function that models the percent of light, P, that passes through n layers of glass.

b) Determine how many layers of glass are needed for only 25% of light to pass through.

C

15. Solve each equation, then verify the solution graphically.

a) $2^{(x^2)} = 16$　　　　　**b)** $9^{x+4} = 3^{(x^2)}$

16. For what values of k does the equation $9^{(x^2)} = 27^{x+k}$ have no real solution?

Multiple-Choice Questions

1. Which number cannot be written as 2^n, where n is an integer?

A. $\sqrt{32}$ **B.** $\frac{1}{4}$ **C.** 1   **D.** 6

2. Which value of x is a solution of the equation $8\left(4^{\frac{1}{3}}\right) = \left(\frac{1}{4}\right)^x$?

A. $x = -\frac{11}{6}$ **B.** $x = -1$ **C.** $x = -\frac{2}{3}$ **D.** $x = \frac{7}{3}$

Study Note

Use examples to describe two strategies for solving an exponential equation.

ANSWERS

Check Your Understanding

1. a) $x = -4$ **b)** $x = 2$ **2. a)** $x = \frac{10}{3}$ **b)** $x = -\frac{1}{18}$ **3.** approximately 12.75 years

4. approximately 3 km

Exercises

3. a) 2^4 **b)** 2^7 **c)** 2^{-5} **d)** 2^0 **4. a)** 5^3 **b)** cannot be written as a power of 5

c) 5^{-2} **d)** 5^0 **5. a)** $3^{\frac{5}{3}}$ **b)** $3^{\frac{5}{2}}$ **c)** $3^{-\frac{1}{2}}$ **d)** $3^{\frac{7}{2}}$ **6. a)** $x = 8$ **b)** $x = 3$ **c)** $x = 4$

d) $x = 5$ **e)** $x = 6$ **f)** $x = -\frac{13}{3}$ **7. a)** $x \doteq 3.3$ **b)** $x \doteq 4.2$ **c)** $x \doteq 2.6$

d) $x \doteq 5.9$ **9. a)** $x = \frac{10}{3}$ **b)** $x = \frac{9}{2}$ **c)** $x = \frac{2}{3}$ **d)** $x = \frac{3}{4}$ **e)** $x = \frac{11}{8}$ **f)** $x = \frac{1}{3}$

10. a) $x = -6$ **b)** $x = -\frac{4}{3}$ **c)** $x = -\frac{10}{3}$ **d)** $x = -\frac{5}{4}$ **e)** $x = \frac{11}{9}$ **f)** $x = -\frac{9}{13}$

11. a) $x \doteq 14.2$ **b)** $x \doteq 6.6$ **c)** $x \doteq 7.1$ **d)** $x \doteq 4.4$ **12.** approximately 9.4 years

13. a) i) 18 years   **ii)** 12 years   **iii)** 9 years   **iv)** 8 years   **v)** 6 years

14. a) $P = 100(0.95)^n$ **b)** 27 layers   **15. a)** $x = \pm 2$ **b)** $x = -2, x = 4$

16. $k < -\frac{3}{8}$

Multiple Choice

1. D   **2.** A

Additional Workspace

Self-Assess

Can you . . .	Try *Checkpoint* question	For review, see
sketch, with technology, the graph of an exponential function of the form $y = a^x, a > 0$?	1	Page 341 in Lesson 5.1 (Question 1)
sketch, without technology, the graph of an exponential function of the form $y = a^x, a > 0$?	3	Page 345 in Lesson 5.2 (Example 1)
identify the characteristics of the graph of an exponential function of the form $y = a^x, a > 0$?	3	Page 345 in Lesson 5.2 (Example 1)
sketch the graph of a function by applying a set of transformations to the graph of the exponential function $y = a^x, a > 0$?	4	Page 347 in Lesson 5.2 (Example 2)
determine the solution of an exponential equation in which the bases are powers of each other?	6	Page 359 in Lesson 5.3 (Example 1)
determine the solution of an exponential equation in which the bases are not powers of each other?	7	Page 362 in Lesson 5.3 (Example 3)
solve a problem that involves exponential growth or decay?	8	Page 362 in Lesson 5.3 (Example 3)
solve a problem that involves the application of exponential equations to investments?	8	Page 362 in Lesson 5.3 (Example 3)

Assess Your Understanding

5.1

1. Use technology to graph each function below. Sketch or print the graph. For each graph, identify its intercepts and the equation of its asymptote.

   a) $y = 0.7^x$ **b)** $y = 4.25^x$

2. Multiple Choice Which equation describes a function whose graph can be obtained by compressing the graph of $y = 10^x$ horizontally by a factor of $\frac{1}{3}$, then translating the graph 2 units up?

A. $y - 2 = 10^{3x}$ **B.** $y = 3(10^{x-2})$

C. $y - 2 = \frac{1}{3}(10^x)$ **D.** $y + 2 = 10^{\frac{x}{3}}$

3. Graph each exponential function below. Determine:

    i) whether the function is increasing or decreasing
    ii) the intercepts
    iii) the equation of the asymptote
    iv) the domain of the function
    v) the range of the function

a) $y = \left(\frac{3}{4}\right)^x$ **b)** $y = 6^x$

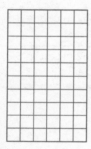   

4. a) Use transformations to sketch the graph of $y + 2 = 2^{3x}$.

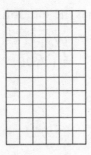

b) Determine:

   i) whether the function is increasing or decreasing

   ii) the intercepts

   iii) the equation of the asymptote

   iv) the domain of the function

   v) the range of the function

5. Multiple Choice Which equation has the solution $x = -3$?

A. $5^x = \left(\sqrt[3]{625}\right)^{x+1}$ B. $5^x = \left(\sqrt[3]{625}\right)^{x-1}$

C. $5^{x+1} = \left(\sqrt[3]{625}\right)^{x}$ D. $5^{x-1} = \left(\sqrt[3]{625}\right)^{x}$

6. Solve each equation.

a) $9^{x+2} = 27^x$ b) $\left(\dfrac{1}{8}\right)^x = 4\sqrt{2}$

7. Use graphing technology to solve each equation. Give the solution to the nearest tenth.

a) $2^x = 50$ b) $4^{x-2} = 3^{x-1}$

8. A principal of $500 is invested in a savings account that pays 3.5% annual interest, compounded quarterly. To the nearest half year, when will the amount be $700?

ANSWERS

1. a), b) no x-intercept; y-intercept: 1; asymptote: $y = 0$
2. A   3. a) i) decreasing   ii) no x-intercept; y-intercept: 1   iii) $y = 0$ iv) $x \in \mathbb{R}$
v) $y > 0$ b) i) increasing   ii) no x-intercept; y-intercept: 1   iii) $y = 0$ iv) $x \in \mathbb{R}$
v) $y > 0$ 4. b) i) increasing   ii) x-intercept: $\frac{1}{3}$; y-intercept: -1 iii) $y = -2$
iv) $x \in \mathbb{R}$ v) $y > -2$ 5. D   6. a) $x = 4$ b) $x = -\dfrac{5}{6}$
7. a) $x \doteq 5.6$ b) $x \doteq 5.8$ 8. approximately 9.5 years

5.4 Logarithms and the Logarithmic Function

Investigate logarithmic functions and relate them to exponential functions.

Get Started

How are these graphs related?

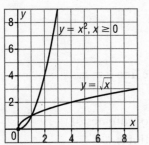

Construct Understanding

> Complete the table of values below for $y = 2^x$.
> Use the completed table to graph $y = 2^x$ and its inverse.
> What are the equations of the asymptotes for the graphs?
> State the domain and the range of each function.

$y = 2^x$

x	y
−2	
−1	
0	
1	
2	
3	

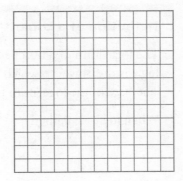

The term **logarithm** is used to describe the inverse of a power. For example, the inverse of 10^x is the logarithm to the base 10 of x, which is written as $\log_{10}x$. We say: log base 10 of x

Here is the graph of $y = 10^x$ and its inverse.

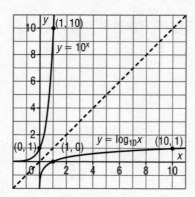

Each graph is a reflection of the other graph in the line $y = x$. The inverse of $y = 10^x$ is $y = \log_{10}x$.

To understand what a logarithm is, consider the coordinates of corresponding points on the graphs of these functions:

$y = 10^x$

x	y	Points
0	$10^0 = 1$	(0, 1)
1	$10^1 = 10$	(1, 10)
2	$10^2 = 100$	(2, 100)

$y = \log_{10}x$

x	y	Points
1	$\log_{10}1 = 0$	(1, 0)
10	$\log_{10}10 = 1$	(10, 1)
100	$\log_{10}100 = 2$	(100, 2)

$\uparrow$

$\log_{10}100 = 2$ means that 10 is raised to the power 2 to get 100; that is, $10^2 = 100$

Definition of a Logarithm

The logarithm of a number is an exponent.
$\log_b c$ is the power to which b is raised to get c.
The base of the logarithm is the same as the base of the power.

When $\log_b c = a$, then $c = b^a$, where $b > 0, b \neq 1, c > 0$

Example 1 | **Writing Expressions in Different Forms**

a) Write each exponential expression as a logarithmic expression.

i) $2^5 = 32$　　ii) $3^{-4} = \dfrac{1}{81}$　　iii) $7^0 = 1$

b) Write each logarithmic expression as an exponential expression.

i) $\log_3 81 = 4$　　ii) $\log_5 125 = 3$　　iii) $\log_6 1 = 0$

SOLUTION

Use the definition of a logarithm.

a) i) $2^5 = 32$　　ii) $3^{-4} = \dfrac{1}{81}$　　iii) $7^0 = 1$

The base is 2.　　The base is 3.　　The base is 7.
The logarithm is　The logarithm is　The logarithm is
the exponent 5.　the exponent -4.　the exponent 0.
So, $5 = \log_2 32$　So, $-4 = \log_3\left(\dfrac{1}{81}\right)$　So, $0 = \log_7 1$

b) i) $\log_3 81 = 4$　　ii) $\log_5 125 = 3$　　iii) $\log_6 1 = 0$

The base is 3.　　The base is 5.　　The base is 6.
The exponent is 4.　The exponent is 3.　The exponent is 0.
So, $81 = 3^4$　　So, $125 = 5^3$　　So, $6^0 = 1$

Check Your Understanding

1. a) Write each exponential expression as a logarithmic expression.

i) $3^3 = 27$

ii) $5^{-2} = \dfrac{1}{25}$

iii) $4^0 = 1$

b) Write each logarithmic expression as an exponential expression.

i) $\log_7 49 = 2$

ii) $\log_4\left(\dfrac{1}{64}\right) = -3$

iii) $\log_{10}\left(\dfrac{1}{10\,000}\right) = -4$

Since our number system is based on powers of 10, $\log_{10} x$ is called the **common logarithm** of x. When logarithms to base 10 are written, the base is often not shown; that is, $\log_{10} x$ is written as $\log x$.
On scientific and graphing calculators, use the $\boxed{\text{LOG}}$ key to enter a logarithm with base 10.

For logarithms to bases other than 10, other strategies are used to evaluate them.
Consider these logarithms:
$\log_2 2^3$ is the power to which 2 is raised to get 2^3, which is 3.
So, $\log_2 2^3 = 3$
$\log_4 4^6$ is the power to which 4 is raised to get 4^6, which is 6.
So, $\log_4 4^6 = 6$
These examples illustrate this general result:

$$\log_b b^n = n$$

This equation and a related equation can be derived from the fact that
$f(x) = \log_b x$ and $g(x) = b^x$ are inverses:
$f(g(n))$: $\log_b b^n = n$
$g(f(n))$: $b^{\log_b n} = n$
These equations can be used to simplify expressions involving exponents or logarithms.

Example 2   **Evaluating Logarithms**

2. Evaluate each logarithm.

   a) $\log_5 3125$

   b) $\log_6\left(\dfrac{1}{216}\right)$

   c) $\log_8\left(2\sqrt[3]{2}\right)$

Evaluate each logarithm.

a) $\log_3 729$ **b)** $\log_4\left(\dfrac{1}{32}\right)$ **c)** $\log_2\left(\sqrt[3]{4}\right)$

SOLUTION

a) $\log_3 729$ Write 729 as a power of 3.

     $\log_3 729 = \log_3 3^6$

               $= 6$

b) $\log_4\left(\dfrac{1}{32}\right)$ Write $\dfrac{1}{32}$ as a power of 2.

     $\log_4\left(\dfrac{1}{32}\right) = \log_4(2^{-5})$ Write 2^{-5} with a base of 4.

                $= \log_4(2^2)^{-\frac{5}{2}}$

                $= \log_4 4^{-\frac{5}{2}}$

                $= -\dfrac{5}{2}$, or -2.5

c) $\log_2\left(\sqrt[3]{4}\right)$ Write $\sqrt[3]{4}$ as a power of 2.

     $\log_2\left(\sqrt[3]{4}\right) = \log_2 4^{\frac{1}{3}}$

                $= \log_2 2^{\frac{2}{3}}$

                $= \dfrac{2}{3}$

In *Example 2*, the logarithm of each number could be determined because the number could be written as a power of the base of the logarithm. If a number cannot be written this way, benchmarks can be used to estimate the value of a logarithm.

Example 3 | **Using Benchmarks to Estimate the Value of a Logarithm**

To the nearest tenth, estimate the value of $\log_2 10$.

3. To the nearest tenth, estimate the value of $\log_5 100$.

SOLUTION

$\log_2 10$ has base 2, so use the powers of 2 closest to 10 as benchmarks:
$2^3 = 8$ and $2^4 = 16$
$\log_2 2^3 < \log_2 10 < \log_2 2^4$
So, $3 < \log_2 10 < 4$
10 is closer to 8, so $\log_2 10$ is likely closer to 3.
An estimate is: $\log_2 10 \doteq 3.3$
Check the estimate.
Calculate: $2^{3.3} = 9.8491\ldots$ This is less than 10, but close to 10.
Calculate: $2^{3.4} = 10.5560\ldots$ This is greater than 10, but not as close.
So, $\log_2 10 \doteq 3.3$

Example 4 | **Identifying the Characteristics of the Graph of a Logarithmic Function**

a) Graph $y = \log_3 x$.
b) Identify the intercepts, the equations of any asymptotes, and the domain and range of the function.

4. a) Graph $y = \log_4 x$.

b) Identify the intercepts, the equations of any asymptotes, and the domain and range of the function.

SOLUTION

a) $y = \log_3 x$ is the inverse of $y = 3^x$, so construct a table of values for $y = 3^x$, then interchange the coordinates for a table of values for $y = \log_3 x$.

For $y = 3^x$

x	y
-2	$\frac{1}{9}$
-1	$\frac{1}{3}$
0	1
1	3
2	9

For $y = \log_3 x$

x	y
$\frac{1}{9}$	-2
$\frac{1}{3}$	-1
1	0
3	1
9	2

b) The graph does not intersect the y-axis, so it does not have a y-intercept.
The graph has x-intercept 1.
The y-axis is a vertical asymptote; its equation is $x = 0$.
The domain of the function is $x > 0$.
The range of the function is $y \in \mathbb{R}$.

The graph in *Example 4* illustrates the characteristics of a **logarithmic function**.

Definition of a Logarithmic Function

The logarithmic function $y = \log_b x$, $b > 0$, $b \neq 1$, is the inverse of the exponential function $y = b^x$.
The domain of $y = \log_b x$ is $x > 0$.

THINK FURTHER

In the definition of a logarithmic function, why is $b \neq 1$?

Discuss the Ideas

1. What is a logarithm? Explain what $\log_5 25$ means.

2. Why is it not possible to determine $\log_3(-27)$?

3. If $\log_b a < 0$ and $b > 1$, what can you say about a?

Exercises

4. Evaluate each logarithm.

    a) $\log_4 16$ **b)** $\log 100\,000$

    c) $\log_6 1296$ **d)** $\log_2 2$

5. Write each exponential expression as a logarithmic expression.

    a) $2^6 = 64$ **b)** $10^4 = 10\,000$

    c) $4^{-\frac{1}{2}} = \frac{1}{2}$ **d)** $3^{\frac{2}{3}} = \sqrt[3]{9}$

6. a) Write each logarithmic expression as an exponential expression.

    i) $\log_7 16\,807 = 5$ **ii)** $\log_9 3 = \frac{1}{2}$

    iii) $\log 0.01 = -2$ **iv)** $\log_3\left(\frac{\sqrt{3}}{3}\right) = -\frac{1}{2}$

b) Use one pair of statements from part a to explain the relationship between a logarithmic expression and an exponential expression.

B

7. Evaluate each logarithm.

a) $\log_4 8$

b) $\log_9\left(\frac{1}{27}\right)$

c) $\log_6 1$

d) $\log_2\left(4\sqrt[4]{2}\right)$

8. a) Write 3 as a logarithm with base 2.

b) Write 2 as a logarithm with base 3.

9. Determine the value of $\log_b 1$. Justify the answer.

10. How are the domain and range of the functions $y = b^x$ and $y = \log_b x$ related?

11. a) Use a table of values to graph $y = \log_5 x$.

b) Identify the intercepts, the equation of the asymptote, the domain, and the range of the function.

c) What is the significance of the asymptote?

12. a) Use technology to graph $y = \log x$. Identify the intercepts, the equation of the asymptote, the domain, and the range of the function.

b) What is the equation of the inverse of $y = \log x$?

13. Use benchmarks to estimate the value of each logarithm, to the nearest tenth.

a) $\log_3 12$

b) $\log_2 100$

14. Write the equations of an exponential function and a logarithmic function with the same base. Use graphs of these functions to demonstrate that each function is the inverse of the other.

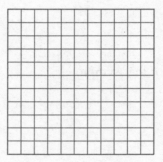

15. Use benchmarks to estimate the value of each logarithm to the nearest tenth.

a) $\log_2 6.5$

b) $\log_3 1.8$

16. Graph $y = \log_{\frac{1}{2}} x$. How is the graph of this function related to the graph of $y = \log_2 x$?

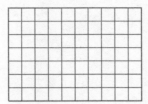

17. On a graphing calculator, the key $\boxed{\text{LN}}$ calculates the value of a logarithm whose base is the irrational number e. The number e is known as Euler's constant. Logarithms with base e are called *natural logarithms*.

a) Graph $y = \ln x$. Sketch the graph.

b) Determine the value of e to the nearest thousandth.

Multiple-Choice Questions

1. Given $a^b = c$, which statement is true?

A. $\log_a b = c$ **B.** $\log_b a = c$ **C.** $\log_a c = b$ **D.** $\log_b c = a$

2. For which value of x is $y = \log_3 x$ not defined?

A. $x = 9$ **B.** $x = 1$ **C.** $x = \frac{1}{3}$ **D.** $x = -3$

Study Note

Describe the relationship between the functions $y = \log_b x$, $b > 0$, $b \neq 1$, $x > 0$ and $y = b^x$, $b > 0$, $b \neq 1$. Sketch the graph of each function and list its characteristics.

Check Your Understanding

1. a) i) $3 = \log_3 27$ **ii)** $-2 = \log_5\left(\dfrac{1}{25}\right)$ **iii)** $0 = \log_4 1$ **b) i)** $49 = 7^2$

ii) $\dfrac{1}{64} = 4^{-3}$ **iii)** $\dfrac{1}{10\,000} = 10^{-4}$ **2. a)** 5   **b)** -3 **c)** $\dfrac{4}{9}$ **3.** approximately 2.9

4. b) no y-intercept, x-intercept: 1; asymptote: $x = 0$; domain: $x > 0$; range: $y \in \mathbb{R}$

Exercises

4. a) 2   **b)** 5   **c)** 4   **d)** 1   **5. a)** $6 = \log_2 64$ **b)** $4 = \log 10\,000$ **c)** $-\dfrac{1}{2} = \log_4\left(\dfrac{1}{2}\right)$

d) $\dfrac{2}{3} = \log_3 \sqrt[3]{9}$ **6. a) i)** $16\,807 = 7^5$ **ii)** $3 = 9^{\frac{1}{2}}$ **iii)** $0.01 = 10^{-2}$ **iv)** $\dfrac{\sqrt{3}}{3} = 3^{-\frac{1}{2}}$

7. a) $\dfrac{3}{2}$ **b)** $-\dfrac{3}{2}$ **c)** 0   **d)** $\dfrac{9}{4}$ **8. a)** $3 = \log_2 8$ **b)** $2 = \log_3 9$ **9.** 0

11. b) no y-intercept, x-intercept: 1; asymptote: $x = 0$; domain: $x > 0$; range: $y \in \mathbb{R}$
12. a) no y-intercept, x-intercept: 1; asymptote: $x = 0$; domain: $x > 0$; range: $y \in \mathbb{R}$
b) $y = 10^x$ **13. a)** approximately 2.3   **b)** approximately 6.6
15. a) approximately 2.7   **b)** approximately 0.5   **17. b)** approximately 2.718

Multiple Choice
1. C   **2.** D

Additional Workspace

5.5   The Laws of Logarithms

FOCUS Develop and use the laws of logarithms.

Get Started

Use the exponent laws to simplify each expression.

$$2^5 \cdot 2^3 \qquad \frac{3^8}{3^2} \qquad \frac{7^3}{7^6} \qquad \left(7^5\right)^2$$

Construct Understanding

Use the exponent laws and the relationship between exponents and logarithms to complete each statement with a natural number. Describe your strategies. Use a calculator to check.

$\log 2 + \log 3 = \log\,?$
$\log 8 - \log 2 = \log\,?$
$3 \log 2 = \log\,?$

For each statement above, write two more statements using the same operation.

Compare your results with those of your classmates.

Write rules for:
- adding two logarithms with the same base
- subtracting two logarithms with the same base
- multiplying a logarithm by an integer

Operations on logarithms with the same base obey the
laws of logarithms.

Laws of Logarithms

When $x > 0$ and $y > 0$

Product law: $\log_b xy = \log_b x + \log_b y, b > 0, b \neq 1$

Quotient law: $\log_b\left(\dfrac{x}{y}\right) = \log_b x - \log_b y, b > 0, b \neq 1$

Power law: $\log_b x^k = k \log_b x, b > 0, b \neq 1, k \in \mathbb{R}$

THINK FURTHER

In the power law for logarithms, why is $k \in \mathbb{R}$, while $b > 0$, $b \neq 1$?

The definition of a logarithm can be used to prove that the laws above are true for all logarithms.

Here is a proof of the product law.
To prove that $\log_b xy = \log_b x + \log_b y$:

Let $\log_b x = m$ and $\log_b y = n$ Apply the definition of a logarithm.

Then $x = b^m$ $y = b^n$

   So, $xy = b^m \cdot b^n$ Use the product rule for exponents.

     $xy = b^{m+n}$ Write this exponential statement as a logarithmic statement.

$\log_b xy = m + n$ Substitute for m and n.

$\log_b xy = \log_b x + \log_b y$

The proofs of the other two laws of logarithms are in the Exercises.

Example 1 — Applying the Laws of Logarithms to Logarithms with Base 10

Example 1 | **Applying the Laws of Logarithms to Logarithms with Base 10**

1. Simplify each expression. Use a calculator to verify the answer.

a) $\log 7 + \log 8$

b) $5 \log 2$

c) $\log 80 - \log 16$

Use a law of logarithms to simplify each expression.
Use a calculator to verify the answer.

a) $\log 50 - \log 25$ b) $\log 5 + \log 12$ c) $3 \log 4$

SOLUTION

a) Use the quotient law.
$$\log 50 - \log 25 = \log\left(\frac{50}{25}\right)$$
$$= \log 2$$
Verify: $\log 50 - \log 25 = 0.3010\ldots$
$$\log 2 = 0.3010\ldots$$

b) Use the product law.
$$\log 5 + \log 12 = \log(5 \cdot 12)$$
$$= \log 60$$
Verify: $\log 5 + \log 12 = 1.7781\ldots$
$$\log 60 = 1.7781\ldots$$

c) Use the power law.
$$3 \log 4 = \log 4^3$$
$$= \log 64$$
Verify: $3 \log 4 = 1.8061\ldots$
$$\log 4^3 = 1.8061\ldots$$

Example 2 — Using the Laws of Logarithms to Simplify Expressions

Example 2 | **Using the Laws of Logarithms to Simplify Expressions**

2. Write each expression as a single logarithm.

a) $\log x + 3 \log y$

b) $\log x + 2 \log y - 4 \log z$

c) $\log_2 6 - 3$

Write each expression as a single logarithm.

a) $2 \log x - \log y$

b) $\frac{1}{2} \log x - 3 \log y + 2 \log z$

c) $2 + \log_4 3$

SOLUTION

a) $2 \log x - \log y$ Use the power law to write $2 \log x$ as $\log x^2$.
$$= \log x^2 - \log y$$ Use the quotient law.
$$= \log\left(\frac{x^2}{y}\right)$$

b) $\frac{1}{2}\log x - 3\log y + 2\log z$ Use the power law.

$= \log x^{\frac{1}{2}} - \log y^3 + \log z^2$ Use the quotient law.

$= \log\left(\dfrac{x^{\frac{1}{2}}}{y^3}\right) + \log z^2$ Use the product law.

$= \log\left(\dfrac{x^{\frac{1}{2}}z^2}{y^3}\right)$

c) $2 + \log_4 3$

Write 2 as a logarithm base 4:

$2 = \log_4 4^2$, or $\log_4 16$

So, $2 + \log_4 3 = \log_4 16 + \log_4 3$ Use the product law.

$\qquad\qquad\qquad = \log_4(16 \cdot 3)$

$\qquad\qquad\qquad = \log_4 48$

<table>
<tr><td>**Example 3**</td><td>**Writing a Logarithm as a Sum or Difference of Logarithms**</td></tr>
</table>

Write each expression in terms of $\log a$, $\log b$, and/or $\log c$.

a) $\log a^2 c$ **b)** $\log\left(\dfrac{a^2}{bc^3}\right)$

SOLUTION

a) $\log a^2 c$ Use the product law.

$= \log a^2 + \log c$ Use the power law.

$= 2\log a + \log c$

b) $\log\left(\dfrac{a^2}{bc^3}\right)$ Use the quotient law.

$= \log a^2 - \log bc^3$ Use the power law and product law.

$= 2\log a - (\log b + \log c^3)$

$= 2\log a - \log b - \log c^3$ Use the power law.

$= 2\log a - \log b - 3\log c$

Check Your Understanding

3. Write each expression in terms of $\log a$, $\log b$, and/or $\log c$.

a) $\log\left(\dfrac{a}{b^2}\right)$ **b)** $\log\left(\dfrac{a^2 b^{\frac{1}{3}}}{c}\right)$

Example 4 | Using the Laws of Logarithms to Evaluate

4. Evaluate each expression.

    a) $3 \log_9 6 - \log_9 72$

    b) $2 \log_4 6 - 3 \log_4 3 + \log_4 12$

Evaluate each expression.

a) $2 \log_2 6 - \log_2 9$ **b)** $\log_9 2 + 3 \log_9 6 - 4 \log_9 2$

SOLUTION

a) $2 \log_2 6 - \log_2 9$ Use the power law.

$= \log_2 6^2 - \log_2 9$

$= \log_2 36 - \log_2 9$ Use the quotient law.

$= \log_2 \left(\dfrac{36}{9} \right)$

$= \log_2 4$ Write the number as a power of 2.

$= \log_2 2^2$ Use $\log_b b^n = n$.

$= 2$

b) $\log_9 2 + 3 \log_9 6 - 4 \log_9 2$ Use the power law.

$= \log_9 2 + \log_9 6^3 - \log_9 2^4$

$= \log_9 2 + \log_9 216 - \log_9 16$ Use the product law.

$= \log_9 (2 \cdot 216) - \log_9 16$ Use the quotient law.

$= \log_9 \left(\dfrac{2 \cdot 216}{16} \right)$

$= \log_9 27$ Write the number as a power of 9.

$= \log_9 (9 \cdot 3)$

$= \log_9 \left(9 \cdot 9^{\frac{1}{2}} \right)$

$= \log_9 9^{\frac{3}{2}}$

$= \dfrac{3}{2}$

Discuss the Ideas

1. How is the product law for logarithms related to the product law for exponents?

2. How is the quotient law for logarithms related to the quotient law for exponents?

3. How is the power law for logarithms related to the power law for exponents?

Exercises

A

4. Simplify each expression. Use a calculator to verify the answer.

   a) $\log 6 + \log 5$ **b)** $3 \log 2$

   c) $\log 48 - \log 6$ **d)** $\log 8 + \log 5$

5. Write each expression as a single logarithm.

   a) $\log a - \log b$ **b)** $\log x + \log y$

   c) $5 \log m$ **d)** $\log x - \log y + \log z$

B

6. Use each law of logarithms to write an expression that is equal to $\log 16$. Use a calculator to verify each expression.

   a) the product law

   b) the quotient law

   c) the power law

7. Substitute values of a and b to verify each statement.

   a) $\dfrac{\log a}{\log b} \neq \log\left(\dfrac{a}{b}\right)$ **b)** $\log(a + b) \neq \log ab$

8. Write each expression as a single logarithm.

    a) $\log x - 5 \log y$ **b)** $\frac{1}{2} \log x + 3 \log y$

    c) $\frac{2}{3} \log_5 x - 4 \log_5 y - 3 \log_5 z$ **d)** $5 + \log_2 x$

9. Explain each step in this proof of the power law for logarithms.
To prove that $\log_b x^k = k \log_b x$:

    Let: $\log_b x = n$
       Then $x = b^n$
           $x^k = (b^n)^k$
           $x^k = b^{kn}$
       $\log_b x^k = \log_b b^{kn}$
       $\log_b x^k = kn$
       $\log_b x^k = k \log_b x$

10. Use the strategy from the proof of the product law for logarithms to
prove the quotient law: $\log_b \left(\frac{x}{y}\right) = \log_b x - \log_b y$

11. Use two different strategies to write $2(\log x + \log y)$ as a single logarithm.

12. Write each expression as a single logarithm.

   a) $3 \log 2 + \log 6$ **b)** $\frac{1}{2} \log 9 + 2 \log 5$

   c) $3 \log_2 6 - 2$ **d)** $5 \log_5 2 - \log_5 4 + 2$

13. Evaluate each expression.

   a) $2 \log_3 6 - 3 \log_3 2 + \log_3 18$ **b)** $\frac{1}{2} \log_2 36 + \log_2 12 - 2 \log_2 3$

   c) $9 \log_9 3 - \log_9 75 + 2 \log_9 5$ **d)** $\log_4 98 - 2 \log_4 7 - 2$

14. Given $\log a \doteq 1.301$, determine an approximate value for each logarithm.

a) $\log a^3$

b) $\log 10a$

c) $\log \left(\dfrac{a^2}{100} \right)$

15. Identify the errors in the solution to the question below. Write the correct solution.

Write $\log \left(\dfrac{a^{\frac{1}{2}}}{c^3 b^2} \right)$ in terms of $\log a$, $\log b$, and $\log c$.

$\log \left(\dfrac{a^{\frac{1}{2}}}{c^3 b^2} \right)$

$= \log a^{\frac{1}{2}} - \log c^3 b^2$

$= \log a^{\frac{1}{2}} - \log c^3 + \log b^2$

$= \dfrac{1}{2} \log a - \log 3c + 2 \log b$

16. Write each expression in terms of $\log a$, $\log b$, and/or $\log c$.

a) $\log a^3 b^{\frac{1}{2}}$

b) $\log ab^2 c^{\frac{2}{3}}$

c) $\log \left(\dfrac{a^3}{b^2} \right)$

d) $\log \left(\dfrac{a^4 b^{\frac{3}{5}}}{c} \right)$

17. Given $\log 3 \doteq 0.477$ and $\log 7 \doteq 0.845$, determine the approximate value of $\log (132\ 300)$ without using a calculator.

18. Write each expression as a single logarithm.

  a) $3 \log x + \log (2x - 3)$ **b)** $\log (x + 1) + \log (2x - 1)$

  c) $\log (x^2 - 1) - \log (x - 1)$ **d)** $\log (2x^2 + x - 3) - \log (x^2 - 1)$

19. Without using the power law, prove the law of logarithms for radicals:
$\log_b \sqrt[k]{x} = \frac{1}{k} \log_b x, b > 0, b \neq 1, k \in \mathbb{N}, x > 0$

Multiple-Choice Questions

1. Which statement is not correct for $x > 0, y > 0$?

   A. $\log x + \log y = \log xy$

   B. $2 + \log x = \log (x + 2)$

   C. $3 \log x = \log x^3$

   D. $\log x - \log 4 = \log \left(\frac{1}{4}x\right)$

2. Which logarithm is equal to $3 + \log_2 5$?

   A. $\log_2 15$ **B.** $\log_2 30$ **C.** $\log_2 40$ **D.** $\log_2 625$

Study Note

List the three laws of logarithms and provide an example to show how each law is applied.

ANSWERS

Check Your Understanding

1. a) $\log 56$ b) $\log 32$ c) $\log 5$ 2. a) $\log xy^3$ b) $\log \left(\frac{xy^2}{z^4}\right)$ c) $\log_2\left(\frac{3}{4}\right)$

3. a) $\log a - 2 \log b$ b) $2 \log a + \frac{1}{3} \log b - \log c$ 4. a) $\frac{1}{2}$ b) 2

Exercises

4. a) $\log 30$ b) $\log 8$ c) $\log 8$ d) $\log 40$ 5. a) $\log \left(\frac{a}{b}\right)$ b) $\log xy$ c) $\log m^5$

d) $\log \left(\frac{xz}{y}\right)$ 8. a) $\log \left(\frac{x}{y^5}\right)$ b) $\log \left(x^{\frac{1}{2}}y^3\right)$ c) $\log_5 \left(\frac{x^{\frac{2}{3}}}{y^4 z^3}\right)$ d) $\log_2 32x$

11. $\log x^2 y^2$ or $\log (xy)^2$ 12. a) $\log 48$ b) $\log 75$ c) $\log_2 54$ d) $\log_5 200$

13. a) 4 b) 3 c) 4 d) $-\frac{3}{2}$ 14. a) 3.903 b) 2.301 c) 0.602

16. a) $3 \log a + \frac{1}{2} \log b$ b) $\log a + 2 \log b + \frac{2}{3} \log c$ c) $3 \log a - 2 \log b$

d) $4 \log a + \frac{3}{5} \log b - \log c$ 17. 5.121 18. a) $\log x^3(2x - 3)$

b) $\log (x + 1)(2x - 1)$ c) $\log (x + 1), x \neq 1$ d) $\log \left(\frac{2x + 3}{x + 1}\right), x \neq \pm 1$

Multiple Choice

1. B   2. C

Additional Workspace

5.6 Analyzing Logarithmic Functions

FOCUS Use technology to graph transformations of logarithmic functions.

Get Started

Use a calculator to evaluate each expression.

$\log 5$ $\qquad$ $2 \log 2$ $\qquad$ $\dfrac{\log 3}{\log 4}$

Construct Understanding

Evaluate $\log_2 6$.
Determine a strategy to verify your answer using graphing technology.

To use technology to evaluate a logarithm with base other than 10, the base of the logarithm has to be changed to 10.

Consider: $y = \log_b x$ $\qquad$ Write this statement in exponential form.

$b^y = x$ $\qquad$ Take the common logarithm of both sides.

$\log b^y = \log x$ $\qquad$ Apply the power law to the left side.

$y \log b = \log x$ $\qquad$ Divide both sides by $\log b$.

$y = \dfrac{\log x}{\log b}$ $\qquad$ Substitute $\log_b x$ for y.

So, $\log_b x = \dfrac{\log x}{\log b}$

A similar relationship can be used to change the base b of a logarithm to any other base a.

Changing the Base of a Logarithm

$$\log_b x = \frac{\log_a x}{\log_a b}, \text{ where } a, b > 0; a, b \neq 1; x > 0$$

Example 1	Using Technology to Approximate the Value of a Logarithm

Check Your Understanding

1. Approximate the value of each logarithm, to the nearest thousandth. Write the related exponential expression.

a) $\log_5 50$ **b)** $\log_8 6$

Approximate the value of each logarithm, to the nearest thousandth. Write the related exponential expression.

a) $\log_6 100$ **b)** $\log_3 2$

SOLUTION

Use the change of base formula.

a) $\log_6 100 = \dfrac{\log 100}{\log 6}$ **b)** $\log_3 2 = \dfrac{\log 2}{\log 3}$

$ = 2.5701\ldots$ $= 0.6309\ldots$

$\log_6 100 \doteq 2.570$ $\log_3 2 \doteq 0.631$

So, $100 \doteq 6^{2.570}$ So, $2 \doteq 3^{0.631}$

THINK FURTHER

In *Example 1a*, explain why $\log_6 100 = \dfrac{2}{\log 6}$.

Example 2	Using Technology to Graph a Logarithmic Function

Check Your Understanding

2. a) Use a graphing calculator to graph $y = \log_8 x$.

  b) Identify the intercepts and the equation of the asymptote of the graph, and the domain and range of the function.

a) Use a graphing calculator to graph $y = \log_4 x$.

b) Identify the intercepts and the equation of the asymptote of the graph, and the domain and range of the function.

SOLUTION

a) Use the change of base formula to change $y = \log_4 x$ to a logarithmic function with base 10.

$\log_4 x = \dfrac{\log x}{\log 4}$

Graph: $y = \dfrac{\log x}{\log 4}$

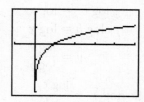

b) Press 2nd TRACE 2 for the zero feature from the CALC menu.
The x-intercept is 1.
Since log x is not defined for $x \leq 0$, there is no y-intercept.
The equation of the asymptote is $x = 0$.
The domain of the function is $x > 0$.
The range of the function is $y \in \mathbb{R}$.

THINK FURTHER

In *Example 2*, what other strategy could you use to verify the domain of the function?

Transformations can be applied to the graph of a logarithmic function.

The Function $y - k = c \log_a d(x - h)$, $a > 0$, $c \neq 0$, $d \neq 0$

When the graph of $y = \log_a x$ is:
- stretched vertically by a factor of $|c|$
- stretched horizontally by a factor of $\dfrac{1}{|d|}$
- reflected in the x-axis when $c < 0$
- reflected in the y-axis when $d < 0$
- translated k units vertically
- translated h units horizontally

the equation of the image graph is: $y - k = c \log_a d(x - h)$, $a > 0$

The general transformation is: (x, y) corresponds to $\left(\dfrac{x}{d} + h, cy + k \right)$

| **Example 3** | **Transforming the Graph of a Logarithmic Function** |

a) Create a table of values for $y = \log_3 x$.
b) How is the graph of $y = \log_3(2x + 6)$ related to the graph of $y = \log_3 x$? Sketch these two graphs on the same grid.
c) Identify the intercepts and the equation of the asymptote of the graph of $y = \log_3(2x + 6)$, and the domain and range of the function.

Check Your Understanding

3. a) Create a table of values for $y = \log_2 x$.
b) How is the graph of $y = \log_2 2x - 1$ related to the graph of $y = \log_2 x$? Sketch these two graphs on the same grid.

c) Identify the intercepts and the equation of the asymptote of the graph of $y = \log_2 2x - 1$, and the domain and range of the function.

SOLUTION

a) To create the table of values, write $y = \log_3 x$ as $3^y = x$.

x	y
$\frac{1}{9}$	-2
$\frac{1}{3}$	-1
1	0
3	1
9	2

b) Write $y = \log_3(2x + 6)$ as $y = \log_3 2(x + 3)$.

Compare $y = \log_3 2(x + 3)$ with $y - k = c \log_3 d(x - h)$:

$k = 0, c = 1, d = 2$, and $h = -3$

The graph of $y = \log_3 2(x + 3)$ is the image of the graph of $y = \log_3 x$ after a horizontal compression by a factor of $\frac{1}{2}$, then a translation of 3 units left.

Use the general transformation:

(x, y) corresponds to $\left(\dfrac{x}{d} + h, cy + k\right)$

The point (x, y) on $y = \log_3 x$ corresponds to the point $\left(\dfrac{x}{2} - 3, y\right)$

on $y = \log_3 2(x + 3)$. Use the points (x, y) on $y = \log_3 x$.

(x, y)	$\left(\dfrac{x}{2} - 3, y\right)$
$\left(\frac{1}{9}, -2\right)$	$\left(-\frac{53}{18}, -2\right)$
$\left(\frac{1}{3}, -1\right)$	$\left(-\frac{17}{6}, -1\right)$
$(1, 0)$	$(-2.5, 0)$
$(3, 1)$	$(-1.5, 1)$
$(9, 2)$	$(1.5, 2)$

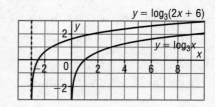

c) From the graph of $y = \log_3(2x + 6)$:

The x-intercept is -2.5.

For the y-intercept, substitute $x = 0$ in $y = \log_3(2x + 6)$.

$y = \log_3 6$

$y = \dfrac{\log 6}{\log 3}$

$y = 1.6309\ldots$

The y-intercept is approximately 1.6.

The equation of the asymptote is $x = -3$.

The domain of the function is $x > -3$.

The range of the function is $y \in \mathbb{R}$.

Discuss the Ideas

1. Scientific and graphing calculators have a $\boxed{\text{LOG}}$ key that calculates the value of a common logarithm. How can you use this key to calculate the value of $\log_b x$ for any value of $x > 0$, and $b > 0$, $b \neq 1$?

2. When c, d, h, and k are positive constants, how is the graph of $y - k = -c \log d(x - h)$ related to the graph of $y = \log x$?

Exercises

A

3. Approximate the value of each logarithm, to the nearest thousandth.

   a) $\log_2 9$ b) $\log_2 100$

4. Order these logarithms from greatest to least:
   $\log_2 80$, $\log_3 900$, $\log_4 5000$, $\log_5 10\ 000$

5. Approximate the value of each logarithm, to the nearest thousandth. Write the related exponential expression.

    a) $\log_7 400$ b) $\log_3\left(\dfrac{1}{2}\right)$

6. a) Use technology to graph $y = \log_5 x$. Sketch the graph.

    b) Identify the intercepts and the equation of the asymptote of the graph, and the domain and range of the function.

    c) Choose the coordinates of two points on the graph. Multiply their x-coordinates and add their y-coordinates. What do you notice about the new coordinates? Explain the result.

7. a) Use a graphing calculator to graph $y = \log_2 x$, $y = \log_4 x$, and $y = \log_8 x$. Sketch the graphs.

b) In part a, what happened to the graph of $y = \log_b x$, $b > 0$, $b \neq 1$, as the base changed?

8. a) The graphs of a logarithmic function and its transformation image are shown. The functions are related by translations, and corresponding points are indicated. Identify the translations.

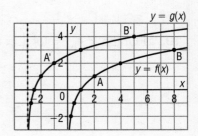

b) Given that $f(x) = \log_2 x$, what is $g(x)$? Justify your answer.

9. a) How is the graph of $y = 2\log_2(2x - 8)$ related to the graph of $y = \log_2 x$? Sketch both graphs on the same grid.

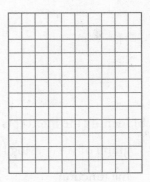

b) Identify the intercepts and the equation of the asymptote of the graph of $y = 2\log_2(2x - 8)$, and the domain and range of the function. Use graphing technology to verify.

10. a) Graph $y = -\dfrac{1}{4}\log_2\left(\dfrac{1}{2}x\right) + 1$.

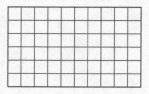

b) Identify the intercepts and the equation of the asymptote of the graph of $y = -\dfrac{1}{4}\log_2\left(\dfrac{1}{2}x\right) + 1$, and the domain and range of the function.

11. Graph each function below, then identify the intercepts and the equation of the asymptote of the graph, and the domain and range of the function.

a) $y = -\log_2(x + 4) - 3$

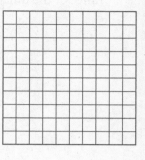

b) $y = 4\log_2(-x - 3)$

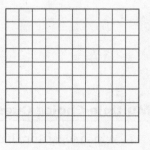

12. Graph the function $y = -\frac{1}{3}\log_3(-2x - 4) + 5$, then identify the intercepts, the equation of the asymptote, and the domain and range of the function.

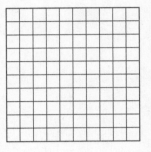

Multiple-Choice Questions

1. Which logarithm has the least value?

   A. $\log_2 7$ **B.** $\log_3 20$ **C.** $\log_5 12$ **D.** $\log_4 30$

2. Which equation describes the image graph after stretching the graph of $y = \log_3 x$ vertically by a factor of 2, then translating that graph 3 units down?

   A. $y = 2\log_3(x - 3)$ **B.** $y = \log_3(2x - 3)$

   C. $y = 2\log_3 x - 3$ **D.** $y = \log_3 2x - 3$

Study Note

Choose a value of b for the function $y = \log_b x$, $b > 0$, $b \neq 1$.
Graph the function. Choose 3 different transformations.
Apply these transformations to your graph and graph the image.
Write its equation and list its characteristics.

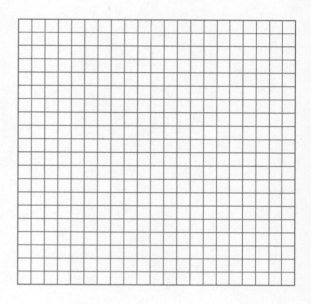

ANSWERS

Check Your Understanding

1. a) approximately 2.431; $5^{2.431}$ **b)** approximately 0.862; $8^{0.862}$

2. b) no y-intercept; x-intercept: 1; asymptote: $x = 0$; domain: $x > 0$; range: $y \in \mathbb{R}$

3. c) no y-intercept; x-intercept: 1; asymptote: $x = 0$; domain: $x > 0$; range: $y \in \mathbb{R}$

Exercises

3. a) approximately 3.170 **b)** approximately 6.644

4. $\log_2 80$, $\log_3 900$, $\log_4 5000$, $\log_5 10\,000$ **5. a)** $400 \doteq 7^{3.079}$ **b)** $\frac{1}{2} \doteq 3^{-0.631}$

6. b) x-intercept: 1; no y-intercept; asymptote: $x = 0$; domain: $x > 0$; range: $y \in \mathbb{R}$

8. a) 3 units left and 1 unit up **b)** $g(x) = \log_2(x + 3) + 1$

9. b) x-intercept: 4.5; no y-intercept; asymptote: $x = 4$; domain: $x > 4$; range: $y \in \mathbb{R}$

10. b) x-intercept: 32; no y-intercept; asymptote: $x = 0$; domain: $x > 0$; range: $y \in \mathbb{R}$

11. a) x-intercept: approximately -3.9; y-intercept: -5; asymptote: $x = -4$; domain: $x > -4$; range: $y \in \mathbb{R}$ **b)** x-intercept: -4; no y-intercept; asymptote: $x = -3$; domain: $x < -3$; range: $y \in \mathbb{R}$ **12.** x-intercept: $x = -7\,174\,455.5$; no y-intercept; asymptote: $x = -2$; domain: $x < -2$; range: $y \in \mathbb{R}$

Multiple Choice

1. C **2.** C

Additional Workspace

Self-Assess

Can you . . .	Try *Checkpoint* question	For review, see
express a logarithmic expression as an exponential expression?	1	Page 377 in Lesson 5.4 (Example 1)
express an exponential expression as a logarithmic expression?	2	Page 377 in Lesson 5.4 (Example 1)
use benchmarks to estimate the value of a logarithm?	3	Page 379 in Lesson 5.4 (Example 3)
determine, without technology, the exact value of a logarithm?	4	Page 378 in Lesson 5.4 (Example 2)
sketch, without technology, the graph of a logarithmic function of the form $y = \log_b x$, $b > 1$, and identify its characteristics?	5	Page 379 in Lesson 5.4 (Example 4)
determine, using the laws of logarithms, an equivalent expression for a logarithmic expression?	7	Page 390 in Lesson 5.5 (Example 2)
determine, with technology, the approximate value of a logarithmic expression?	10	Page 402 in Lesson 5.6 (Example 1)
sketch, with technology, the graph of a logarithmic function of the form $y = \log_b x$, $b > 1$, and identify its characteristics?	9	Page 402 in Lesson 5.6 (Example 2)
sketch the graph of a function by applying a set of transformations to the graph of $y = \log_b x$, $b > 1$, and state the characteristics of the graph?	11	Page 403 in Lesson 5.6 (Example 3)

Assess Your Understanding

5.4

1. **Multiple Choice** Given that $\log_m n = p$, which statement is correct?

   A. $m^n = p$ **B.** $n = m^p$ **C.** $n^p = m$ **D.** $n = p^m$

2. Write each exponential expression as a logarithmic expression.

   a) $8^3 = 512$ **b)** $36^{\frac{1}{2}} = 6$

3. Use benchmarks to estimate the value of each logarithm to the nearest tenth.

a) $\log_4 60$ **b)** $\log_9 8$

4. Evaluate each logarithm.

a) $\log_2 64$ **b)** $\log_9 243$ **c)** $\log_2\left(\dfrac{1}{128}\right)$

5. a) Graph $y = \log_4 x$.

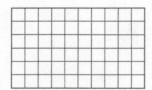

b) Identify the intercepts and the equation of the asymptote of the graph, and the domain and range of the function.

6. Multiple Choice Which expression is equal to $\log_3\left(\dfrac{x}{y}\right)$?

    A. $\log_3 x + \log_3 y$ **B.** $\log_3 x - \log_3 y$

    C. $\dfrac{\log_3 x}{\log_3 y}$ **D.** $3(\log_3 x - \log_3 y)$

7. Write each expression as a single logarithm.

    a) $4 \log x - \dfrac{1}{2} \log y$ **b)** $3 \log x + 5 \log y$

    c) $\log x + 3$

8. Multiple Choice How is the graph of $y = \log_3 x$ transformed to obtain the graph of $y = \log_3 2x - 3$?

    A. a horizontal stretch by a factor of 2 and a translation of 3 units down

    B. a vertical stretch by a factor of 2 and a translation of 3 units down

    C. a vertical stretch by a factor of 2 and a translation of 3 units up

    D. a horizontal compression by a factor of $\dfrac{1}{2}$ and a translation of 3 units down

9. Use technology to graph $y = \log_9 x$. Identify the intercepts and the equation of the asymptote of the graph, and the domain and range of the function.

10. Approximate the value of each logarithm, to the nearest thousandth.

a) $\log_2 35$ b) $\log_3\left(\dfrac{3}{4}\right)$

11. Graph $y = 3\log_2(-x + 4)$, then state the characteristics of the function.

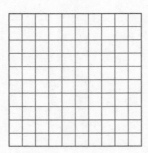

ANSWERS

1. B   2. a) $3 = \log_8 512$ b) $\dfrac{1}{2} = \log_{36} 6$ 3. a) approximately 3.0

b) approximately 0.9   4. a) 6   b) $\dfrac{5}{2}$ c) -7

5. b) x-intercept: 1; no y-intercept; asymptote: $x = 0$; domain: $x > 0$; range: $y \in \mathbb{R}$

6. B   7. a) $\log\left(\dfrac{x^4}{y^{\frac{1}{2}}}\right)$ b) $\log x^3 y^5$ c) $\log 1000x$ 8. D

9. x-intercept: 1; no y-intercept; asymptote: $x = 0$; domain: $x > 0$; range: $y \in \mathbb{R}$
10. a) approximately 5.129   b) approximately -0.262
11. x-intercept: 3; y-intercept: 6; asymptote: $x = 4$; domain: $x < 4$; range: $y \in \mathbb{R}$

5.7   Solving Logarithmic and Exponential Equations

FOCUS Solve logarithmic and exponential equations algebraically.

Get Started

Simplify each expression.

$\log_4 100 + \log_4 2$ $\log_5 35 - \log_5 7$

Construct Understanding

Use algebra to solve this equation: $\log_2 x + \log_2 x = 2$

Verify the solution.

A **logarithmic equation** is an equation that contains the logarithm of a variable.

The laws of logarithms may be used to solve logarithmic equations.

Example 1 | Solving a Logarithmic Equation Involving $\log_b dx$

1. Solve: $\log_3 9x + \log_3 x = 4$
Verify the solution.

Solve: $5 = \log_2 x + \log_2 2x$
Verify the solution.

SOLUTION

$5 = \log_2 x + \log_2 2x$ Use the product law of logarithms.

$5 = \log_2 (x)(2x)$

$5 = \log_2 2x^2$ Write as an exponential statement.

$2x^2 = 2^5$

$x^2 = 2^4$

$x^2 = 16$

$x = \pm\sqrt{16}$

$x = \pm 4$

A logarithm is not defined for a negative number, so the solution is $x = 4$.

To verify $x = 4$, substitute in the original equation.

R.S. $= \log_2 x + \log_2 2x$

$= \log_2 4 + \log_2 8$

$= 2 + 3$

$= 5$

$=$ L.S.

Since the left side is equal to the right side, the solution is verified.

The solution of *Example 1* can be verified by solving the equation $5 = \log_2 x + \log_2 2x$ graphically. Use the change of base formula. In a graphing calculator, input:

$y = 5$ and $y = \dfrac{\log(x)}{\log(2)} + \dfrac{\log(2x)}{\log(2)}$

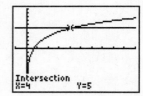

Use the intersect feature from the CALC menu to determine the x-coordinate of the point of intersection. The solution is $x = 4$.

In *Example 1*, $x = -4$ is an extraneous solution.
A logarithm is defined for only positive numbers so, in the equation $5 = \log_2 x + \log_2 2x$, $x > 0$. However, when the laws of logarithms were used to combine the logarithms, the term $\log_2 2x^2$ was obtained. Since x^2 is positive for all values of x except $x = 0$, this new equation is defined for all real numbers except $x = 0$. Therefore $x = -4$ is a solution of the equation $5 = \log_2 2x^2$, but not of the original equation $5 = \log_2 x + \log_2 2x$.

Example 2 | **Solving a Logarithmic Equation Involving $\log_b(dx - a)$**

Solve, then verify each equation.

a) $2 \log x - \log (x + 2) = \log (2x - 3)$

b) $\log_6(x + 3) + \log_6(x + 4) = 1$

2. Solve, then verify each equation.

a) $\log 6x = \log (x + 6) + \log (x - 1)$

b) $3 = \log_2(x + 2) + \log_2 x$

SOLUTION

a) $2 \log x - \log (x + 2) = \log (2x - 3)$

Consider the values of x for which each logarithm is defined.

$x > 0 \quad x + 2 > 0 \quad 2x - 3 > 0$
$\qquad\qquad x > -2 \qquad x > 1.5$

So, $x > 1.5$

$2 \log x - \log (x + 2) = \log (2x - 3)$ Use the laws of logarithms.

$\log x^2 - \log (x + 2) = \log (2x - 3)$

$\log \left(\dfrac{x^2}{x + 2}\right) = \log (2x - 3)$

Write both sides as exponents of 10.

$\dfrac{x^2}{x + 2} = 2x - 3$ \qquad Multiply each side by $x + 2$.

$x^2 = (2x - 3)(x + 2)$

$x^2 = 2x^2 + x - 6$

$x^2 + x - 6 = 0$ \qquad Solve by factoring.

$(x + 3)(x - 2) = 0$

$x + 3 = 0 \quad$ or $\quad x - 2 = 0$

$x = -3 \qquad\qquad x = 2$

Since $x > 1.5$, $x = -3$ is non-permissible, so it is an extraneous root.

Substitute $x = 2$ in the original equation to verify this solution.

L.S. $= 2 \log x - \log (x + 2)$ \qquad R.S. $= \log (2x - 3)$

$\quad = 2 \log 2 - \log (2 + 2)$ \qquad\qquad $= \log (2(2) - 3)$

$\quad = \log 2^2 - \log 4$ \qquad\qquad\qquad $= \log 1$

$\quad = \log 4 - \log 4$ \qquad\qquad\qquad\quad $= 0$

$\quad = 0$

Since the left side is equal to the right side, the solution is verified.

b) $\log_6(x + 3) + \log_6(x + 4) = 1$

Consider the values of x for which each logarithm is defined.

$x + 3 > 0 \qquad x + 4 > 0$

$\quad x > -3 \qquad\quad x > -4$

So, $x > -3$

$\log_6(x + 3) + \log_6(x + 4) = 1$ \qquad Use the product law.

$\log_6[(x + 3)(x + 4)] = 1$

$\log_6(x^2 + 7x + 12) = 1$ \qquad Write in exponential form.

$x^2 + 7x + 12 = 6^1$

$x^2 + 7x + 6 = 0$ \qquad Factor.

$(x + 6)(x + 1) = 0$

$x + 6 = 0 \quad$ or $\quad x + 1 = 0$

$x = -6 \qquad\qquad x = -1$

Since $x > -3$, $x = -6$ is an extraneous root.
Substitute $x = -1$ in the original equation to verify this solution.

$$\begin{aligned} \text{L.S.} &= \log_6(x + 3) + \log_6(x + 4) \qquad \text{R.S.} = 1 \\ &= \log_6(-1 + 3) + \log_6(-1 + 4) \\ &= \log_6 2 + \log_6 3 \\ &= \log_6(2)(3) \\ &= \log_6 6 \\ &= 1 \end{aligned}$$

Since the left side is equal to the right side, the solution is verified.

In Lesson 5.3, algebra was used to solve exponential equations for which both sides of an equation could be written with the same base. Most exponential equations cannot be written this way. Logarithms can be used to solve these equations.

Example 3	Using Logarithms to Solve Exponential Equations

Solve each exponential equation algebraically.
Give the solution to the nearest hundredth.
a) $9^x = 50$ **b)** $2(5^{x-2}) = 100$ **c)** $2^{x+3} = 6^{x-1}$

SOLUTION

a)
$$\begin{aligned} 9^x &= 50 && \text{Take the logarithm base 9 of each side.} \\ \log_9 9^x &= \log_9 50 \\ x &= \log_9 50 && \text{Apply the change of base formula.} \\ x &= \frac{\log 50}{\log 9} \\ x &\doteq 1.78 \end{aligned}$$

b)
$$\begin{aligned} 2(5^{x-2}) &= 100 && \text{Divide each side by 2.} \\ 5^{x-2} &= 50 && \text{Take the logarithm base 5 of each side.} \\ \log_5 5^{x-2} &= \log_5 50 \\ (x - 2) &= \log_5 50 && \text{Solve for } x. \\ x &= \log_5 50 + 2 && \text{Apply the change of base formula.} \\ x &= \frac{\log 50}{\log 5} + 2 \\ x &\doteq 4.43 \end{aligned}$$

Check Your Understanding

3. Solve each exponential equation algebraically. Give the solution to the nearest hundredth.

a) $12 = 4^x$ **b)** $36 = 3(2^{x+1})$

c) $3^{x+1} = 6^x$

DO NOT COPY. ©P

c)

$$2^{x+3} = 6^{x-1}$$

Take the common logarithm of each side.

$$\log 2^{x+3} = \log 6^{x-1}$$

Apply the power law.

$$(x + 3) \log 2 = (x - 1) \log 6$$

Apply the distributive law.

$$x \log 2 + 3 \log 2 = x \log 6 - 1 \log 6$$

Collect like terms.

$$3 \log 2 + \log 6 = x \log 6 - x \log 2$$

Apply the power law. Remove x as a common factor.

$$\log 2^3 + \log 6 = x(\log 6 - \log 2)$$

Apply the product and quotient laws.

$$\log (8 \cdot 6) = x \log \left(\frac{6}{2}\right)$$

$$\log 48 = x \log 3$$

Solve for x.

$$x = \frac{\log 48}{\log 3}$$

$$x \doteq 3.52$$

THINK FURTHER

In *Example 3c*, could logarithms with a different base be applied instead of common logarithms? Justify your answer. Why do you think common logarithms were used?

Discuss the Ideas

1. Why is it necessary to verify the solution of a logarithmic equation?

2. Is the root of a logarithmic equation always positive? Explain.

Exercises

A

3. Write each expression as a single logarithm.
   a) $\log 24 - \log 3$ **b)** $\log 2 + \log 4$

   c) $2 \log 4 - \log 4$ **d)** $3 \log 2 + 2 \log 3$

4. Write each expression as a single logarithm.
   a) $\log_5(x + 2) + \log_5 x$ **b)** $\log_3(x - 5) + \log_3(x + 3)$

   c) $\log (x - 7) + \log (x + 7)$ **d)** $\log_6(3x - 2) - 2 \log_6 x$

5. Use substitution or logical reasoning to determine whether $x = 2$ is a root of each equation.
   a) $\log_2 x + \log_2 2x = 3$ **b)** $\log (x - 4) + \log (x - 7) = 1$

6. Explain why $\dfrac{\log 80}{\log 4} \neq \log 20$. Use a calculator to verify.

7. Solve each exponential equation. Give the solution to the nearest hundredth.

   a) $60 = 3^{x+1}$

   b) $5^{x-3} = 200$

8. Consider the exponential equation $3^x = 30$.

   a) Solve this equation algebraically. Give the root to the nearest hundredth.

   b) Verify the solution by graphing.

9. Solve, then verify each logarithmic equation.

    a) $4 = \log_2 x + \log_2(x + 6)$ **b)** $\log_6 x + \log_6(x - 16) = 2$

10. Consider the equation $4^{x+2} = 8^{x-1}$.

    a) Solve this equation algebraically using logarithms.

    b) Solve this equation using a different algebraic strategy.

    c) Which strategy in parts a and b is more efficient?
    Justify your answer.

11. Solve, then verify each logarithmic equation.

    a) $\log_6 48 = \log_6(x + 7) + \log_6(x - 1)$

    b) $\log(2x + 4) - \log(x + 2) = \log(x + 1)$

12. Solve each exponential equation algebraically. Write the solution to the nearest hundredth.

    a) $200 = 5\left(2^{x-1}\right)$ **b)** $4^x = 6^{x-2}$

    c) $5^{x+2} = 10^{x-1}$ **d)** $3\left(2^x\right) = 6^{x-1}$

13. Solve, then verify each logarithmic equation.

a) $\log (2x - 7) + \log (x - 1) = \log (x + 1) + \log (x - 3)$

b) $\log_2 (x + 4) - \log_2 (x - 2) = 1 + \log_2 (2x - 1) - \log_2 (x + 1)$

14. a) Solve the equation $10^x = k$, where $k > 0$.

b) Explain the result.

15. Consider the equation $\log_2(x - 1) + \log_2(x - 3) = 1$.

    a) Use graphing technology to solve the equation. Write the solution to the nearest hundredth.

    b) Solve the equation algebraically to determine the exact value of x.

Multiple-Choice Questions

  1. What is the solution of the equation $3(4^{x+1}) = 36$?

    A. $x = \dfrac{\log 3}{\log 4}$ **B.** $x = \log 2$

    C. $x = \dfrac{\log 3}{\log 12}$ **D.** $x = \dfrac{\log 8}{\log 4}$

  2. Which equation has the solution $x = 6$?

    A. $\log_3(x + 5) + \log_3(x + 11) = 2$

    B. $2 = \log_5(x + 6) + \log_5(2x + 7)$

    C. $\log(2x - 1) + \log(4x - 1) = \log(6x + 1)$

    D. $\log x + \log(x - 2) = \log 3 + \log(x + 2)$

Study Note

When would you use logarithms to solve an exponential equation?
Include an example of an exponential equation and its solution
in your response.

Check Your Understanding

1. $x = 3$ **2. a)** $x = 3$ **b)** $x = 2$ **3. a)** $x \doteq 1.79$ **b)** $x \doteq 2.58$ **c)** $x \doteq 1.58$

Exercises

3. a) $\log 8$ **b)** $\log 8$ **c)** $\log 4$ **d)** $\log 72$ **4. a)** $\log_5(x^2 + 2x)$

b) $\log_3(x^2 - 2x - 15)$ **c)** $\log(x^2 - 49)$ **d)** $\log_6\left(\dfrac{3x - 2}{x^2}\right)$ **5. a)** yes   **b)** no

7. a) $x \doteq 2.73$ **b)** $x \doteq 6.29$ **8. a)** $x \doteq 3.10$ **9. a)** $x = 2$ **b)** $x = 18$
10. a), b) $x = 7$ **11. a)** $x = 5$ **b)** $x = 1$ **12. a)** $x \doteq 6.32$ **b)** $x \doteq 8.84$
c) $x \doteq 7.97$ **d)** $x \doteq 2.63$ **13. a)** $x = 5$ **b)** $x = 5$ **14. a)** $x = \log k$
15. a) $x \doteq 3.73$ **b)** $x = 2 + \sqrt{3}$

Multiple Choice
1. A   **2.** D

FOCUS Use exponents and logarithms to model and solve problems.

Get Started

Use the formula for the sum of a geometric series to determine the sum of this series: $4 + 4.4 + 4.84 + 5.324 + 5.8564$

Construct Understanding

A principal of $5000 is invested at 3% annual interest, compounded monthly. Use algebra to determine the time, to the nearest year, it will take for the investment to double.

Use graphing technology to verify the answer.

THINK FURTHER

For the problem on page 430, how would the solution change if the interest was compounded semi-annually instead of monthly?

When a series of equal investments is made at equal time intervals, and the compounding period for the interest is equal to the time interval for the investments, the amount in dollars, or *future value FV*, of these investments can be determined using this formula:

$$FV = \frac{R[(1 + i)^n - 1]}{i}$$

where R dollars is the regular investment,
i is the interest rate per compounding period, and
n is the number of investments

Example 1	Solving a Problem Involving Future Value

Determine how many monthly investments of $100 would have to be made into a savings account that pays 6% annual interest, compounded monthly, for the future value to be $100 000.

Check Your Understanding

1. Determine how many monthly investments of $200 would have to be made into an account that pays 6% annual interest, compounded monthly, for the future value to be $100 000.

SOLUTION

Use: $FV = \dfrac{R[(1 + i)^n - 1]}{i}$, where n is the number of monthly investments

Substitute: $FV = 100\,000$; $R = 100$; $i = \dfrac{0.06}{12}$, or 0.005

$$100\,000 = \frac{100[(1 + 0.005)^n - 1]}{0.005} \qquad \text{Simplify.}$$

$100\,000 = 20\,000(1.005^n - 1)$ Divide each side by 20 000.

$5 = 1.005^n - 1$

$6 = 1.005^n$ Take the common logarithm of each side.

$\log 6 = \log 1.005^n$ Apply the power law.

$\log 6 = n \log 1.005$ Solve for n.

$$n = \frac{\log 6}{\log 1.005}$$

$n = 359.2470\ldots$

The number of investments is 360.

THINK FURTHER

In *Example 1*, suppose 180 monthly investments of $100 were made into the account. Would the future value be $50 000? Justify the answer.

Many people borrow money to finance a purchase. A loan is usually repaid by making regular equal payments for a fixed period of time. The amount borrowed is called the *present value, PV,* of the loan. The following formula relates the present value to n equal payments of R dollars each, when the interest rate per compounding period is i. The compounding period is equal to the time between payments. The first payment is made after a time equal to the compounding period.

$$PV = \frac{R[1 - (1 + i)^{-n}]}{i}$$

Example 2	Solving a Problem Involving Loans

A person wants to borrow $200 000 as a mortgage to buy a house. The person can afford to pay $1500 a month. The mortgage will be repaid with equal monthly payments at 4% annual interest, compounded monthly. How many monthly payments will the person make?

SOLUTION

Use the formula:

$$PV = \frac{R[1 - (1 + i)^{-n}]}{i}$$ Substitute: $PV = 200\,000$, $R = 1500$, $i = \frac{0.04}{12}$

$$200\,000 = \frac{1500\left[1 - \left(1 + \frac{0.04}{12}\right)^{-n}\right]}{\frac{0.04}{12}}$$ Simplify.

$$\frac{200\,000\left(\frac{0.04}{12}\right)}{1500} = 1 - \left(1 + \frac{0.04}{12}\right)^{-n}$$

$$\frac{4}{9} = 1 - \left(1 + \frac{0.04}{12}\right)^{-n}$$

$$\left(1 + \frac{0.04}{12}\right)^{-n} = \frac{5}{9}$$ Take the logarithm of each side.

$$\log\left(1 + \frac{0.04}{12}\right)^{-n} = \log\left(\frac{5}{9}\right)$$

$$-n \log\left(1 + \frac{0.04}{12}\right) = \log\left(\frac{5}{9}\right)$$

$$n = \frac{\log\left(\frac{5}{9}\right)}{-\log\left(1 + \frac{0.04}{12}\right)}$$

$$n = 176.6297\ldots$$

There will be 177 monthly payments; the last payment will be less than the others.

When physical quantities have a large range of values, they are measured using a *logarithmic scale*. Some examples include the Richter scale, the decibel scale, and the pH scale.

In 1935, Charles Richter defined the magnitude, M, of an earthquake to be:

$$M = \log\left(\frac{I}{S}\right)$$

The intensity of the vibrations of an earthquake, I microns, is measured on a seismograph that is 100 km away from the *epicentre* of the earthquake. This intensity is compared to the intensity, S, of a standard earthquake, which has a seismograph reading of 1 micron and can barely be detected. The logarithmic scale for measuring the intensity of earthquakes is the **Richter scale**. Each increase of 1 unit on the logarithmic scale represents a 10-fold increase in intensity. For example, an earthquake of magnitude 9.0 in Japan in March 2011 was 100 times as intense as an earthquake of magnitude 7.0 in the same country in July 2011.

Example 3	Solving a Problem Involving the Richter Scale

In June 2010, Ontario and Quebec experienced an earthquake with magnitude 5.0. In January of the same year, Haiti experienced an earthquake with magnitude 7.0.

a) Calculate the intensity of the Haiti earthquake in terms of a standard earthquake.

b) Calculate the intensity of the Ontario-Quebec earthquake in terms of a standard earthquake.

c) How many times as intense as the Ontario-Quebec earthquake was the Haiti earthquake?

Check Your Understanding

3. The most intense earthquake ever recorded was in Chile in May 1960, with a magnitude of 9.5.

a) Calculate the intensity of the earthquake in Chile in terms of a standard earthquake.

b) How many times as intense as the Haiti earthquake was the Chile earthquake? Give the answer to the nearest whole number.

SOLUTION

a) Use: $M = \log\left(\dfrac{I}{S}\right)$ Substitute: $M = 7$

$\quad$ $7 = \log\left(\dfrac{I}{S}\right)$ To solve for I, write an exponential equation.

$\quad$ $\dfrac{I}{S} = 10^7$

$\quad$ $I = 10^7 S$

The earthquake was 10^7 times as intense as a standard earthquake.

b) Use: $M = \log\left(\dfrac{I}{S}\right)$ Substitute: $M = 5$

$\quad$ $5 = \log\left(\dfrac{I}{S}\right)$

$\quad$ $\dfrac{I}{S} = 10^5$

$\quad$ $I = 10^5 S$

The earthquake was 10^5 times as intense as a standard earthquake.

c) To compare the two earthquakes, divide their intensities.

$$\frac{\text{the intensity of the Haiti earthquake}}{\text{the intensity of the Ontario-Quebec earthquake}} = \frac{10^7 S}{10^5 S}$$

$$= 10^2, \text{ or } 100$$

The earthquake in Haiti was 100 times as intense as the Ontario-Quebec earthquake.

Example 3 illustrates that an increase of 2 units on the Richter scale represents an earthquake intensity that is 100 times as great.

Discuss the Ideas

1. How are the formulas for present value and future value alike? How are they different?

2. Why is the Richter scale called a *logarithmic scale*? Why are the intensities of two earthquakes compared instead of calculated?

Exercises

A

3. Use the equation $200 = 100(1.05)^t$ to determine the time in years it will take an investment of $100 to double when it is invested in an account that pays 5% annual interest, compounded annually.

B

4. In 1949, Vancouver Island experienced an earthquake with a magnitude of 8.1. How many times as intense as the 5.0-magnitude Ontario-Quebec earthquake in 2010 was the Vancouver Island earthquake? Give the answer to the nearest whole number.

5. Why is the intensity of an earthquake with magnitude 6 not twice the intensity of an earthquake with magnitude 3?

6. A student is saving money to buy a used car. The student deposits $150 monthly in a savings account that pays 3% annual interest, compounded monthly.

a) How long will it take the student to save $5000?

b) How much money did the student deposit in the savings account?

7. A student borrows $5000 to buy a used car. The loan payments are $150 a month at 9% annual interest, compounded monthly.

a) How long will it take the student to repay the loan?

b) How much money did the student pay?

8. Look at the answers to questions 6 and 7. Which may be the better way to finance the purchase of a car? Explain.

9. The acidity or alkalinity of a solution is measured using a logarithmic scale called the *pH scale*. A solution that has a pH of 7 is neutral. For each increase of 1 pH, a solution is 10 times as alkaline. For each decrease of 1 pH, a solution is 10 times as acidic.

    a) A sample of soda water has a pH of 3.8. A sample of vinegar has a pH of 2.8.

      i) Which sample is more acidic?

      ii) How many times as acidic is the sample?

    b) A sample of household ammonia has a pH of 11.5. A sample of sea water has a pH of 8.4.

      i) Which sample is more alkaline?

      ii) How many times as alkaline is the sample? Give the answer to the nearest whole number.

10. The *decibel scale* measures the intensity of sound. The loudness of a sound, L decibels (dB), can be determined using the function $L = 10 \log\left(\dfrac{I}{I_0}\right)$, where I is the intensity of the sound and I_0 is the intensity of the quietest sound that can be detected.

    a) The loudness of normal conversation is 60 dB. Calculate the intensity of this sound in terms of I_0.

    b) The loudness of a rock concert is 120 dB. Calculate the intensity of this sound in terms of I_0.

    c) How many times as intense as the sound of normal conversation is the sound of a rock concert?

11. The loudness of city traffic is 80 dB and the loudness of a car horn is 110 dB. Use the formula in question 10. How many times as intense as the sound of city traffic is the sound of a car horn?

12. Each of two people has a mortgage of $200 000 with an annual interest rate of 3.5%. Person A makes payments of $500.00 every two weeks, and the interest is compounded every two weeks. Person B makes monthly payments of $1000, and the interest is compounded monthly. Who pays off the mortgage first? How much sooner is it paid?

Multiple-Choice Questions

1. The loudness of sound in a gymnasium ranges from 75 dB to 115 dB. How many times as intense as the quieter sound is the louder sound?

   A. approximately 1.5 times   **B.** 40 times

   C. 10^4 times   **D.** 10^{40} times

2. Tomato juice has a pH of 4.0. Which pH solution is approximately 5 times as acidic?

    A. pH of 20.0   **B.** pH of 1.25   **C.** pH of 0.8   **D.** pH of 3.3

Study Note

Create a problem that can be modelled using a function involving exponents and that requires the use of logarithms to solve it. Solve the problem.

ANSWERS

Check Your Understanding

1. 252 investments   2. 58   3. a) $10^{9.5}S$ b) approximately 316 times

Exercises

3. approximately 14 years   4. approximately 1259 times

6. a) approximately $2\frac{2}{3}$ years b) \$4800   7. a) approximately 3.25 years

b) approximately \$5775   9. a) i) vinegar ii) 10 times b) i) household ammonia

ii) approximately 1259 times   10. a) $10^{6}I_{0}$ b) $10^{12}I_{0}$ c) 10^{6} times   11. 10^{3} times

12. person A; 3 years

Multiple Choice

1. C   2. D

STUDY GUIDE

Concept Summary

Big Ideas	Applying the Big Ideas
An exponential function can be described by the equation $y = a^x$, $a > 0$.	This means that: • The graph of the exponential function $y = a^x$, $a > 0$, has a y-intercept of 1, no x-intercept, and an asymptote with equation $y = 0$. • The exponential function $y = a^x$, $a > 0$, has domain $x \in \mathbb{R}$, and range $y > 0$. • The graph of $y = a^x$ is increasing when $a > 1$ and decreasing when $0 < a < 1$.
A logarithmic function is the inverse of an exponential function.	• The graph of a logarithmic function, $y = \log_b x$, $b > 0$, $b \neq 1$, has an x-intercept of 1, no y-intercept, and an asymptote with equation $x = 0$. • The logarithmic function, $y = \log_b x$, $b > 0$, $b \neq 1$ has domain $x > 0$ and range $y \in \mathbb{R}$.
Functions involving exponents and logarithms can be used to model financial and physical situations.	• When a situation has been modelled using exponents or logarithms, a related problem may be solved by solving an exponential or logarithmic equation. • Logarithms can be used to solve for the variable in an exponential equation. • A logarithmic equation may be solved by writing any logarithmic expression as an exponential expression.

Chapter Study Notes

• How do you know from the graphs of $y = 4^x$ and $y = \log_4 x$ that an exponential function and its related logarithmic function are inverses?

• How are exponential growth and decay alike? How are they different?

Skills Summary

Skill	Description	Example
Solve an exponential equation whose powers can be written with the same base. **(5.3)**	Write each power with the same base, then equate the exponents.	Solve: $4^x = 8^{x-1}$ $(2^2)^x = (2^3)^{x-1}$ $2^{2x} = 2^{3x-3}$ $2x = 3x - 3$ $x = 3$
Solve an exponential equation whose powers cannot be written with the same base. **(5.3, 5.7)**	To solve by graphing, move all the terms to one side of the equation. Graph the corresponding function $y = f(x)$, then determine the zeros. To solve algebraically, take the same logarithm of each side, then use the laws of logarithms.	Solve: $3^x = 10$ Graph $y = 3^x - 10$ and determine the zeros. Use algebra. $\log 3^x = \log 10$ $x \log 3 = 1$ $x = \dfrac{1}{\log 3}$ $x = 2.0959\ldots$
Write a logarithmic expression as an exponential expression, and vice versa. **(5.4)**	Identify the base and the exponent. The logarithm is an exponent.	Write $\log_3 81 = 4$ as an exponential expression. The base is 3. The exponent is 4. $81 = 3^4$ Write $6^2 = 36$ as a logarithmic expression. The base is 6. The exponent is 2. $\log_6 36 = 2$
Use the laws of logarithms to simplify and evaluate logarithmic expressions. **(5.5)**	• $\log x + \log y = \log xy$ • $\log x - \log y = \log\left(\dfrac{x}{y}\right)$ • $k \log x = \log x^k$	Write as a single logarithm: $2 \log x + \log y - 3 \log z$ $= \log x^2 + \log y - \log z^3$ $= \log x^2 y - \log z^3$ $= \log\left(\dfrac{x^2 y}{z^3}\right)$
Solve a logarithmic equation algebraically. **(5.7)**	Identify non-permissible values, then express each side of the equation as one logarithm, and equate the terms or numbers whose logarithms are equal. Solve for the variable. Identify extraneous roots, then verify the solution.	Solve: $\log (x - 2) + \log x = \log 8$ $x > 2, x > 0,$ so $x > 2$ $\log x(x - 2) = \log 8$ $\log (x^2 - 2x) = \log 8$ $x^2 - 2x = 8$ $x^2 - 2x - 8 = 0$ $(x - 4)(x + 2) = 0$ $x = 4$ or $x = -2$ $x = -2$ is extraneous. Use mental math to verify. The solution is $x = 4$.

5.1

1. Complete the table of values, then graph $y = \left(\frac{1}{4}\right)^x$.

x	−2	−1	0	1	2
y					

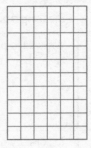

5.2

2. a) Graph $y = 3.5^x$ for $-2 \leq x \leq 2$.

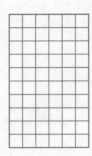

    b) Determine:

        i) whether the function is increasing or decreasing

        ii) the intercepts

        iii) the equation of the asymptote

        iv) the domain of the function

        v) the range of the function

3. Use technology to graph each function below. For each graph:

    i) identify the intercepts

    ii) identify the equation of the asymptote and state why it is significant

    a) $y = 0.8^x$ **b)** $y = 2.75^x$

4. a) Sketch the graph of $y = -\dfrac{1}{2}(3^{2x}) - 1$.

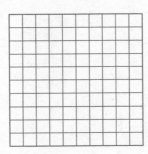

b) From the graph, identify:

   i) whether the function is increasing or decreasing

   ii) the intercepts

   iii) the equation of the asymptote

   iv) the domain of the function

   v) the range of the function

5.3

5. Solve each equation.

   a) $4^x = 128$

   b) $27^{x+1} = 81^{x-2}$

   c) $9^x = 27\sqrt[4]{3}$

   d) $\dfrac{\sqrt[3]{2}}{8} = 4^x$

6. Solve the equation $1.04^{2x} = 2$. Give the solution to the nearest tenth.

7. A new combine, used for harvesting wheat, costs $370 000. Its value depreciates by 10% each year. The value of the combine, v thousands of dollars, after t years can be modelled by this function:
$v = 370(0.9)^t$

a) What is the value of the combine when it is 5 years old? Give the answer to the nearest thousand dollars.

b) When will the combine be worth $100 000? Give the answer to the nearest half year.

8. A principal of $2500 is invested at 3% annual interest, compounded semi-annually. To the nearest year, how long will it be until the amount is $3000?

5.4

9. a) Write each logarithmic expression as an exponential expression.

    i) $\log_3 729 = 6$ **ii)** $\log_4 2\sqrt{2} = \frac{3}{4}$

b) Write each exponential expression as a logarithmic expression.

    i) $4^5 = 1024$ **ii)** $5^{-4} = \dfrac{1}{625}$

10. For each logarithm below, determine its exact value or use benchmarks to determine its approximate value to the nearest tenth.

    a) $\log_7 343$ **b)** $\log_8 100$

    c) $\log_2 20$ **d)** $\log_4\left(\dfrac{1}{32}\right)$

11. a) Graph $y = \log_6 x$.

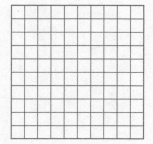

b) Identify the intercepts and the equation of the asymptote of the graph, and the domain and range of the function.

c) How could you use the graph of $y = \log_6 x$ to graph $y = 6^x$? Use your strategy to graph $y = 6^x$ on the grid in part a.

5.5

12. Write each expression as a single logarithm.

   a) $3 \log x + \dfrac{1}{2} \log y - 2 \log z$ b) $4 + \log_2 3$

13. Evaluate: $2 \log_4 6 - \log_4 18 + \log_4 8$

5.6

14. Approximate the value of each logarithm, to the nearest thousandth.

   a) $\log_5 600$ b) $\log_3 0.1$

15. Use technology to graph $y = \log_9 x$. Identify the intercepts and the equation of the asymptote of the graph, and the domain and range of the function.

16. a) Sketch the graph of $y = \log_5(3x - 6) + 3$.

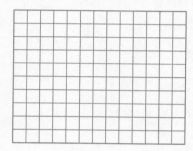

b) Identify the intercepts and the equation of the asymptote of the graph of $y = \log_5(3x - 6) + 3$, and the domain and range of this function.

17. Solve, then verify each logarithmic equation.

    a) $3 = \log_2(x + 5) + \log_2(x + 7)$ **b)** $\log x + \log(x + 1) = \log(7x - 8)$

18. Solve each equation algebraically. Give the solution to the nearest hundredth.

    a) $5(3^x) = 60$ **b)** $3^{x+4} = 5^{x+1}$

19. The pH of a solution can be described by the equation
pH $= -\log [H^+]$, where $[H^+]$ is the hydrogen-ion concentration in moles/litre.

a) Determine the hydrogen-ion concentration in pure water with a pH of 7.

b) How are the hydrogen-ion concentrations of these liquids related: black coffee with a pH of 5 and pure water?

ANSWERS

2. b) i) increasing   **ii)** no x-intercept; y-intercept: 1   **iii)** $y = 0$ **iv)** $x \in \mathbb{R}$
v) $y > 0$ **3. a), b) i)** no x-intercept; y-intercept: 1   **ii)** $y = 0$
4. b) i) decreasing   **ii)** no x-intercept; y-intercept: -1.5 **iii)** $y = -1$

iv) $x \in \mathbb{R}$ **v)** $y < -1$ **5. a)** $x = 3.5$ **b)** $x = 11$ **c)** $x = 1.625$ **d)** $x = -\dfrac{4}{3}$

6. $x \doteq 8.8$ **7. a)** approximately \$218 000   **b)** approximately 12.5 years
8. approximately 6 years   **9. a) i)** $729 = 3^6$ **ii)** $2\sqrt{2} = 4^{\frac{3}{4}}$ **b) i)** $5 = \log_4 1024$

ii) $-4 = \log_5\left(\dfrac{1}{625}\right)$ **10. a)** 3   **b)** approximately 2.2   **c)** approximately 4.3   **d)** $-\dfrac{5}{2}$

11. b) no y-intercept; x-intercept: 1; asymptote: $x = 0$; domain: $x > 0$; range: $y \in \mathbb{R}$

12. a) $\log\left(\dfrac{x^3 y^{\frac{1}{2}}}{z^2}\right)$ **b)** $\log_2 48$ **13.** 2   **14. a)** approximately 3.975

b) approximately -2.096 **15.** x-intercept: 1; no y-intercept; asymptote: $x = 0$;

domain: $x > 0$; range: $y \in \mathbb{R}$ **16. b)** x-intercept: $\dfrac{751}{375}$; no y-intercept;

asymptote: $x = 2$; domain: $x > 2$; range: $y \in \mathbb{R}$ **17. a)** $x = -3$ **b)** $x = 2, x = 4$
18. a) $x \doteq 2.26$ **b)** $x \doteq 5.45$ **19. a)** 10^{-7} moles/litre

1. Multiple Choice Which logarithm has the greatest value?

   A. $\log_3 30$ **B.** $\log_2 9$ **C.** $\log_4 60$ **D.** $\log_7 360$

2. Multiple Choice Which function describes this graph?

   A. $f(x) = 2^{x+1} + 3$

   B. $f(x) = 2^{x-1} - 3$

   C. $f(x) = 2^{x+1} - 3$

   D. $f(x) = 2^{x-1} + 3$

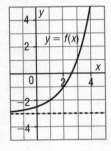

3. a) Graph $y = 3^x$. Identify the intercepts and the equation of the asymptote of the graph, and the domain and range of the function.

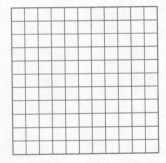

b) Sketch the graph of $y = \log_3 x$ on the grid in part a. Identify the intercepts and the equation of the asymptote of the graph, and the domain and range of the function.

c) How do the graphs in parts a and b show that these functions are inverses?

4. Solve each equation. Where necessary, give the solution to the nearest hundredth.

a) $5^x = 400$

b) $8^{x+1} = 16^{x-2}$

c) $\log_4(x - 8) + \log_4(x + 4) = 3$ **d)** $\log_2(3x + 4) = \log_2(x + 4) + \log_2(x - 2)$

5. a) Graph $y = 5^x$.

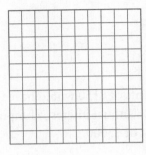

b) Which transformations would be applied to the graph of $y = 5^x$ so that the equation of its image is $y = \frac{1}{2}(5^{-x+4}) + 3$?

c) Graph $y = \frac{1}{2}(5^{-x+4}) + 3$ on the grid in part a. Identify the intercepts and the equation of the asymptote of the graph, and the domain and range of the function.

6. How would you add two logarithms with different bases? Include an example in your explanation.

7. How many monthly investments of $150 would have to be paid into a savings account that pays 3% annual interest, compounded monthly, to obtain an amount of $5000?

ANSWERS

1. B   2. B

3. a) no *x*-intercept; *y*-intercept: 1; asymptote: $y = 0$; domain: $x \in \mathbb{R}$; range: $y > 0$
b) no *y*-intercept; *x*-intercept: 1; asymptote: $x = 0$: domain: $x > 0$; range: $y \in \mathbb{R}$
4. a) $x \doteq 3.72$ b) $x = 11$ c) $x = 12$ d) $x = 4$
5. c) no *x*-intercept; *y*-intercept: 315.5; asymptote: $y = 3$; domain: $x \in \mathbb{R}$; range: $y > 3$
7. 32

1. When $bx^5 + x^4 - 5x^3 + x^2 + 2x - 4b$ is divided by $x + 1$, the remainder is -10. Determine the value of b.

2

2. For the graph of each rational function below, determine without technology:

   i) the equations of any asymptotes and the coordinates of any hole

   ii) the domain of the function

   Use graphing technology to verify the characteristics.

   a) $y = \dfrac{x^2 - 6x + 8}{x - 3}$

   b) $y = \dfrac{-3x + 12}{x^2 + 3}$

3. Describe how the graph of $y = \sqrt{x}$ has been translated to create the graph of each function below. Use graphing technology to check.

a) $y = \sqrt{x} + 3$

b) $y = \sqrt{x + 1} + 1$

4. Here is the graph of $y = f(x)$. On the same grid, sketch and label the graph of each function.

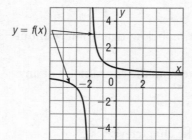

$y = f(x)$

a) $y = f(-x)$

b) $y = -f(x)$

5. Graph $y = \sqrt{x}$, then apply transformations to sketch the graph of
$y - 2 = -\frac{1}{2}\sqrt{3x}$. What are the domain and range of this function?

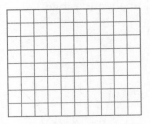

6. For each graph of a relation below, sketch the graph of its inverse.
Is the inverse a function? How do you know?

a)

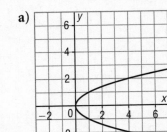

b)

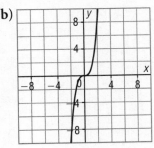

7. Use the graphs of $y = f(x)$ and $y = g(x)$ to sketch the graph of each function below, then identify its domain and range.

a) $y = f(x) - g(x)$

b) $y = \dfrac{f(x)}{g(x)}$

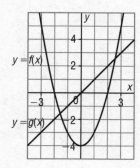

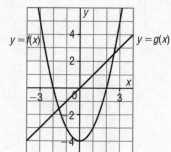

8. Given that $f(x) = 2 + x^2$, $g(x) = -3x + 5$, and $h(x) = \sqrt{2 - 4x}$, write an explicit equation for $k(x)$ then state its domain.

a) $k(x) = f(x) + g(x) + h(x)$ **b)** $k(x) = f(x) \cdot g(x) - h(x)$

9. Use the functions $f(x) = x^2 - x$, $g(x) = \dfrac{1}{3 - x}$, and $h(x) = |x + 1|$.

a) Determine each value.

   i) $f(g(4))$ **ii)** $g(h(-3))$

b) Write an explicit equation for each composite function, then state its domain.

   i) $h(g(x))$ **ii)** $f(f(x))$

10. For the function $y = 3x^2 - 12x + 5$, determine possible functions f and g so that $y = f(g(x))$.

11. Use transformations to graph $y = -4^{2(x+3)}$. Describe the transformations, then state the characteristics of the graph; include the intercepts, equation of the asymptote, domain, and range.

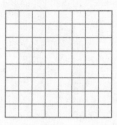

12. A cup of coffee contains 150 mg of caffeine. In a healthy adult, the mass, m grams, that remains after t hours is modelled by the function $m = 150(0.5)^{0.2t}$. Use technology.

a) To the nearest half hour, how long will it take until only 10 mg of caffeine remain?

b) To the nearest tenth of a milligram, how much caffeine remains after 24 h?

13. Solve each equation.

a) $9^{2x+1} = \dfrac{\sqrt[4]{27}}{81}$

b) $\log_3(x + 5) + \log_3(x - 1)$
$= 2 + \log_3(x + 1)$

14. Write each expression in terms of $\log a$, $\log b$, and $\log c$.

a) $\log\left(\dfrac{a^3\sqrt{b}}{c}\right)$

b) $\log\left(\dfrac{a^{\frac{2}{3}}}{b\sqrt[4]{c^3}}\right)$

15. Write each expression as a single logarithm.

a) $4\log 3 - 2\log 6 + 2\log 2$ **b)** $2\log_7 x - \log_7 y - \dfrac{1}{4}\log_7 z$

16. On March 11, 2011, an earthquake off the coast of Japan had a magnitude of 9.0 and it caused a tsunami. To the nearest tenth, determine the magnitude of an earthquake that is one-half as intense as this earthquake.

ANSWERS

1. 3   **2. a) i)** $x = 3$; $y = x - 3$ **ii)** $x \neq 3$ **b) i)** $y = 0$ **ii)** $x \in \mathbb{R}$

5. domain: $x \geq 0$; range: $y \leq 2$ **6. a)** yes   **b)** yes

7. a) domain: $x \in \mathbb{R}$; range: $y \geq -4.25$ **b)** domain: $x \neq 0$; range: $y \in \mathbb{R}$

8. a) $k(x) = x^2 - 3x + 7 + \sqrt{2 - 4x}$; $x \leq 0.5$

b) $k(x) = -3x^3 + 5x^2 - 6x + 10 - \sqrt{2 - 4x}$; $x \leq 0.5$

9. a) i) 2   **ii)** 1   **b) i)** $h(g(x)) = \left| \dfrac{4 - x}{3 - x} \right|$; $x \neq 3$ **ii)** $f(f(x)) = x^4 - 2x^3 + x$; $x \in \mathbb{R}$

11. y-intercept: -4096; asymptote: $y = 0$; domain: $x \in \mathbb{R}$; range: $y < 0$

12. a) approximately 19.5 h   **b)** approximately 5.4 mg

13. a) $x = -\dfrac{21}{16}$ **b)** $x = 7$ **14. a)** $3 \log a + \dfrac{1}{2} \log b - \log c$

b) $\dfrac{2}{3} \log a - \log b - \dfrac{3}{4} \log c$ **15. a)** $\log 9$ **b)** $\log_7 \left(\dfrac{x^2}{yz^{\frac{1}{4}}} \right)$ **16.** approximately 8.7

6 Trigonometry

BUILDING ON

- definitions of trigonometric ratios for angles between 0° and 360°

- transformations of the graphs of functions

- circle geometry

BIG IDEAS

- The trigonometric ratio for an angle $\theta < 0°$ or $\theta > 360°$ is the value of that ratio for the related angle in standard position.

- The radian measure of an angle is a real number.

- A sine or cosine function can be used to model periodic behaviour.

LEADING TO

- solving trigonometric equations

- identifying and proving trigonometric identities

NEW VOCABULARY

coterminal angles	periodic function
unit circle	period
reciprocal trigonometric ratio	sinusoidal function
secant, cosecant, cotangent	amplitude
radian	phase shift
trigonometric function	

Get Started

Determine the exact coordinates of P.

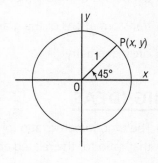

Determine the value of tan 45°.

α is an angle between 0° and 360°.
Determine the values of α that satisfy each equation:

• $\sin \alpha = \sin 45°$

• $\cos \alpha = \cos 45°$

• $\tan \alpha = \tan 45°$

Construct Understanding

Each diagram of a clock face shows 3:00 A.M.
Use arcs to show how the hour hand would rotate from this
position to indicate each time. State the angle through which the
hand rotates.

3:00 P.M. the same day

9:00 P.M. the same day

6:00 A.M. the next day

10:00 A.M. the next day

Recall that when a ray rotates 130° counterclockwise about the origin from the positive x-axis, it forms a positive angle in standard position.

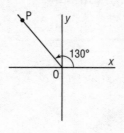

Suppose the ray continues to rotate. When the ray first reaches its starting position, it forms an angle of 360°. After rotating another 200°, the ray forms an angle greater than 360°.
560° = 360° + 200°

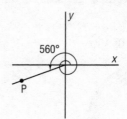

When a ray rotates 130° clockwise about the origin from the positive x-axis, it forms a negative angle in standard position.

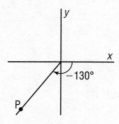

When a ray rotates more than 1 revolution clockwise, it forms a negative angle less than −360°.
−560° = −360° + (−200°)

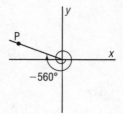

Angles in standard position with the same terminal arm are **coterminal angles**. For example, consider the angle 40° in standard position.

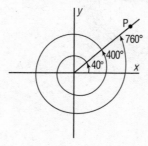

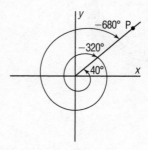

THINK FURTHER

Why do the angles that are coterminal with a given angle form an arithmetic sequence?

400° = 360° + 40°

760° = 2(360°) + 40°

−320° = −360° + 40°

−680° = 2(−360°) + 40°

There are infinitely many angles that are coterminal with a given angle.

The measures of the positive angles that are coterminal with 40° form an arithmetic sequence: 40°, 400°, 760°, ..., with general term: 40° + k360°, where k is a whole number

The measures of the negative angles that are coterminal with 40° form an arithmetic sequence: −320°, −680°, ..., with general term: 40° − k360°, where k is a natural number

So, the measure of any angle coterminal with 40° in standard position can be written as: 40° + k360°, k ∈ ℤ

Example 1   Determining and Sketching Coterminal
Angles

a) Determine the measures of all the angles in standard position between −1000° and 1000° that are coterminal with an angle of 150° in standard position. Sketch the angles.

b) Write an expression for the measures of all the angles that are coterminal with an angle of 150° in standard position.

1. a) Determine the measures of all the angles in standard position between −800° and 800° that are coterminal with an angle of 85° in standard position. Sketch the angles.

b) Write an expression for the measures of all the angles that are coterminal with an angle of 85° in standard position.

SOLUTION

a) Between 0° and 1000°, the measures of angles that are coterminal with 150° are:

150°
150° + 360° = 510°
150° + 2(360°) = 870°

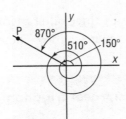

Between −1000° and 0°, the measures of angles that are coterminal with 150° are:

150° − 360° = −210°
150° − 2(360°) = −570°
150° − 3(360°) = −930°

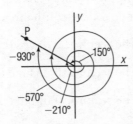

b) The measures of all the angles that are coterminal with 150° can be represented by the expression: 150° + k360°, $k \in \mathbb{Z}$.

Suppose a terminal point P(x, y), in any quadrant, lies 1 unit from the origin O. As the terminal arm OP rotates, P traces a circle.

The Pythagorean Theorem can be used to relate the radius of the circle and the coordinates of P.
In right △OPN,
$x^2 + y^2 = 1^2$, which simplifies to
$x^2 + y^2 = 1$
This is the equation of a circle with centre (0, 0) and radius 1. This is the **unit circle**.

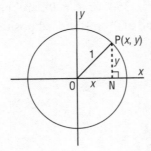

Equation of the Unit Circle

A circle, centre the origin and radius 1 unit, has equation:
$x^2 + y^2 = 1$

Recall that when the terminal point P(x, y) of an angle θ in standard position lies on a circle with radius r, the coordinates of P are:
$x = r \cos \theta$ and $y = r \sin \theta$

For the unit circle, $r = 1$, so the coordinates of P are:
$x = \cos \theta$ and $y = \sin \theta$

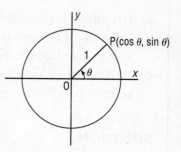

From these definitions, when P(x, y) is the point where the terminal arm of angle θ intersects the unit circle, then:

$\cos \theta = x \qquad \sin \theta = y \qquad \tan \theta = \dfrac{y}{x}$

There are three other trigonometric ratios that are related to the primary trigonometric ratios. These are the **reciprocal trigonometric ratios**.

Reciprocal Trigonometric Ratios

Suppose P(x, y) is the point where the terminal arm of angle θ intersects the unit circle.

The reciprocal of $\cos \theta$ is the **secant ratio** for angle θ: $\sec \theta = \dfrac{1}{x}$

The reciprocal of $\sin \theta$ is the **cosecant ratio** for angle θ: $\csc \theta = \dfrac{1}{y}$

The reciprocal of $\tan \theta$ is the **cotangent ratio** for angle θ: $\cot \theta = \dfrac{x}{y}$

The coordinates of points on the unit circle can be used to identify the exact trigonometric ratios of certain angles in Quadrant 1, and the trigonometric ratios of the angles in the other quadrants with the same reference angle.

The trigonometric ratios for an angle θ in standard position, where $\theta > 360°$ or $\theta < 0°$, are the same as these ratios for the angle between 0° and 360° in standard position that is coterminal with θ.

Example 2 **Determining the Six Trigonometric Ratios for an Angle**

a) Determine the exact values of the six trigonometric ratios for 510°.

b) Determine the approximate values of the six trigonometric ratios for −416°, to the nearest thousandth.

2. a) Determine the exact values of the six trigonometric ratios for −420°.

   b) Determine the approximate values of the six trigonometric ratios for 586°, to the nearest thousandth.

SOLUTION

a) Sketch 510° in standard position, then determine the coordinates of point $P(x, y)$ on the terminal arm that intersects the unit circle. The measure of a coterminal angle in standard position is: $510° − 360° = 150°$ The terminal arm of this angle lies

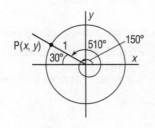

in Quadrant 2, where the sine ratio is positive, and the cosine and tangent ratios are negative. The reference angle is 30°.

$$x = \cos 150° \quad \text{and} \quad y = \sin 150°$$
$$= -\cos 30° \qquad\qquad = \sin 30°$$
$$= -\frac{\sqrt{3}}{2} \qquad\qquad = \frac{1}{2}$$

Then,

$$\cos 510° = \cos 150° \qquad \sec 510° = \frac{1}{\cos 510°}$$
$$= -\frac{\sqrt{3}}{2} \qquad\qquad = -\frac{2}{\sqrt{3}}$$

$$\sin 510° = \sin 150° \qquad \csc 510° = \frac{1}{\sin 510°}$$
$$= \frac{1}{2} \qquad\qquad = 2$$

$$\tan 510° = \tan 150° \qquad \cot 510° = \frac{1}{\tan 510°}$$
$$= \frac{\frac{1}{2}}{-\frac{\sqrt{3}}{2}} \qquad\qquad = -\sqrt{3}$$
$$= -\frac{1}{\sqrt{3}}$$

b) Use technology and the $\boxed{x^{-1}}$ key to determine the values of the reciprocal ratios.

$$\cos(-416°) = 0.5591... \qquad \sec(-416°) = \frac{1}{\cos(-416°)}$$
$$\doteq 0.559 \qquad\qquad\qquad \doteq 1.788$$

$$\sin(-416°) = -0.8290... \qquad \csc(-416°) = \frac{1}{\sin(-416°)}$$
$$\doteq -0.829 \qquad\qquad\qquad \doteq -1.206$$

$$\tan(-416°) = -1.4825... \qquad \cot(-416°) = \frac{1}{\tan(-416°)}$$
$$\doteq -1.483 \qquad\qquad\qquad \doteq -0.675$$

A terminal point $P(x, y)$ lies r units from the origin O. As the terminal arm OP rotates, P traces a circle. The Pythagorean Theorem can be used to relate the radius of the circle and the coordinates of P. In right $\triangle$OPN,
$x^2 + y^2 = r^2$

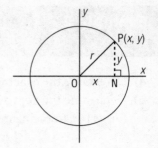

This is the equation of a circle with centre $(0, 0)$ and radius r.

Equation of a Circle

A circle, centre the origin and radius r units, has equation:
$$x^2 + y^2 = r^2$$

For any angle θ in standard position, with terminal point $P(x, y)$ on a circle, radius r,

$\cos \theta = \frac{x}{r}$ $\sin \theta = \frac{y}{r}$ $\tan \theta = \frac{y}{x}$

$\sec \theta = \frac{r}{x}$ $\csc \theta = \frac{r}{y}$ $\cot \theta = \frac{x}{y}$

Example 3   Determining All Trigonometric Ratios Given the Coordinates of a Point on the Terminal Arm

Check Your Understanding

3. $P(-1, -4)$ is a terminal point of angle θ in standard position. Determine the exact values of the six trigonometric ratios for θ.

$P(-2, 5)$ is a terminal point of angle θ in standard position. Determine the exact values of the six trigonometric ratios for θ.

SOLUTION

Sketch a diagram.
Let the length of OP be r.
Use: $x^2 + y^2 = r^2$ Substitute: $x = -2, y = 5$
$(-2)^2 + 5^2 = r^2$
$r = \sqrt{29}$

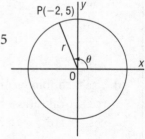

$\sin \theta = \frac{y}{r}$ $\csc \theta = \frac{r}{y}$

$= \frac{5}{\sqrt{29}}$ $= \frac{\sqrt{29}}{5}$

$\cos \theta = \frac{x}{r}$ $\sec \theta = \frac{r}{x}$

$= -\frac{2}{\sqrt{29}}$ $= -\frac{\sqrt{29}}{2}$

$\tan \theta = \frac{y}{x}$ $\cot \theta = \frac{x}{y}$

$= -\frac{5}{2}$ $= -\frac{2}{5}$

Example 4 — Determining All Trigonometric Ratios and Angle Measures Given One Trigonometric Ratio

Suppose $\csc \theta = 3$.

a) Determine the exact values of the other trigonometric ratios for $0° \leq \theta \leq 180°$.

b) To the nearest degree, determine possible values of θ in the domain $-360° \leq \theta \leq 360°$.

Check Your Understanding

4. Suppose $\sec \theta = 4$.

a) Determine the exact values of the other trigonometric ratios for $0° \leq \theta \leq 180°$.

b) To the nearest degree, determine possible values of θ in the domain $-360° \leq \theta \leq 360°$.

SOLUTION

a) Let $P(x, y)$ on a circle, radius r, be the terminal point of angle θ in standard position.

Then, $\csc \theta = \dfrac{r}{y}$

$\dfrac{r}{y} = \dfrac{3}{1}$, so choose $r = 3$ and $y = 1$

Use: $x^2 + y^2 = r^2$ Substitute: $y = 1, r = 3$

$\qquad x^2 + 1^2 = 3^2$

$\qquad\qquad x^2 = 8$

$\qquad\qquad x = \pm\sqrt{8}$

Since $\csc \theta$ is positive, the terminal arm of angle θ lies in Quadrant 1 or 2, where x is positive or negative.

$\sin \theta = \dfrac{y}{r} \qquad \cos \theta = \dfrac{x}{r} \qquad \sec \theta = \dfrac{r}{x}$

$\quad = \dfrac{1}{3} \qquad\quad = \pm\dfrac{\sqrt{8}}{3} \qquad = \pm\dfrac{3}{\sqrt{8}}$

$\tan \theta = \dfrac{y}{x} \qquad \cot \theta = \dfrac{x}{y}$

$\quad = \pm\dfrac{1}{\sqrt{8}} \qquad\quad = \pm\sqrt{8}$

b) $\sin \theta = \dfrac{1}{3}$, so:

In Quadrant 1, $\theta = \sin^{-1}\left(\dfrac{1}{3}\right)$

$\qquad\qquad\quad \doteq 19°$

In Quadrant 2, $\theta \doteq 180° - 19°$, or $161°$

Sketch a diagram.

The angles between $-360°$ and $0°$ that are coterminal with the angles above are:

$-360° + 19° = -341°$ and $-360° + 161° = -199°$

Possible values of θ are approximately: $19°$, $161°$, $-341°$, and $-199°$.

THINK FURTHER

In *Example 4a*, which other values of r and y could you use? Where would P be situated then?

Discuss the Ideas

1. A terminal point $P(x, y)$ of an angle θ in standard position lies on the unit circle. How can the coordinates of P be used to determine the six trigonometric ratios for that angle?

2. For which values of θ is each of $\csc \theta$, $\sec \theta$, and $\cot \theta$ not defined?

Exercises

A

3. Use technology to determine the value of each trigonometric ratio to the nearest thousandth.

   a) $\sin 415°$ b) $\cos(-65°)$ c) $\cot 72°$ d) $\csc 285°$

4. Sketch each angle in standard position, then identify the reference angle.

   a) $460°$ b) $-350°$

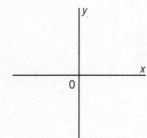
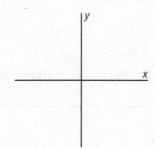

c) 695°   d) −500°

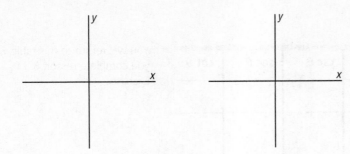

5. For each angle in standard position below:
   i) Determine the measures of angles that are coterminal with the angle in the given domain.
   ii) Write an expression for the measures of all the angles that are coterminal with the angle in standard position.

a) 75°;
   for −500° ≤ θ ≤ 500°

b) −105°;
   for −600° ≤ θ ≤ 600°

c) 215°;
   for −700° ≤ θ ≤ 700°

d) −290°;
   for −800° ≤ θ ≤ 800°

6. Use exact values to complete this table.

θ	sin θ	cos θ	tan θ	csc θ	sec θ	cot θ
0°						
30°						
45°						
60°						
90°						
120°						
135°						
150°						
180°						
210°						
225°						
240°						
270°						
300°						
315°						
330°						
360°						

You will return to this table when you complete Lesson 6.3 Exercises.

7. Determine the exact values of the 6 trigonometric ratios for each angle.

a) 480°

b) −855°

8. For each point P(x, y) on the terminal arm of an angle θ in standard position, determine the exact values of the six trigonometric ratios for θ.

a) P(2, 1)

b) P(3, −4)

9. For each point $P(x, y)$ on the terminal arm of an angle θ in standard position, determine possible measures of θ in the given domain. Give the answers to the nearest degree.

a) $P(-4, 2)$;
   for $-360° \leq \theta \leq 0°$

b) $P(-4, -8)$;
   for $-360° \leq \theta \leq 360°$

10. For each trigonometric ratio, determine the exact values of the other 5 trigonometric ratios for θ in the given domain.

a) $\cos \theta = \dfrac{1}{\sqrt{2}}$;
   for $0° \leq \theta \leq 180°$

b) $\cot \theta = -\sqrt{3}$;
   for $90° \leq \theta \leq 270°$

11. For each value of the trigonometric ratio below, determine possible measures of angle θ in the given domain. Give the angles to the nearest degree.

a) $\sin \theta = -\dfrac{1}{2}$; for $-360° \leq \theta \leq 360°$

b) $\cot \theta = 1$; for $0° \leq \theta \leq 720°$

c) $\sec \theta = -11$; for $0° \leq \theta \leq 360°$

C

12. Perpendicular lines are drawn from the axes to the terminal arm of an angle θ in standard position. Lines DC and EF are tangents to the unit circle. Explain why each trigonometric ratio is equal to the length of the indicated line segment.

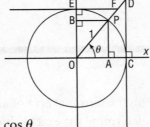

a) $PA = \sin \theta$

b) $PB = \cos \theta$

c) $OF = \csc \theta$

d) $DC = \tan \theta$

e) $FE = \cot\theta$ **f)** $DO = \sec\theta$

Multiple-Choice Questions

1. Which angle is coterminal with an angle of 300° in standard position?

    A. −60°   **B.** 60°   **C.** −300°   **D.** 780°

2. Given $\tan\theta = \frac{2}{3}$, which statement is true for all possible values of θ?

    A. $\cot\theta = \frac{3}{2}$

    B. $\cot\theta = -\frac{3}{2}$

    C. $\cot\theta = -\frac{2}{3}$

    D. $\cot\theta$ cannot be determined

Study Note

Choose the coordinates of a point on the terminal arm of an angle in standard position. Explain how to determine the exact values of the 6 trigonometric ratios of that angle.

Check Your Understanding

1. a) $85°, 445°, -275°, -635°$ b) $85° + k360°, k \in \mathbb{Z}$

2. a) $\cos(-420°) = \frac{1}{2}$; $\sec(-420°) = 2$; $\sin(-420°) = -\frac{\sqrt{3}}{2}$;

$\csc(-420°) = -\frac{2}{\sqrt{3}}$; $\tan(-420°) = -\sqrt{3}$; $\cot(-420°) = -\frac{1}{\sqrt{3}}$

b) $\cos 586° \doteq -0.695$; $\sec 586° \doteq -1.440$; $\sin 586° \doteq -0.719$; $\csc 586° \doteq -1.390$; $\tan 586° \doteq 1.036$; $\cot 586° \doteq 0.966$

3. $\sin\theta = -\frac{4}{\sqrt{17}}$; $\csc\theta = -\frac{\sqrt{17}}{4}$; $\cos\theta = -\frac{1}{\sqrt{17}}$; $\sec\theta = -\sqrt{17}$; $\tan\theta = 4$; $\cot\theta = \frac{1}{4}$

4. a) $\cos\theta = \frac{1}{4}$; $\sin\theta = \frac{\sqrt{15}}{4}$; $\csc\theta = \frac{4}{\sqrt{15}}$; $\tan\theta = \sqrt{15}$; $\cot\theta = \frac{1}{\sqrt{15}}$

b) approximately $\pm76°$ and $\pm284°$

Exercises

3. a) approximately 0.819   b) approximately 0.423   c) approximately 0.325
d) approximately -1.035 4. a) $80°$ b) $10°$ c) $25°$ d) $40°$ 5. a) i) $75°, 435°, -285°$
ii) $75° + k360°, k \in \mathbb{Z}$ b) i) $255°, -105°, -465°$ ii) $-105° + k360°, k \in \mathbb{Z}$
c) i) $215°, 575°, -145°, -505°$ ii) $215° + k360°, k \in \mathbb{Z}$
d) i) $70°, 430°, 790°, -290°, -650°$ ii) $-290° + k360°, k \in \mathbb{Z}$

7. a) $\sin 480° = \frac{\sqrt{3}}{2}$, $\cos 480° = -\frac{1}{2}$, $\tan 480° = -\sqrt{3}$, $\csc 480° = \frac{2}{\sqrt{3}}$,

$\sec 480° = -2$, $\cot 480° = -\frac{1}{\sqrt{3}}$ b) $\sin(-855°) = \cos(-855°) = -\frac{1}{\sqrt{2}}$,

$\tan(-855°) = \cot(-855°) = 1$, $\csc(-855°) = \sec(-855°) = -\sqrt{2}$

8. a) $\sin\theta = \frac{1}{\sqrt{5}}$, $\csc\theta = \sqrt{5}$, $\cos\theta = \frac{2}{\sqrt{5}}$, $\sec\theta = \frac{\sqrt{5}}{2}$, $\tan\theta = \frac{1}{2}$, $\cot\theta = 2$

b) $\sin\theta = -\frac{4}{5}$, $\csc\theta = -\frac{5}{4}$, $\cos\theta = \frac{3}{5}$, $\sec\theta = \frac{5}{3}$, $\tan\theta = -\frac{4}{3}$, $\cot\theta = -\frac{3}{4}$

9. a) approximately $-207°$ b) approximately: $243°, -117°$

10. a) $\sec\theta = \sqrt{2}$, $\sin\theta = \frac{1}{\sqrt{2}}$, $\csc\theta = \sqrt{2}$, $\tan\theta = 1$, $\cot\theta = 1$

b) $\tan\theta = -\frac{1}{\sqrt{3}}$, $\sin\theta = \frac{1}{2}$, $\csc\theta = 2$, $\cos\theta = -\frac{\sqrt{3}}{2}$, $\sec\theta = -\frac{2}{\sqrt{3}}$

11. a) $210°, 330°, -150°, -30°$ b) $45°, 225°, 405°, 585°$ c) approximately: $95°, 265°$

Multiple Choice

1. A   2. A

6.2 Angles in Standard Position and Arc Length

FOCUS Relate an angle in standard position to the length of the arc that subtends the angle.

Get Started

A tire has an outside diameter of 78 cm. To the nearest centimetre, how far will the tire travel when it rolls forward $2\frac{3}{4}$ turns?

Construct Understanding

A. Angle POB is in standard position with a terminal point on the unit circle.

• Use a proportion to write the length of arc BP as a fraction of the circumference of the circle.

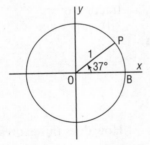

Recall that an arc of a circle *subtends* an angle at the centre of the circle; this is the *central angle*.

• What is the length of arc BP as a fraction of π?

B. Repeat Part A for 3 different angles of your choice.

C. For any angle θ in standard position, what is the length of the arc on the unit circle that subtends angle θ? Give the answer as a fraction of π.

D. For any angle θ in standard position, what is the length of the arc on the circle with radius r that subtends angle θ? Give the answer as a fraction of π.

How does this expression compare with the expression in Part C?

Assess Your Understanding

1. As a fraction of π, determine the length of the arc that subtends each central angle in the unit circle.

   a) 180°

   b) 135°

   c) 150°

   d) −45°

2. As a fraction of π, determine the length of the arc that subtends each central angle in a circle with radius r. Include a labelled sketch of the arc on the circle.

   a) 90°; $r = 6$ units

   b) 240°; $r = 5$ units

   c) 300°; $r = 3$ units

   d) −160°; $r = 4$ units

3. A bicycle wheel has radius 30 cm. Suppose a positive angle of rotation corresponds to the wheel moving forward. Determine the distance and the direction the wheel will roll when it turns through each angle. Express the exact distance in terms of π.

a) 30° b) 60°

c) 315° d) −225°

4. A winch has diameter 10 cm. As the winch rotates, it pulls in a cable. Exactly how much cable is pulled in when the winch turns through each angle?

a) 720° b) 480°

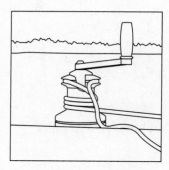

c) 432° d) 2000°

ANSWERS

1. a) π b) $\frac{3}{4}\pi$ c) $\frac{5}{6}\pi$ d) $\frac{1}{4}\pi$ 2. a) 3π b) $\frac{20}{3}\pi$ c) 5π d) $\frac{32}{9}\pi$

3. a) 5π cm forward b) 10π cm forward c) 52.5π cm forward

d) 37.5π cm backward 4. a) 20π cm b) $\frac{40}{3}\pi$ cm c) 12π cm d) $\frac{500}{9}\pi$ cm

6.3 Radian Measure

Develop the relationship between the degree and radian measures of angles.

Get Started

A unicycle wheel has diameter 70 cm. The wheel rolls forward 15 m. Approximately how many revolutions does the wheel make? To the nearest degree, through which angle does the wheel turn?

Construct Understanding

The diagram shows a circle, radius 4 units, and terminal points for some angles in standard position.
Use the diagram to complete the table on the next page.
When you know the measure of a central angle, how can you determine the length of the arc that subtends that angle?

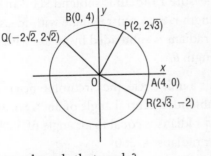

Angle	Angle measure (degrees)	Length of arc that subtends the angle (as a fraction of π)
∠BOA		
∠POA		
∠QOA		
Reflex ∠ROA		

Consider an angle of 108° in standard position in a unit circle.
The angle is determined by its degree measure of 108° and by the length of the arc, PB, that subtends the angle. The arc length is proportional to the circumference:

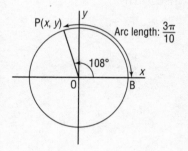

Arc length: $\frac{3\pi}{10}$

$$\frac{\text{arc PB}}{\text{circumference}} = \frac{108°}{360°}$$

So, arc PB $= \frac{108°}{360°}(2\pi)$

$$= \frac{3\pi}{5}$$

Another unit for measuring angles is the *radian*. In a circle with radius r, a central angle with measure **1 radian** is subtended by an arc with length r. So, a central angle with measure θ radians is subtended by an arc with length θr.

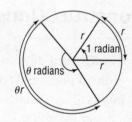

For a unit circle, the circumference is 2π and it subtends a central angle of 360°. So, an angle of 2π radians is equal to an angle of 360°.

2π radians $= 360°$

So, 1 radian $= \dfrac{360°}{2\pi}$

$$= \frac{180°}{\pi}$$

$$\doteq 57°$$

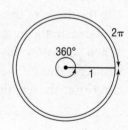

And, $1° = \dfrac{\pi}{180}$ radians

Radian Measure

In a circle with radius r:

- A central angle of 1 radian is subtended by an arc with length r.
- A central angle of θ radians is subtended by an arc with length θr; conversely, the length of an arc, a, that subtends a central angle of θ radians is: $a = \theta r$

$$1 \text{ radian} = \frac{180°}{\pi} \qquad 1° = \frac{\pi}{180} \text{ radians}$$

$$\pi \text{ radians} = 180° \qquad 360° = 2\pi \text{ radians}$$

Example 1 — Converting between Degree and Radian Measures

a) Given $\theta = 255°$, determine its measure in radians. Give the exact measure and its approximate value to the nearest hundredth.

b) Given $\theta = -\dfrac{5\pi}{7}$ radians
   i) Sketch the angle in standard position.
   ii) Determine its measure to the nearest tenth of a degree.

c) Given $\theta = -8.25$ radians, determine its measure to the nearest tenth of a degree.

SOLUTION

a) Since $1° = \dfrac{\pi}{180}$ radians

   Then, $255° = 255\left(\dfrac{\pi}{180}\right)$ radians, or $\dfrac{17}{12}\pi$ radians

   $$= 4.4505\ldots \text{ radians}$$

   An angle of $255°$ is equal to $\dfrac{17}{12}\pi$ radians, or approximately 4.45 radians.

b) i) Estimate $\dfrac{5}{7}$ of $-\pi$, then draw a terminal arm and label the angle.

   ii) Since π radians $= 180°$

   Then, $-\dfrac{5\pi}{7}$ radians $= \dfrac{5}{7}(-180°)$

   $$= -128.5714\ldots°$$

   An angle of $-\dfrac{5\pi}{7}$ radians is approximately $-128.6°$.

c) Since 1 radian $= \dfrac{180°}{\pi}$

   Then, -8.25 radians $= (-8.25)\left(\dfrac{180°}{\pi}\right)$

   $$= -472.6901\ldots°$$

   An angle of -8.25 radians is approximately $-472.7°$.

Check Your Understanding

1. a) Given $\theta = 170°$, determine its measure in radians. Give the exact measure and its approximate value to the nearest hundredth.

   b) Given $\theta = -\dfrac{12\pi}{11}$ radians
      i) Sketch the angle in standard position.
      ii) Determine its measure to the nearest tenth of a degree.

   c) Given $\theta = 7.5$ radians, determine its measure to the nearest tenth of a degree.

Coterminal angles do not depend on the units used to measure them; so, for example, the measures of angles coterminal with $\dfrac{2\pi}{3}$ radians are obtained by rotating the terminal arm of that angle:

counterclockwise through multiples of 2π to form:

$$\dfrac{2\pi}{3} + 2\pi = \dfrac{2\pi}{3} + \dfrac{6\pi}{3}, \text{ or } \dfrac{8\pi}{3}$$

$$\dfrac{2\pi}{3} + 4\pi = \dfrac{2\pi}{3} + \dfrac{12\pi}{3}, \text{ or } \dfrac{14\pi}{3},$$

and so on

or clockwise through multiples of 2π to form:

$$\dfrac{2\pi}{3} - 2\pi = \dfrac{2\pi}{3} - \dfrac{6\pi}{3}, \text{ or } -\dfrac{4\pi}{3}$$

$$\dfrac{2\pi}{3} - 4\pi = \dfrac{2\pi}{3} - \dfrac{12\pi}{3}, \text{ or } -\dfrac{10\pi}{3},$$

and so on

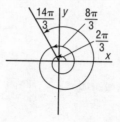
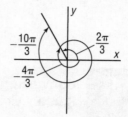

When θ is measured in radians, the general form of a coterminal angle is: $(\theta + 2\pi k)$ radians, $k \in \mathbb{Z}$

This diagram shows the exact coordinates of points on the unit circle that lie on the terminal arms of certain angles in standard position, measured in degrees or radians.

THINK FURTHER

What is the minimum information you need to memorize to be able to reconstruct this diagram?

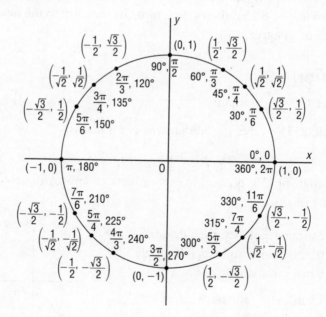

The trigonometric ratios for an angle of θ radians, outside the domain $0 \le \theta \le 2\pi$, are the same as those of the trigonometric ratios for the coterminal angle within that domain. To determine a trigonometric ratio for an angle in radians, first set the scientific or graphing calculator to RADIAN mode.

When an angle is written in terms of π or as a decimal, it is assumed to be measured in radians and the unit is not usually given.

Example 2 | **Determining the Trigonometric Ratios of Angles in Radians**

a) Determine the exact value of $\tan\left(-\dfrac{7\pi}{3}\right)$.

b) Determine the value of $\csc\dfrac{2\pi}{7}$ to the nearest hundredth.

2. a) Determine the exact value of $\sin\left(-\dfrac{13\pi}{6}\right)$.

b) Determine the value of $\cot\dfrac{12\pi}{5}$ to the nearest hundredth.

SOLUTION

a) Sketch $-\dfrac{7\pi}{3}$ on a unit circle.

$-\dfrac{6\pi}{3}$, which equals -2π, is coterminal with 0.

So, $-\dfrac{7\pi}{3}$, which equals $-\dfrac{6\pi}{3} - \dfrac{\pi}{3}$, is coterminal with $-\dfrac{\pi}{3}$ and $\dfrac{5\pi}{3}$.

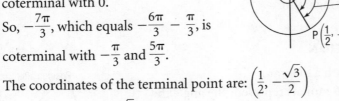

The coordinates of the terminal point are: $\left(\dfrac{1}{2}, -\dfrac{\sqrt{3}}{2}\right)$

So, $\tan\left(-\dfrac{7\pi}{3}\right) = \dfrac{-\dfrac{\sqrt{3}}{2}}{\dfrac{1}{2}}$

$= -\sqrt{3}$

b) To determine $\csc\dfrac{2\pi}{7}$, set the calculator to RADIAN mode.

$\csc\dfrac{2\pi}{7} = \dfrac{1}{\sin\dfrac{2\pi}{7}}$

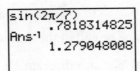

$= 1.2790\ldots$

$\doteq 1.28$

THINK FURTHER

In *Example 2a*, what other strategy could you use to determine the exact value of $\tan\left(-\dfrac{7\pi}{3}\right)$?

Example 3

3. An approximate model of the motion of the international space station is that it travels at a speed of 27 600 km/h in a circular orbit at an altitude of 400 km. The radius of Earth is approximately 6400 km.

a) Visualize a line segment joining the space station to the centre of Earth. To the nearest tenth of a radian, through which angle will the segment have rotated after 40 min?

b) To the nearest 100 km, what is the straight-line distance between the initial and final positions of the space station?

A centre-pivot irrigation system traces out a circular path as it irrigates farm fields. One system has an arm 36 m long. The speed of the end of the arm is 3 m/min.

a) In radians, through which angle will the arm have rotated after 30 min?

b) To the nearest metre, how far will the end of the arm be from its starting point?

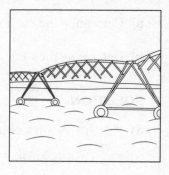

SOLUTION

a) Sketch a diagram.
Let θ radians represent the angle the arm has rotated through after 30 min.
At 3 m/min, the arc length will be:
$30(3 \text{ m}) = 90 \text{ m}$
Use: $a = r\theta$ Substitute: $a = 90, r = 36$
$\qquad 90 = 36\theta$
$\qquad \theta = \dfrac{90}{36}$, or 2.5 radians

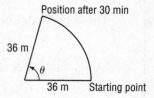

Position after 30 min

The end of the arm will have rotated through 2.5 radians.

b) Sketch a diagram.
The distance between the end of the arm and its starting point is the length of line segment TS.
Use the Cosine Law in $\triangle$TCS.
$c^2 = t^2 + s^2 - 2ts \cos C$
$c = \sqrt{t^2 + s^2 - 2ts \cos C}$
Substitute: $t = 36, s = 36, \angle C = 2.5$
Set the calculator to RADIAN mode.
$c = \sqrt{36^2 + 36^2 - 2(36)(36) \cos 2.5}$
$c = 68.3268\ldots$
After 30 min, the end of the arm will be approximately 68 m from its starting point.

Example 4 — Determining Angle Measures Given a Terminal Point

Check Your Understanding

a) $P(-9, -5)$ is a terminal point of angle θ in standard position. To the nearest tenth of a radian, determine possible values of θ in the domain $-2\pi \le \theta \le 2\pi$.

b) Given $\sec \theta = 2.5$; to the nearest tenth of a radian, determine the values of θ in the domain $-2\pi \le \theta \le 2\pi$.

SOLUTION

a) Sketch a diagram.

$$\tan \theta = \frac{y}{x}$$

$$= \frac{-5}{-9}, \text{ or } \frac{5}{9}$$

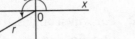

The terminal arm of angle θ lies in Quadrant 3.

The reference angle is:

$$\tan^{-1}\left(\frac{5}{9}\right) = 0.5070\ldots$$

So, $\theta = \pi + 0.5070\ldots$

$ = 3.6486\ldots$

The angle between -2π and 0 that is coterminal with $3.6486\ldots$ is:

$-2\pi + 3.6486\ldots = -2.6344\ldots$

Possible values of θ are approximately: 3.6 and -2.6

b) $\sec \theta = 2.5$, so $\cos \theta = \frac{1}{2.5}$, or $\frac{2}{5}$

The cosine ratio is positive in Quadrants 1 and 4.

In Quadrant 1, $\theta = \cos^{-1}\left(\frac{2}{5}\right)$

$ = 1.1592\ldots$

In Quadrant 4, $\theta = 2\pi - 1.1592\ldots$

$ = 5.1239\ldots$

Sketch a diagram.

The angles between -2π and 0 that are coterminal with the angles above are: $-1.1592\ldots$ and $-5.1239\ldots$

Possible values of θ are approximately: 1.2, 5.1, -1.2, and -5.1

4. a) $P(-4, 3)$ is a terminal point of angle θ in standard position. To the nearest tenth of a radian, determine possible values of θ in the domain $-2\pi \le \theta \le 2\pi$.

b) Given $\cot \theta = -2$; to the nearest tenth of a radian, determine the values of θ in the domain $-2\pi \le \theta \le 2\pi$.

Discuss the Ideas

1. What is a radian?

2. How can you determine the length of the arc that subtends an angle of θ radians at the centre of a circle with radius r?

3. For which angles, measured in radians, can you determine the exact or undefined values of the 6 trigonometric ratios? How can you determine these values?

Exercises

A

4. Sketch each angle in standard position.

a) $\dfrac{\pi}{4}$ b) $\dfrac{\pi}{2}$

c) $\dfrac{5\pi}{3}$ d) $\dfrac{3\pi}{4}$

e) $-\dfrac{\pi}{6}$ f) $-\dfrac{3\pi}{4}$

5. a) Convert each angle to radians.

i) $60°$ ii) $720°$ iii) $-450°$

b) Convert each angle to degrees. Give the answer to the nearest degree where necessary.

   i) 7π **ii)** 5 **iii)** $-\dfrac{5\pi}{6}$

6. Determine the value of each trigonometric ratio to the nearest hundredth.

   a) $\cos \dfrac{\pi}{10}$ **b)** $\sin 2.5$ **c)** $\cot\left(-\dfrac{3\pi}{5}\right)$

B

7. Sketch each angle in radians in standard position.

   a) 1 **b)** 2.4

   c) -4 **d)** -7.5

8. Determine the length of the arc that subtends each central angle in a circle with each radius. Give the answers to the nearest tenth where necessary.

   a) 3; radius 4 cm   **b)** 1; radius 5 cm

c) $\frac{\pi}{4}$; radius 6.5 cm   **d)** $\frac{3\pi}{2}$; radius 2.5 cm

9. An arc with length 2 cm is marked on the circumference of a circle with radius 3 cm.

   a) To the nearest tenth of a radian, determine the measure of the central angle subtended by the arc.

   b) The area of the sector of a circle is proportional to the central angle. Determine the area of the sector of the circle formed by the arc and the radii that intersect the endpoints of the arc.

10. A wheel with diameter 35 cm is rotating at 20 revolutions per minute.

   a) What is the speed of the rotating wheel in radians per second? This is the *angular velocity* of the wheel.

   b) Suppose the wheel travels in a straight line. To the nearest centimetre, how far will it travel in 50 s?

11. For each angle in standard position below:

    i) Determine the measures of angles that are coterminal with the angle in the given domain. Give the angles to the nearest tenth where necessary.

    ii) Write an expression for the measures of all possible angles that are coterminal with the angle.

a) $\frac{\pi}{3}$; for $-2\pi \leq \theta \leq 2\pi$ **b)** $\frac{2\pi}{5}$; for $-2\pi \leq \theta \leq 2\pi$

c) 5; for $-2\pi \leq \theta \leq 2\pi$ **d)** -2; for $-2\pi \leq \theta \leq 2\pi$

e) $-\frac{7\pi}{6}$; for $-4\pi \leq \theta \leq 4\pi$

f) -8; for $-4\pi \leq \theta \leq 4\pi$

12. Return to Lesson 6.1, question 6, page 476. In the first column, write the equivalent angles in radians.

    a) Use the completed table to determine the exact value of each trigonometric ratio.

        i) $\sin \frac{\pi}{4}$ **ii)** $\cos \frac{\pi}{6}$ **iii)** $\tan \frac{5\pi}{3}$ **iv)** $\sec \frac{\pi}{3}$

b) Determine the exact value of each trigonometric ratio.

    i) $\csc 3\pi$ **ii)** $\cot\left(-\dfrac{5\pi}{6}\right)$

    iii) $\cos\left(-\dfrac{7\pi}{3}\right)$ **iv)** $\sin\dfrac{11\pi}{4}$

c) Describe the strategy you used to complete part b.

13. For each point $P(x, y)$ on the terminal arm of an angle θ in standard position
    i) Determine the exact values of the 6 trigonometric ratios for θ.
    ii) To the nearest tenth of a radian, determine possible values of θ
        in the domain $-2\pi \le \theta \le 2\pi$.
  a) $P(1, -2)$ **b)** $P(-3, 2)$

14. For each trigonometric ratio

    i) Determine the exact values of the other 5 trigonometric ratios for θ in the given domain.

    ii) To the nearest tenth of a radian, determine possible values of θ in the domain $-2\pi \leq \theta \leq 2\pi$.

    a) $\cos \theta = \frac{2}{3}$; for $0 \leq \theta \leq \pi$ **b)** $\cot \theta = \frac{3}{5}$; for $\pi \leq \theta \leq 2\pi$

15. Earth completes one orbit of the sun in 1 year. The orbit approximates a circle with radius 150 million kilometres.

   a) To the nearest hundred thousand kilometres, what is the length of the arc along Earth's orbit after 30 days?

   b) To the nearest hundred thousand kilometres, what is the straight-line distance between the ends of this arc?

C

16. Points on the circumferences of these circles move at the same speed. When the smaller circle rotates through 1.4 radians, the larger circle rotates through 0.9 radians. The radius of the smaller circle is 10 cm. What is the radius of the larger circle, to the nearest tenth of a centimetre?

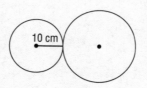

17. Determine the exact area of the shaded region in this circle, centre O.

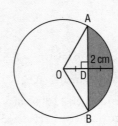

Multiple-Choice Questions

1. Which angle is not coterminal with an angle of $\frac{7\pi}{4}$ in standard position?

A. $-\frac{7\pi}{4}$ **B.** $-\frac{\pi}{4}$ **C.** $\frac{15\pi}{4}$ **D.** $-\frac{9\pi}{4}$

2. A circle has diameter 10 cm. An arc on the circle is 8 cm long. Which central angle does the arc subtend?

A. 0.625   **B.** 0.8   **C.** 1.25   **D.** 1.6

Study Note

Explain how the degree measure and radian measure of an angle are related.

ANSWERS

Check Your Understanding

1. a) $\frac{17}{18}\pi$ radians $\doteq 2.97$ radians **b) ii)** approximately $-196.4°$

c) approximately $430.0°$ **2. a)** $-\frac{1}{2}$ **b)** approximately 0.32

3. a) approximately 2.7 radians **b)** approximately $13\,300$ km

4. a) approximately: $2.5, -3.8$ **b)** approximately: $2.7, 5.8, -3.6, -0.5$

Exercises

5. a) i) $\frac{\pi}{3}$ **ii)** 4π **iii)** $-\frac{5\pi}{2}$ **b) i)** $1260°$ **ii)** approximately $286°$ **iii)** $-150°$

6. a) approximately 0.95 **b)** approximately 0.60 **c)** approximately 0.32

8. a) 12 cm **b)** 5 cm **c)** approximately 5.1 cm **d)** approximately 11.8 cm

9. a) approximately 0.7 **b)** 3 cm^2 **10. a)** $\frac{2}{3}\pi$ radians/s **b)** approximately 18.33 m

11. a) i) $\frac{\pi}{3}, -\frac{5\pi}{3}$ **ii)** $\frac{\pi}{3} + 2\pi k, k \in \mathbb{Z}$ **b) i)** $\frac{2\pi}{5}, -\frac{8\pi}{5}$ **ii)** $\frac{2\pi}{5} + 2\pi k, k \in \mathbb{Z}$

c) i) 5, approximately -1.3 **ii)** $5 + 2\pi k, k \in \mathbb{Z}$ **d) i)** -2, approximately 4.3

ii) $-2 + 2\pi k, k \in \mathbb{Z}$ **e) i)** $-\frac{7\pi}{6}, -\frac{19\pi}{6}, \frac{5\pi}{6}, \frac{17\pi}{6}$ **ii)** $-\frac{7\pi}{6} + 2\pi k, k \in \mathbb{Z}$

f) i) -8, approximately: $-1.7, 4.6, 10.8$ **ii)** $-8 + 2\pi k, k \in \mathbb{Z}$

12. a) i) $\frac{1}{\sqrt{2}}$ **ii)** $\frac{\sqrt{3}}{2}$ **iii)** $-\sqrt{3}$ **iv)** 2 **b) i)** undefined **ii)** $\sqrt{3}$ **iii)** $\frac{1}{2}$ **iv)** $\frac{1}{\sqrt{2}}$

13. a) i) $\sin\theta = -\frac{2}{\sqrt{5}}$, $\csc\theta = -\frac{\sqrt{5}}{2}$, $\cos\theta = \frac{1}{\sqrt{5}}$, $\sec\theta = \sqrt{5}$, $\tan\theta = -2$, $\cot\theta = -\frac{1}{2}$

ii) approximately: $5.2, -1.1$ **b) i)** $\sin\theta = \frac{2}{\sqrt{13}}$, $\csc\theta = \frac{\sqrt{13}}{2}$, $\cos\theta = -\frac{3}{\sqrt{13}}$,

$\sec\theta = -\frac{\sqrt{13}}{3}$, $\tan\theta = -\frac{2}{3}$, $\cot\theta = -\frac{3}{2}$ **ii)** approximately: $2.6, -3.7$

14. a) i) $\sec\theta = \frac{3}{2}$, $\sin\theta = \frac{\sqrt{5}}{3}$, $\csc\theta = \frac{3}{\sqrt{5}}$, $\tan\theta = \frac{\sqrt{5}}{2}$, $\cot\theta = \frac{2}{\sqrt{5}}$

ii) approximately: $0.8, -5.4$ **b) i)** $\tan\theta = \frac{5}{3}$, $\sin\theta = -\frac{5}{\sqrt{34}}$, $\csc\theta = -\frac{\sqrt{34}}{5}$,

$\cos\theta = -\frac{3}{\sqrt{34}}$, $\sec\theta = -\frac{\sqrt{34}}{3}$ **ii)** approximately: $4.2, -2.1$

15. a) approximately $77\,500\,000$ km **b)** approximately $76\,600\,000$ km

16. approximately 15.6 cm **17.** $\left(\frac{16\pi}{3} - 4\sqrt{3}\right)$ cm^2

Multiple Choice

1. A **2.** D

Self-Assess

Can you. . .	Try *Checkpoint* question	For review, see
sketch a positive or negative angle in standard position?	1, 7	Page 468 in Lesson 6.1
determine the measures of all angles in a given domain that are coterminal with a given angle in standard position; and determine the general form of the measures?	1, 7	Page 469 in Lesson 6.1 (Example 1)
determine the exact value of a trigonometric ratio for a multiple of 0°, 30°, 45°, or 60°; or for a multiple of 0, $\frac{\pi}{6}$, $\frac{\pi}{4}$, or $\frac{\pi}{3}$ radians?	2, 9	Page 471 in Lesson 6.1 (Example 2)
determine the exact values of the six trigonometric ratios for an angle, given the coordinates of a point on the terminal arm of the angle in standard position?	10	Page 472 in Lesson 6.1 (Example 3)
determine the possible measures of an angle in a specified domain, given a point on the terminal arm of the angle in standard position?	3	Page 493 in Lesson 6.3 (Example 4)
determine the exact values of the other trigonometric ratios for an angle, given the value of one trigonometric ratio in a specified domain?	4	Page 473 in Lesson 6.1 (Example 4)
determine the possible measures of an angle in a specified domain, given the value of a trigonometric ratio for the angle?	4	Page 493 in Lesson 6.3 (Example 4)
convert between the degree and radian measures of an angle?	11	Page 489 in Lesson 6.3 (Example 1)
solve problems that involve an arc of a circle subtending a central angle in radians?	12	Page 492 in Lesson 6.3 (Example 3)

Assess Your Understanding

6.1

1. a) Sketch each angle θ in standard position.

i) $\theta = -405°$ **ii)** $\theta = 760°$

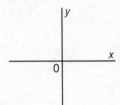 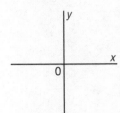

b) For each angle θ in part a

- Determine the measures of angles that are coterminal with θ in the domain $-800° \leq \theta \leq 800°$.

- Write an expression for all angles that are coterminal with θ.

2. Determine the exact value of each trigonometric ratio.

a) $\cos 30°$ **b)** $\tan(-60°)$ **c)** $\csc 90°$

d) $\sin(-300°)$ **e)** $\sec 225°$ **f)** $\cot 495°$

3. P$(2, -3)$ is a terminal point of angle θ in standard position. To the nearest degree, determine possible values of θ in the domain $-360° \leq \theta \leq 360°$.

4. Given $\cos \theta = \dfrac{1}{3}$

  a) Determine the exact values of the other trigonometric ratios for $180° \leq \theta \leq 360°$.

  b) To the nearest degree, determine all possible values of θ in the domain $-360° \leq \theta \leq 360°$.

5. Multiple Choice Point P$(-2, -1)$ lies on the terminal arm of angle θ in standard position. Which statement is correct?

  A. $\tan \theta = \dfrac{1}{2}$

  B. $\sin \theta = -\dfrac{2}{\sqrt{5}}$

  C. $\cos \theta = -\dfrac{1}{\sqrt{5}}$

  D. $\csc \theta = \dfrac{\sqrt{5}}{2}$

6. In terms of π, determine the length of the arc that subtends a central angle of 240° in a circle with radius 9 cm.

7. a) Sketch each angle θ in standard position.

   i) $\theta = -3\pi$ ii) $\theta = \dfrac{13\pi}{6}$

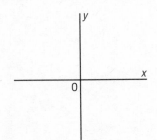   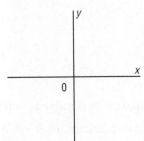

   b) For each angle θ in part a

   • Determine the measures of angles that are coterminal with θ in the domain $-4\pi \leq \theta \leq 4\pi$.

   • Write an expression for all angles that are coterminal with θ.

8. **Multiple Choice** For which pair of values of θ is $\sin \theta = -\cos \theta$?

   A. $\theta = \dfrac{\pi}{4}$ and $\theta = \dfrac{3\pi}{4}$ B. $\theta = \dfrac{3\pi}{4}$ and $\theta = \dfrac{5\pi}{4}$

   C. $\theta = \dfrac{5\pi}{4}$ and $\theta = \dfrac{7\pi}{4}$ D. $\theta = \dfrac{3\pi}{4}$ and $\theta = \dfrac{7\pi}{4}$

9. Determine the exact value of each trigonometric ratio.

a) $\tan \dfrac{\pi}{4}$

b) $\csc \left(-\dfrac{\pi}{6}\right)$

c) $\sin \dfrac{11\pi}{3}$

d) $\sec \left(-\dfrac{8\pi}{3}\right)$

e) $\cot \dfrac{13\pi}{6}$

f) $\cos \left(-\dfrac{11\pi}{4}\right)$

10. $P(-5, -2)$ is a terminal point of angle θ in standard position.

a) State the exact values of all trigonometric ratios for θ.

b) To the nearest tenth of a radian, determine all possible values of θ in the domain $-2\pi \le \theta \le 2\pi$.

11. a) Convert each angle to radians.

    i) $450°$ **ii)** $-115°$

   b) Convert each angle to degrees. Give the exact answer where possible. Write the answer to the nearest degree where necessary.

    i) $\dfrac{7\pi}{4}$ **ii)** $-\dfrac{4\pi}{7}$

12. An arc of length 4.5 cm is marked on the circumference of a circle with radius 10.0 cm. What is the area of the sector of the circle formed by the arc and the radii that join the centre of the circle to the endpoints of the arc?

ANSWERS

1. b) i) $-765°, -405°, -45°, 315°, 675°; -405° + k360°, k \in \mathbb{Z}$
ii) $760°, 400°, 40°, -320°, -680°; 760° + k360°, k \in \mathbb{Z}$

2. a) $\dfrac{\sqrt{3}}{2}$ **b)** $-\sqrt{3}$ **c)** 1 **d)** $\dfrac{\sqrt{3}}{2}$ **e)** $-\sqrt{2}$ **f)** -1 **3.** $-56°, 304°$

4. a) $\sec\theta = 3, \sin\theta = -\dfrac{\sqrt{8}}{3}, \csc\theta = -\dfrac{3}{\sqrt{8}}, \tan\theta = -\sqrt{8}, \cot\theta = -\dfrac{1}{\sqrt{8}}$

b) approximately: $-71°, 289°$ **5.** A   **6.** 12π cm

7. b) i) $\pm\pi, \pm3\pi; -3\pi + 2\pi k, k \in \mathbb{Z}$ **ii)** $\dfrac{13\pi}{6}, \dfrac{\pi}{6}, -\dfrac{11\pi}{6}, -\dfrac{23\pi}{6}; \dfrac{13\pi}{6} + 2\pi k, k \in \mathbb{Z}$

8. D   **9. a)** 1 **b)** -2 **c)** $-\dfrac{\sqrt{3}}{2}$ **d)** -2 **e)** $\sqrt{3}$ **f)** $-\dfrac{1}{\sqrt{2}}$

10. a) $\sin\theta = -\dfrac{2}{\sqrt{29}}, \csc\theta = -\dfrac{\sqrt{29}}{2}, \cos\theta = -\dfrac{5}{\sqrt{29}}, \sec\theta = -\dfrac{\sqrt{29}}{5}, \tan\theta = \dfrac{2}{5},$

$\cot\theta = \dfrac{5}{2}$ **b)** approximately: $3.5, -2.7$ **11. a) i)** $\dfrac{5\pi}{2}$ **ii)** $-\dfrac{23\pi}{36}$ **b) i)** $315°$

ii) approximately $-103°$ **12.** 22.5 cm^2

6.4 Graphing Trigonometric Functions

FOCUS Sketch the graphs of $y = \sin x$, $y = \cos x$, and $y = \tan x$ and determine their characteristics.

Get Started

For the function $y = \dfrac{x - 2}{x + 1}$, identify:

the equations of the asymptotes;
the domain; the range; and the intercepts

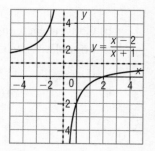

Construct Understanding

A. Complete the tables below, then sketch a graph of $y = \sin x$ for $0 \leq x \leq 2\pi$.

Identify: the domain; the range; and the intercepts of the graph.

x	0	$\dfrac{\pi}{6}$	$\dfrac{\pi}{4}$	$\dfrac{\pi}{3}$	$\dfrac{\pi}{2}$	$\dfrac{2\pi}{3}$	$\dfrac{3\pi}{4}$	$\dfrac{5\pi}{6}$	π
$\sin x$									

x	$\dfrac{7\pi}{6}$	$\dfrac{5\pi}{4}$	$\dfrac{4\pi}{3}$	$\dfrac{3\pi}{2}$	$\dfrac{5\pi}{3}$	$\dfrac{7\pi}{4}$	$\dfrac{11\pi}{6}$	2π
$\sin x$								

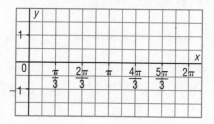

B. Repeat Part A for $y = \cos x$.

x	0	$\frac{\pi}{6}$	$\frac{\pi}{4}$	$\frac{\pi}{3}$	$\frac{\pi}{2}$	$\frac{2\pi}{3}$	$\frac{3\pi}{4}$	$\frac{5\pi}{6}$	π
cos x									

x	$\frac{7\pi}{6}$	$\frac{5\pi}{4}$	$\frac{4\pi}{3}$	$\frac{3\pi}{2}$	$\frac{5\pi}{3}$	$\frac{7\pi}{4}$	$\frac{11\pi}{6}$	2π
cos x								

THINK FURTHER

Suppose you were to graph the reciprocal trigonometric ratios $y = \csc \theta$, $y = \sec \theta$, $y = \cot \theta$. Would the graphs have vertical asymptotes? If so, where?

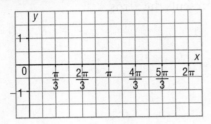

C. Repeat Part A for $y = \tan x$.
Identify the equations of the asymptotes.

x	0	$\frac{\pi}{6}$	$\frac{\pi}{4}$	$\frac{\pi}{3}$	$\frac{\pi}{2}$	$\frac{2\pi}{3}$	$\frac{3\pi}{4}$	$\frac{5\pi}{6}$	π
tan x									

x	$\frac{7\pi}{6}$	$\frac{5\pi}{4}$	$\frac{4\pi}{3}$	$\frac{3\pi}{2}$	$\frac{5\pi}{3}$	$\frac{7\pi}{4}$	$\frac{11\pi}{6}$	2π
tan x								

D. Explain how to extend each graph for $x > 2\pi$ and for $x < 0$.

6.4 Math Lab: Graphing Trigonometric Functions |

Assess Your Understanding

Use graphing technology.

1. Explain why each of $y = \sin x$, $y = \cos x$, and $y = \tan x$ is a function.

2. Graph $y = \sin x$ for $-4\pi \leq x \leq 4\pi$.
Identify the domain, range, and zeros of the graph.
Write a general expression that represents the zeros.

3. Repeat question 2 for $y = \cos x$ for $-4\pi \leq x \leq 4\pi$.

4. Repeat question 2 for $y = \tan x$ for $-4\pi \leq x \leq 4\pi$.
Identify the equations of the asymptotes and write a general expression that represents them.

ANSWERS

2. $-4\pi \leq x \leq 4\pi$; $-1 \leq y \leq 1$; $\pm 4\pi, \pm 3\pi, \pm 2\pi, \pm \pi, 0$; $k\pi, k \in \mathbb{Z}$

3. $-4\pi \leq x \leq 4\pi$; $-1 \leq y \leq 1$; $\pm\dfrac{7\pi}{2}, \pm\dfrac{5\pi}{2}, \pm\dfrac{3\pi}{2}, \pm\dfrac{\pi}{2}$; $(2k + 1)\dfrac{\pi}{2}, k \in \mathbb{Z}$

4. $x \neq \pm\dfrac{\pi}{2}, x \neq \pm\dfrac{3\pi}{2}, x \neq \pm\dfrac{5\pi}{2}, x \neq \pm\dfrac{7\pi}{2}$; $y \in \mathbb{R}$; $\pm 4\pi, \pm 3\pi, \pm 2\pi, \pm \pi, 0$; $k\pi,$

$k \in \mathbb{Z}$; $x = \pm\dfrac{\pi}{2}, x = \pm\dfrac{3\pi}{2}, x = \pm\dfrac{5\pi}{2}, x = \pm\dfrac{7\pi}{2}$; $x = (2k + 1)\dfrac{\pi}{2}, k \in \mathbb{Z}$

FOCUS Define the trigonometric functions and identify single transformations.

Get Started

This graph shows how the number of hours of daylight in Iqaluit varies throughout the year.

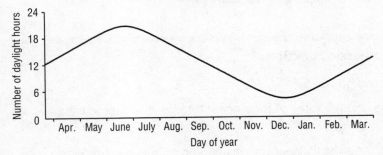

Hours of Daylight per Day for Iqaluit

Approximately how many hours of daylight are there on the longest day of the year?

Approximately how many hours of daylight are there on the shortest day of the year?

Why is it reasonable to expect this pattern to repeat annually?

Construct Understanding

Use graphing technology.
Graph the function $y = a \sin x$ for different integer values of a.
How does the graph of $y = a \sin x$ change as the value of a changes?
What remains the same?

Point P($\cos x$, $\sin x$) lies on the unit circle. OP is the terminal arm of an angle, x radians, in standard position.

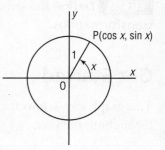

For a central angle in the unit circle, the radian measure of the angle is the length of the arc that subtends the angle, which is a real number. So, radians can be used to define **trigonometric functions** of a real number.

Trigonometric Functions

For any real number x:

- $y = \sin x$ is the value of the sine ratio for an angle measuring x radians

- $y = \cos x$ is the value of the cosine ratio for an angle measuring x radians

- $y = \tan x$ is the value of the tangent ratio for an angle measuring x radians

A function that repeats its values in regular intervals over its domain is a **periodic function**. The length of each interval, or *cycle*, measured along the horizontal axis is called the **period** of the function.

The sine function, $y = \sin x$, is a periodic function with period 2π.

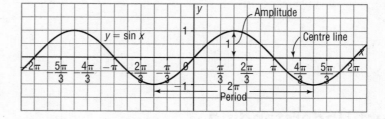

The domain of the sine function is: $x \in \mathbb{R}$

The zeros are: $0, \pm\pi, \pm2\pi, \ldots$; that is, the zeros have the form $k\pi$, $k \in \mathbb{Z}$

The function has a maximum value of 1 and a minimum value of -1. So, the range is: $-1 \leq y \leq 1$

The cosine function, $y = \cos x$, is a periodic function with period 2π.

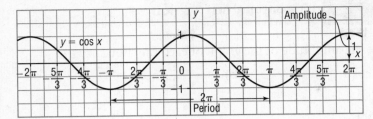

The domain of the cosine function is: $x \in \mathbb{R}$

The zeros are: $\pm\dfrac{\pi}{2}, \pm\dfrac{3\pi}{2}, \ldots$; that is, the zeros have the form $(2k + 1)\dfrac{\pi}{2}, k \in \mathbb{Z}$

The function has a maximum value of 1 and a minimum value of -1. So, the range is: $-1 \le y \le 1$

Functions whose graphs have the same shape as $y = \sin x$ or $y = \cos x$ are **sinusoidal functions**. A sinusoidal function has a maximum value and a minimum value that are equidistant from the *centre line* of the graph; this is the horizontal line that is halfway between the maximum points and the minimum points. The **amplitude** of a sinusoidal function is the distance of a maximum or minimum point from the centre line.

THINK FURTHER

How can you use the position of the centre line and the amplitude to determine the maximum and minimum values of a sinusoidal function and its range?

Transformations can be applied to the graph of a trigonometric function:

- horizontal stretches or compressions
- vertical stretches or compressions
- reflections in horizontal and vertical axes
- horizontal translations
- vertical translations

| Example 1 | Determining the Amplitude of a Trigonometric Function |

Check Your Understanding

1. Determine the amplitude of the graph of each function.

a) $y = \frac{2}{3} \sin x$

b) $y = -4 \cos x$

Determine the amplitude of the graph of each function.

a) $y = 3 \cos x$

b) $y = -\frac{1}{2} \sin x$

SOLUTION

a) The graph of $y = 3 \cos x$ is the image after the graph of $y = \cos x$ has been stretched vertically by a factor of 3.
The amplitude of $y = \cos x$ is 1.
So, the amplitude of $y = 3 \cos x$ is 3.

b) The graph of $y = -\frac{1}{2} \sin x$ is the image after the graph of $y = \sin x$ has been compressed vertically by a factor of $\frac{1}{2}$ and reflected in the x-axis.
The amplitude of $y = \sin x$ is 1.
So, the amplitude of $y = -\frac{1}{2} \sin x$ is $\frac{1}{2}$.

THINK FURTHER

Use the unit circle to explain why the period of the graph of $y = \tan x$ is π.

Graphing technology can be used to verify the amplitudes in *Example 1*.

For part b, $y = -\frac{1}{2} \sin x$:

The y-coordinate of a maximum point is 0.5.

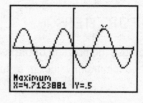

Maximum
X=4.7123881 Y=.5

The tangent function, $y = \tan x$, is a periodic function with period π.

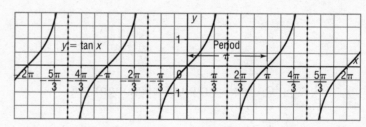

The graph has asymptotes with equations $x = \pm\frac{\pi}{2}, x = \pm\frac{3\pi}{2}, \ldots$; so the domain of the tangent function is: $x \neq \frac{n\pi}{2}$, where n is an odd integer

The zeros are: $0, \pm\pi, \pm2\pi, \ldots$; that is, the zeros have the form $k\pi, k \in \mathbb{Z}$
The function has no maximum or minimum values, so its graph has no amplitude. The range of the function is: $y \in \mathbb{R}$

Example 2	Determining the Period of a Trigonometric Function

Determine the period of each function.

a) $y = \sin 2x$ **b)** $y = \cos \frac{3}{4}x$ **c)** $y = \tan \frac{x}{6}$

SOLUTION

a) The graph of $y = \sin 2x$ is the image after the graph of $y = \sin x$ has been compressed horizontally by a factor of $\frac{1}{2}$.

So, the period of $y = \sin 2x$ is $\frac{1}{2}$ the period of $y = \sin x$.

The period of $y = \sin 2x$ is: $\frac{1}{2}(2\pi) = \pi$

b) The graph of $y = \cos \frac{3}{4}x$ is the image after the graph of $y = \cos x$ has been stretched horizontally by a factor of $\frac{4}{3}$.

So, the period of $y = \cos \frac{3}{4}x$ is $\frac{4}{3}$ the period of $y = \cos x$.

The period of $y = \cos \frac{3}{4}x$ is: $\frac{4}{3}(2\pi) = \frac{8}{3}\pi$

c) The graph of $y = \tan \frac{x}{6}$ is the image after the graph of $y = \tan x$ has been stretched horizontally by a factor of 6.

So, the period of $y = \tan \frac{x}{6}$ is 6 times the period of $y = \tan x$.

The period of $y = \tan \frac{x}{6}$ is: 6π

Graphing technology can be used to check the periods in *Example 2*.

For part c, $y = \tan \frac{x}{6}$:

For the tangent function, adjacent zeros indicate the period.

One zero is 0, the next zero is 6π, as shown.

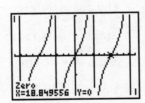

Zero
X=18.849556 Y=0

The results of *Example 2* can be generalized.

Period of a Trigonometric Function

The period of $y = \sin bx$ and $y = \cos bx$ is: $\frac{2\pi}{b}, b > 0$

The period of $y = \tan bx$ is: $\frac{\pi}{b}, b > 0$

Consider the functions $y = \sin x$ and $y = \sin\left(x - \frac{\pi}{3}\right)$.

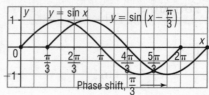

Phase shift, $\frac{\pi}{3}$

The graph of $y = \sin\left(x - \frac{\pi}{3}\right)$ is congruent to the graph of $y = \sin x$, but it has been translated $\frac{\pi}{3}$ units right.

In general, the graph of $y = \sin(x - c)$ is the image after the graph of $y = \sin x$ has been translated c units horizontally; this distance is the **phase shift** of the function.

| **Example 3** | **Determining the Phase Shift of a Trigonometric Function** |

Check Your Understanding

3. a) Determine the phase shift of the function
$y = \cos\left(x - \frac{\pi}{6}\right)$.

b) Sketch graphs of $y = \cos x$ and $y = \cos\left(x - \frac{\pi}{6}\right)$ for $0 \le x \le 2\pi$.

a) Determine the phase shift of the function $y = \tan\left(x + \frac{\pi}{2}\right)$.

b) Sketch graphs of $y = \tan x$ and $y = \tan\left(x + \frac{\pi}{2}\right)$ for $0 \le x \le 2\pi$.

SOLUTION

a) Compare $y = \tan\left(x + \frac{\pi}{2}\right)$

with $\qquad y = \tan(x - c)$

The phase shift is: $-\frac{\pi}{2}$

b) Graph $y = \tan x$, then translate the graph $\frac{\pi}{2}$ units left to obtain the graph of $y = \tan\left(x + \frac{\pi}{2}\right)$.

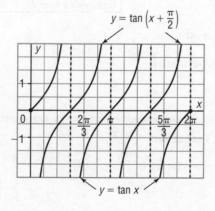

$y = \tan\left(x + \frac{\pi}{2}\right)$

$y = \tan x$

Describe how the graph of each function below relates to the graph of $y = \cos x$. Then, on the same grid, sketch the graphs of $y = \cos x$ and each function below, for $0 \leq x \leq 2\pi$.

a) $y = 2 \cos x$ **b)** $y = \cos 2x$ **c)** $y = \cos x - 2$

4. Describe how the graph of each function below relates to the graph of $y = \sin x$. Then, on the same grid, sketch the graphs of $y = \sin x$ and each function below, for $0 \leq x \leq 2\pi$.

a) $y = 3 \sin x$

b) $y = \sin 3x$

c) $y = \sin x + 3$

SOLUTION

a) The graph of $y = 2 \cos x$ is the image after the graph of $y = \cos x$ has been stretched vertically by a factor of 2.
To graph $y = 2 \cos x$: for points on the graph of $y = \cos x$, multiply each y-coordinate by 2.

b) The graph of $y = \cos 2x$ is the image after the graph of $y = \cos x$ has been compressed horizontally by a factor of $\frac{1}{2}$.

To graph $y = \cos 2x$: for points on the graph of $y = \cos x$, divide each x-coordinate by 2.

c) The graph of $y = \cos x - 2$ is the image after the graph of $y = \cos x$ has been translated 2 units down.
To graph $y = \cos x - 2$, move each point on $y = \cos x$ 2 units down.

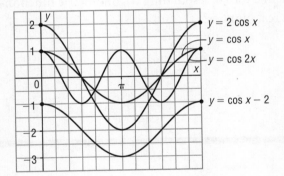

In general:

- The graph of $y = \cos(x - c)$ is the image after the graph of $y = \cos x$ has been translated c units horizontally.

- The graph of $y = a \cos x$ is the image after the graph of $y = \cos x$ has been vertically stretched or compressed by a factor of $|a|$; if $a < 0$, there is also a reflection in the x-axis.

- The graph of $y = \cos bx$ is the image after the graph of $y = \cos x$ has been horizontally stretched or compressed by a factor of $\frac{1}{|b|}$; if $b < 0$, there is also a reflection in the y-axis.

- The graph of $y = \cos x + d$ is the image after the graph of $y = \cos x$ has been translated d units vertically.

Discuss the Ideas

1. What is the essential characteristic of a periodic function?

2. How can the unit circle definitions of the sine and cosine ratios for an angle be used to define the corresponding trigonometric functions of a variable that is a real number?

Exercises

3. Identify the indicated characteristic of each function.

    a) amplitude of $y = 5 \sin x$ **b)** amplitude of $y = 2 \cos x$

    c) period of $y = \sin 10x$ **d)** period of $y = \tan 4x$

    e) phase shift of $y = \sin\left(x - \dfrac{\pi}{7}\right)$ **f)** phase shift of $y = \cos\left(x + \dfrac{\pi}{12}\right)$

4. For each function below, sketch the graph for $-\pi \le x \le \pi$, then identify each characteristic:

    i) amplitude   **ii)** period
    iii) zeros   **iv)** equations of any asymptotes
    v) domain of the function   **vi)** range of the function

    a) $y = \cos x$

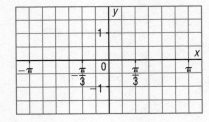

b) $y = \sin x$

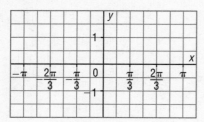

c) $y = \tan x$

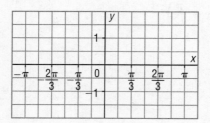

5. Does this graph represent a periodic function? Explain.

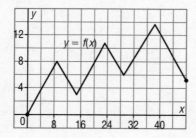

6. Use technology.

a) i) Graph each function.

$$y = 2 \cos x \qquad y = -3 \cos x \qquad y = \frac{1}{3} \cos x$$

ii) How does varying the value of a affect the graph of $y = a \cos x$?

b) i) Graph each function.

$$y = \sin 3x \qquad y = \sin (-4x) \qquad y = \sin \frac{3}{4} x$$

ii) How does varying the value of b affect the graph of $y = \sin bx$?

c) i) Graph each function.

$$y = \cos \left(x - \frac{\pi}{6} \right) \qquad y = \cos \left(x - \frac{\pi}{4} \right) \qquad y = \cos \left(x + \frac{\pi}{3} \right)$$

ii) How does varying the value of c affect the graph of
$y = \cos (x - c)$?

d) i) Graph each function.

$$y = \sin x + 1 \qquad y = \sin x - 2 \qquad y = \sin x + 0.5$$

ii) How does varying the value of d affect the graph of
$y = \sin x + d$?

7. Sketch the graph of each function. Describe your strategy.

a) $y = \cos x + 1$

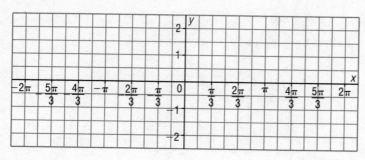

b) $y = \sin 2x$

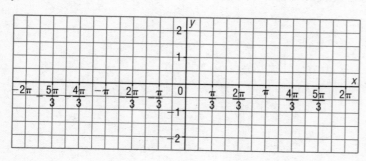

c) $y = \cos\left(x - \dfrac{\pi}{3}\right)$

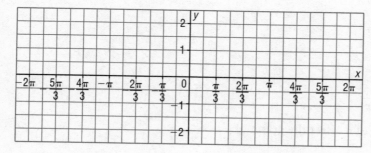

d) $y = 2 \sin x$

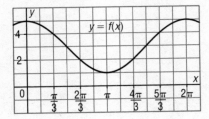

8. Use technology to graph $y = \sin\left(x + \dfrac{\pi}{2}\right)$ and $y = \cos x$.
   Explain the result.

9. A student says that the amplitude of this sinusoidal function is 5.
   Is the student correct? Explain.

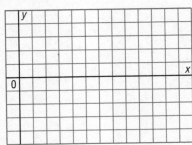

C

10. Sketch the graph of each function. Identify its characteristics.

   a) $y = \csc x$

b) $y = \cot x$

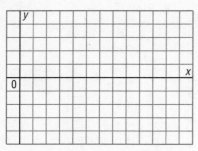

11. Use technology. Graph the function $y = \sin x + \cos x$.
Is it periodic? Explain. Is it sinusoidal? Explain.

Multiple-Choice Questions

1. Which function best describes this graph?

   A. $y = \sin x$

   B. $y = \sin x + 1.5$

   C. $y = 1.5 \sin x$

   D. $y = \sin (x - 1.5)$

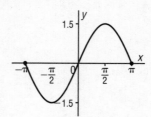

2. Which number is not in the domain of $y = \tan 3x$?

   A. $\dfrac{\pi}{6}$ **B.** $\dfrac{\pi}{4}$ **C.** $\dfrac{\pi}{3}$ **D.** π

Study Note

How are the characteristics of the graph of $y = \sin x$ affected by applying transformations to the graph of the function?

Check Your Understanding

1. a) $\frac{2}{3}$ **b)** 4 **2. a)** $\frac{\pi}{3}$ **b)** $\frac{3\pi}{2}$ **c)** 14π **3. a)** $\frac{\pi}{6}$

Exercises

3. a) 5 **b)** 2 **c)** $\frac{\pi}{5}$ **d)** $\frac{\pi}{4}$ **e)** $\frac{\pi}{7}$ **f)** $-\frac{\pi}{12}$ **4. a) i)** 1 **ii)** 2π **iii)** $\pm\frac{\pi}{2}$

iv) no asymptotes **v)** $x \in \mathbb{R}$ **vi)** $-1 \le y \le 1$ **b) i)** 1 **ii)** 2π **iii)** $0, \pm\pi$

iv) no asymptotes **v)** $x \in \mathbb{R}$ **vi)** $-1 \le y \le 1$ **c) i)** no amplitude. **ii)** π

iii) $0, \pm\pi$ **iv)** $x = \pm\frac{\pi}{2}$ **v)** $x \ne \pm\frac{\pi}{2}$ **vi)** $y \in \mathbb{R}$ **5.** no **9.** no

10. a) no amplitude; period: 2π; no zeros; asymptotes: $x = k\pi, k \in \mathbb{Z}$;
domain: $x \ne k\pi, k \in \mathbb{Z}$; range: $y \ge 1$ or $y \le -1$

b) no amplitude; period: π; zeros: $(2k + 1)\frac{\pi}{2}, k \in \mathbb{Z}$; asymptotes: $x = k\pi, k \in \mathbb{Z}$;

domain: $x \ne k\pi, k \in \mathbb{Z}$; range: $y \in \mathbb{R}$

Multiple Choice

1. C **2.** A

Combining Transformations of Sinusoidal Functions

FOCUS Apply all transformations to graphs of sinusoidal functions.

Get Started

The graph of $y = f(x)$ is shown.

On the same grid, sketch the graph of $y + 3 = \frac{1}{2}f(2(x - 4))$.

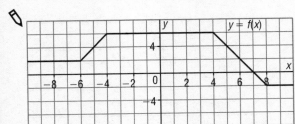

Construct Understanding

The graph of $y = \sin x$ is shown below.

On the same grid, sketch a graph of $y = \sin 2x$.

On the second grid, sketch graphs of:

$y = \frac{1}{2} \sin 2x$ $\qquad$ $y = \frac{1}{2} \sin 2\left(x - \frac{\pi}{4}\right)$

$y = \frac{1}{2} \sin 2\left(x - \frac{\pi}{4}\right) - 3$

Label each image graph with its equation.

Describe how the graph changes with each transformation.

Complete the table below.

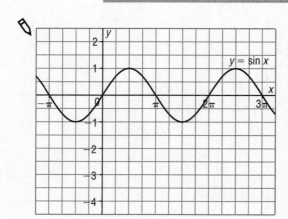
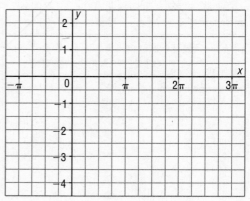

Characteristic	Equation of Function			
	$y = \sin 2x$	$y = \frac{1}{2} \sin 2x$	$y = \frac{1}{2} \sin 2\left(x - \frac{\pi}{4}\right)$	$y = \frac{1}{2} \sin 2\left(x - \frac{\pi}{4}\right) - 3$
Period				
Amplitude				
Domain of function				
Range of function				
Phase shift				
Zeros				

The graph of a function $y = af(b(x - c)) + d$ is the image of the graph of $y = f(x)$ after transformations. The transformations depend on the values of the constants a, b, c, and d.

$y = af(b(x - c)) + d$				
Constant	**a**	**b**	**c**	**d**
Transformation applied to the graph of $y = f(x)$	vertical stretch or compression by a factor of $\lvert a \rvert$; if $a < 0$, there is also a reflection in the x-axis	horizontal stretch or compression by a factor of $\frac{1}{\lvert b \rvert}$; if $b < 0$, there is also a reflection in the y-axis	horizontal translation of c units	vertical translation of d units

In Lesson 6.5, these transformations were applied to the graphs of $y = \sin x$, $y = \cos x$, and $y = \tan x$. The transformations may change the period, the location of the centre line, any zeros, and the amplitude of a sinusoidal function. As a result, the range may also change.

The appearance of the graph of a trigonometric function can be predicted from its equation.

Example 1 | **Using Transformations to Sketch a Graph of a Trigonometric Function**

1. a) Predict how the graph of

$y = \frac{1}{4} \cos 3\left(x + \frac{\pi}{6}\right) + 2$

is related to the graph of $y = \cos x$.

b) Sketch the graph of

$y = \frac{1}{4} \cos 3\left(x + \frac{\pi}{6}\right) + 2$

for $-2\pi \leq x \leq 2\pi$, then list the characteristics of the function.

a) Predict how the graph of $y = 2 \sin \frac{1}{2}\left(x - \frac{\pi}{3}\right) - 1$ is related to the graph of $y = \sin x$.

b) Sketch the graph of $y = 2 \sin \frac{1}{2}\left(x - \frac{\pi}{3}\right) - 1$ for $0 \leq x \leq 4\pi$, then list the characteristics of the function.

SOLUTION

a) The graph of $y = 2 \sin \frac{1}{2}\left(x - \frac{\pi}{3}\right) - 1$ is the image of the graph of $y = \sin x$ after the following transformations have been applied:

- a vertical stretch by a factor of 2
- a horizontal stretch by a factor of 2
- a horizontal translation (phase shift) of $\frac{\pi}{3}$ units right
- a vertical translation of 1 unit down

b) Sketch the graph of $y = \sin x$.

Since the phase shift is $\frac{\pi}{3}$, use a horizontal scale of 1 square represents $\frac{\pi}{3}$.

The horizontal stretch doubles the spacing between the zeros. The phase shift translates these points $\frac{\pi}{3}$ units right, then the vertical shift moves them 1 unit down. Plot these transformed points; they lie on the line $y = -1$, which is the centre line of the image graph. Choose other points on the graph of $y = \sin x$. For each point: double the x-coordinate; double the y-coordinate; shift the point $\frac{\pi}{3}$ units right; then 1 unit down

Plot the points on the grid and join them.

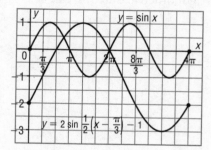

The amplitude is 2; the period is 4π; the phase shift is $\frac{\pi}{3}$; the zeros are $\frac{2\pi}{3}$ and 2π; the domain is $x \in \mathbb{R}$; and the range is $-3 \leq y \leq 1$.

Write an equation for the sinusoidal function graphed below, in terms of sin x.

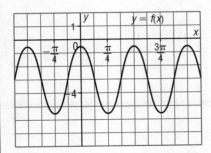

2. Write an equation for the sinusoidal function graphed below, in terms of sin x.

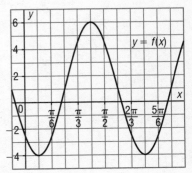

SOLUTION

An equation has the form: $y = a \sin b(x - c) + d$

The equation of the centre line is $y = -3$, so the vertical translation is 3 units down and $d = -3$.

The amplitude is the distance between the centre line and a maximum or minimum point. This distance is: $a = \dfrac{5}{2}$

For the period, choose the x-coordinates of two adjacent minimum

points, such as $-\dfrac{\pi}{4}$ and $\dfrac{\pi}{4}$. The period is: $\dfrac{\pi}{4} - \left(-\dfrac{\pi}{4}\right) = \dfrac{\pi}{2}$

b is: $\dfrac{\text{period of } y = \sin x}{\text{period of given graph}} = \dfrac{2\pi}{\dfrac{\pi}{2}}$, or 4

Draw the line $y = -3$. Look for the closest point on either side of the y-axis where the sine function begins its cycle; that is, where the curve moves up to the right above the line. This point is at $x = -\dfrac{\pi}{8}$ on the given graph, so a possible phase shift is $-\dfrac{\pi}{8}$, and $c = -\dfrac{\pi}{8}$.

An equation is: $y = \dfrac{5}{2} \sin 4\left(x + \dfrac{\pi}{8}\right) - 3$

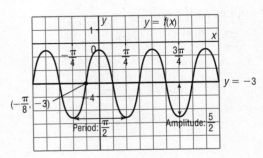

Write an equation in terms of cos *x* for the graph in *Example 2*.

Discuss the Ideas

1. Suppose you are given an equation of the form $y = a \sin b(x - c) + d$. Which characteristics of the graph can you identify?

2. What strategy would you use to sketch the graph of the transformation image of a sinusoidal function?

Exercises

A

3. Identify the transformations that would be applied to the graph of $y = \sin x$ to get the graph of $y = 10 \sin \frac{1}{3}(x - \pi) + 1$.

4. Identify the following characteristics of the graph below: amplitude; period; phase shift; equation of the centre line; zeros; domain; maximum value; minimum value; range

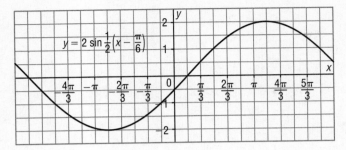

$y = 2 \sin \frac{1}{2}\left(x - \frac{\pi}{6}\right)$

B

5. Use the given data to write an equation for each function.

    a) a sine function with: amplitude 5; period 3π; equation of centre line $y = -2$; and phase shift $\frac{\pi}{3}$

    b) a cosine function with: maximum value 5; minimum value -2; period π; and phase shift $-\frac{\pi}{4}$

6. Determine a possible equation for each function graphed below.

    a)

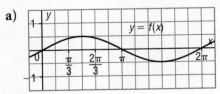

$y = f(x)$

b)

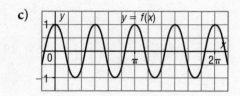

c)

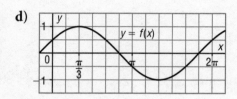

d)

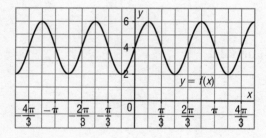

7. a) For the function graphed below, identify the values of a, b, c, and d in $y = a \sin b(x - c) + d$, then write an equation for the function.

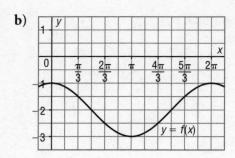

b) For the function graphed below, identify the values of a, b, c, and d in $y = a \cos b(x - c) + d$, then write an equation for the function.

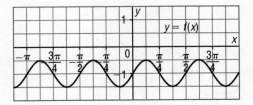

8. a) The graph of $y = \sin x$ is shown below. On the same grid, sketch the graph of $y = 2 \sin 3\left(x - \dfrac{\pi}{2}\right) + 3$. Describe your strategy.

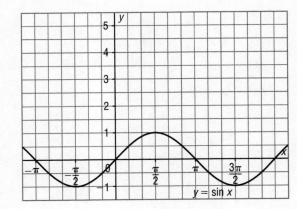

b) List the characteristics of the function $y = 2 \sin 3\left(x - \frac{\pi}{2}\right) + 3$.

9. a) The graph of $y = \cos x$ is shown below. On the same grid, sketch the graph of $y = \cos 4\left(x + \frac{\pi}{3}\right) - 2$. Describe your strategy.

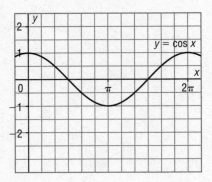

b) List the characteristics of the function $y = \cos 4\left(x + \frac{\pi}{3}\right) - 2$.

10. Sketch the graph of each function for the domain $-2\pi \leq x \leq 2\pi$.

a) $y = 4 \sin \frac{1}{2}\left(x - \frac{\pi}{3}\right) - 3$

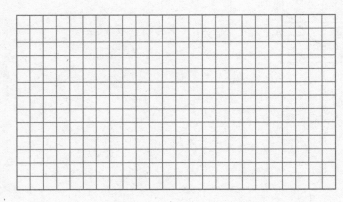

b) $y = \frac{1}{3}\cos 2\left(x + \frac{\pi}{4}\right) + 1$

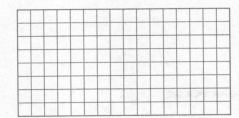

C

11. Use transformations to sketch the graph of $y = -2\sin\left(2x + \frac{\pi}{3}\right) - 2$ for $-2\pi \le x \le 2\pi$.

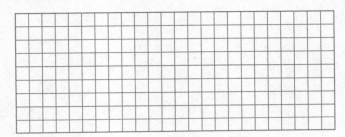

Multiple-Choice Questions

1. Which graph below can be described by $y = \cos 4\left(x + \frac{\pi}{8}\right) + 2$?

A.
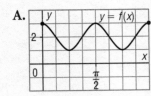

B.
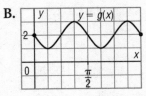

C.
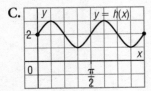

D.
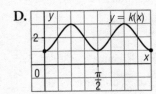

2. What are the phase shift and period respectively of the function

$$y = 3 \sin \frac{1}{2}\left(x + \frac{\pi}{4}\right) + 2?$$

A. $\frac{\pi}{4}, 2\pi$ **B.** $\frac{\pi}{4}, \pi$ **C.** $-\frac{\pi}{4}, 4\pi$ **D.** $-\frac{\pi}{4}, 2\pi$

Study Note

When you are given the graph of a sinusoidal function
$y = af(b(x - c)) + d$, how can you determine the characteristics
of the graph or the function?

ANSWERS

Check Your Understanding

1. b) amplitude: $\frac{1}{4}$; period: $\frac{2\pi}{3}$; phase shift: $-\frac{\pi}{6}$; no zeros; domain: $x \in \mathbb{R}$;
range: $1.75 \leq y \leq 2.25$

Exercises

4. amplitude; 2; period: 4π; phase shift: $\frac{\pi}{6}$; centre line: $y = 0$; zeros: $-\frac{11\pi}{6}, \frac{\pi}{6}$;
domain: $-2\pi \leq x \leq 2\pi$; maximum: 2; minimum: -2; range: $-2 \leq y \leq 2$

5. a) $y = 5 \sin \frac{2}{3}\left(x - \frac{\pi}{3}\right) - 2$ **b)** $y = 3.5 \cos 2 \left(x + \frac{\pi}{4}\right) + 1.5$

8. b) amplitude: 2; period: $\frac{2\pi}{3}$; phase shift: $\frac{\pi}{2}$; domain: $x \in \mathbb{R}$; range: $1 \leq y \leq 5$;
no zeros **9. b)** amplitude: 1; period: $\frac{\pi}{2}$; phase shift: $-\frac{\pi}{3}$ or $\frac{\pi}{6}$; domain: $x \in \mathbb{R}$;
range: $-3 \leq y \leq -1$; no zeros

Multiple Choice

1. B **2.** C

Applications of Sinusoidal Functions

FOCUS Model situations and solve problems using sinusoidal functions.

Get Started

When the last person gets on a Ferris wheel, it begins to rotate. This graph shows the height above the ground of that person, as a function of time.

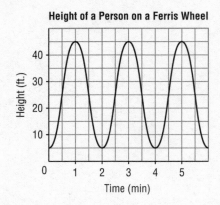

Height of a Person on a Ferris Wheel

How high above the ground is a person when she gets on the Ferris wheel?

What is the radius of the Ferris wheel?

What is the time for one revolution of the wheel?

Construct Understanding

Sketch the graph of $y = 3 \sin \pi(x - 1) + 2$ for $0 \leq x \leq 4$.
Describe your strategy.

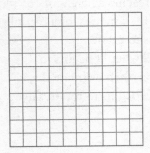

In Lessons 6.4 to 6.6, the scale on the horizontal axis of a sinusoidal graph was in terms of π. When sinusoidal graphs are used in applications, the horizontal axis usually represents time, and the axis is labelled with whole numbers.

Phenomena, such as the oscillation of a mass on a spring or the height of a seat on a rotating Ferris wheel, produce measurements that vary between a maximum value and a minimum value. These phenomena can often be represented by a sinusoidal function. Since the graph of $y = \cos x$ has a maximum point on the y-axis, a cosine function may be used to model the data when the position of the first maximum or minimum is known. Then, the phase shift is the horizontal distance from the vertical axis to this point.

Example 1	Determining a Trigonometric Function that Models a Situation

1. A piston moves vertically in a cylinder starting from its minimum height. Every 20 s, the piston repeats its cycle from a minimum height of 15 cm to a maximum height of 35 cm back to a minimum height of 15 cm.

a) Determine a sinusoidal function that models the height, h centimetres, of the piston at time t seconds after it begins moving.

b) Use technology to graph the function, then estimate the height of the piston 26 s after it begins moving. Give the answer to the nearest centimetre.

The Singapore Flyer is the world's tallest Ferris wheel. People ride the wheel in capsules. The wheel has a diameter of 150 m and completes 1 revolution in approximately 32 min. A capsule reaches a height of 165 m.

a) Determine a function that models the height, h metres, of a capsule at any time t minutes after the wheel begins to rotate.

b) Assume a capsule is at the base of the wheel when it begins to rotate. Use technology to graph the function, then estimate the height of the capsule 20 min after the wheel begins to rotate. Give the answer to the nearest metre.

SOLUTION

a) Sketch a diagram.

A capsule travels along a circle at a constant speed, so its motion can be modelled using a sinusoidal function. The maximum height is 165 m and the diameter of the wheel is 150 m, so the minimum height is: 165 m − 150 m = 15 m

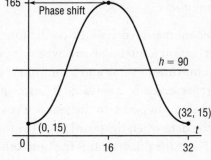

To sketch a graph:
the capsule is at the base of the wheel at time $t = 0$ and height $h = 15$.

So, the graph begins at $(0, 15)$, which is a minimum point.

The maximum height is $h = 165$ after one-half of a revolution at $t = \dfrac{32}{2}$, or 16, so the first maximum point is at $(16, 165)$.

The next minimum point is after 1 rotation and it has coordinates $(32, 15)$.

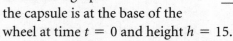

The centre line of the graph has equation: $h = \dfrac{165 + 15}{2}$, or $h = 90$

The position of the first maximum is known, so use a cosine function to describe the motion: $h(t) = a \cos b(t - c) + d$

The amplitude is $165 - 90 = 75$, so $a = 75$.

The period is 32, so $b = \dfrac{2\pi}{32}$, or $\dfrac{\pi}{16}$.

The phase shift is the t-coordinate of the first maximum point, so $c = 16$.

The vertical translation is $d = 90$.

So, an equation is: $h(t) = 75 \cos \dfrac{\pi}{16}(t - 16) + 90$

b) Graph: $Y = 75 \cos \dfrac{\pi}{16}(X - 16) + 90$ (below left)

Determine the height after 20 min (below right).

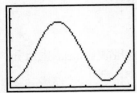 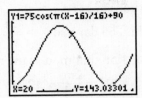

After 20 min, the height of the capsule is approximately 143 m.

The solution to *Example 1b* can be determined algebraically.

To determine the height after 20 min, use:

$h(t) = 75 \cos \dfrac{\pi}{16}(t - 16) + 90$ Substitute: $t = 20$

$h(20) = 75 \cos \dfrac{\pi}{16}(20 - 16) + 90$

$h(20) = 143.0330\ldots$

After 20 min, the height of the car is approximately 143 m.

Consider the graph from Lesson 6.5 *Get Started*, page 513. It shows the number of daylight hours, *n*, against day of the year, *t*, for Iqaluit. This graph approximates a sinusoidal function whose equation can be determined.

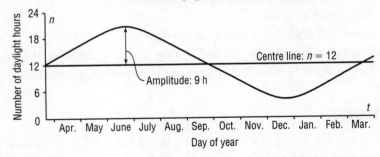

To write a function that models the data, the following assumptions are made:

- March 21 is day 0 on the *Day of year* axis. On this day, there are approximately 12 h of daylight. The maximum daylight is approximately 21 h on June 21.

- The function is sinusoidal with a period of approximately 365 days.

The graph approximates a sine curve with no phase shift, so it can be modelled with a function of the form $n(t) = a \sin bt + d$, where *a* is the amplitude, *b* is $\dfrac{2\pi}{\text{period}}$, and *d* is the vertical translation.

From the graph:

- The equation of the centre line is $n = 12$; so $d = 12$.
- The amplitude is 9 h; so $a = 9$.
- The period is 365 days; so $b = \dfrac{2\pi}{365}$

A possible function that models the number of hours of daylight in Iqaluit is: $n(t) = 9 \sin \dfrac{2\pi t}{365} + 12$

Example 2	Using a Sinusoidal Function to Model Given Data

The Fisheries and Oceans Canada website provides information about tide heights for many locations on the coastal regions of the country. The following data show the tide heights every 2 h for Digby, Nova Scotia, on March 9, 2011.

Time (hours after midnight)	00	02	04	06	08	10	12	14	16	18	20	22
Height (m)	6.3	7.8	6.1	3.2	1.4	2.7	5.6	7.5	6.3	3.7	1.7	2.6

a) Graph the data, then write an equation of a sinusoidal function that models the data.
How well does the function fit the data?

b) Use technology to graph the function in part a. Estimate the tide height at 16:15. Give the answer to the nearest tenth of a metre.

SOLUTION

a) Graph the data. Let h represent the height of the tide in metres, and t represent the time in hours after midnight.

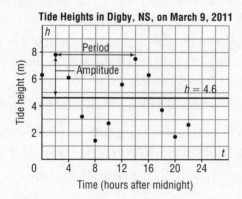

Tide Heights in Digby, NS, on March 9, 2011

The beginning of the period is a maximum point, so use a cosine function to model the data: $h(t) = a \cos b(t - c) + d$

Check Your Understanding

2. The following data show the predicted tide heights every 2 h, starting at midnight, for St. Andrews, PEI, on March 9, 2011:
(00, 4.6), (02, 6.5), (04, 5.7), (06, 3.5), (08, 1.4), (10, 1.7), (12, 4.0), (14, 6.1), (16, 5.8), (18, 3.9), (20, 1.8), (22, 1.7)

a) Graph the data, then write an equation of a sinusoidal function that models the data.

b) Use technology to graph the function in part a. Estimate the tide height at 17:00. Give the answer to the nearest tenth of a metre.

From the graph:

The first maximum point has approximate coordinates (2, 7.8) and the first minimum point has approximate coordinates (8, 1.4),

so the equation of the centre line is approximately: $h \doteq \dfrac{7.8 + 1.4}{2}$,

or $h \doteq 4.6$; so $d \doteq 4.6$

The amplitude is approximately: $7.8 - 4.6 = 3.2$, so $a \doteq 3.2$

The period is approximately 12 h, so $b \doteq \dfrac{2\pi}{12}$, or $\dfrac{\pi}{6}$

The phase shift is the t-coordinate of the first maximum point, so $c \doteq 2$

A function that approximates the data is: $h(t) = 3.2 \cos \dfrac{\pi}{6}(t - 2) + 4.6$
The graph is not a perfect cosine function, but it is close enough to make a sinusoidal model reasonable.

b) Graph: $Y = 3.2 \cos \dfrac{\pi}{6}(X - 2) + 4.6$

Write the time of 16:15 as a decimal of an hour: 16.25
Determine the height of the tide at this time.

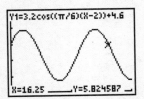

At 16:15, the tide height is approximately 5.8 m.

Discuss the Ideas

1. Suppose you are to graph a sinusoidal function given its equation. How can you tell whether the horizontal axis will be labelled in terms of π or with integers?

2. How do you decide whether to use a sine function or a cosine function to model data that can be described with a sinusoidal function?

Exercises

3. Identify the transformations that would be applied to the graph of
$y = \cos x$ to get the graph of $y = \frac{3}{4} \cos \frac{\pi}{5}(x + 3) - \frac{3}{2}$.

4. Identify the following characteristics of each graph below:
amplitude; period; phase shift; equation of the centre line; domain;
maximum value; minimum value; range

a)

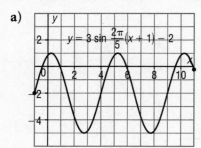

b)

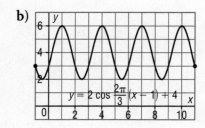

5. a) For the function graphed below, identify the values of a, b, c, and d in $y = a \sin b(x - c) + d$, then write an equation for the function.

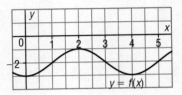

b) For the function graphed below, identify the values of a, b, c, and d in $y = a \cos b(x - c) + d$, then write an equation for the function.

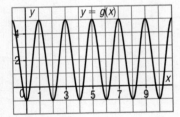

6. Use transformations to sketch a graph of each function for
   $-5 \leq x \leq 5$.

   a) $y = 4 \cos \dfrac{2\pi}{3}(x + 1) - 2$

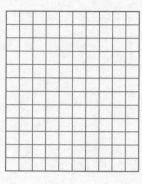

   b) $y = 2 \sin \dfrac{\pi}{4}(x + 3) + 1$

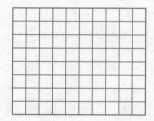

7. A sound wave is a sinusoidal curve, as illustrated by the
   oscilloscope image below. Determine the function that best
   describes this graph.

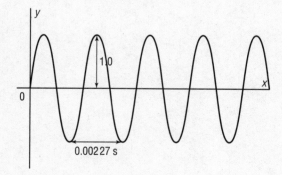

8. A vertical wheel with radius 50 cm rotates about an axle that is 60 cm above the ground. A marker is placed at the top of the wheel. The wheel completes one rotation every 4 s.

a) i) Explain why a cosine function would be an appropriate model for the height, h centimetres, of the marker at any time t seconds.

  ii) For the graph of the cosine function from part i, identify the: period; phase shift; equation of the centre line; and amplitude. Explain how each characteristic relates to the conditions in the problem.

b) Write an equation of a cosine function that models the motion of the wheel.

9. The Fisheries and Oceans Canada website provided the following data for tide heights at Rankin Inlet on May 9, 2011.
Low tide: 1.0 m at 02:09; and 0.9 m at 14:28
High tide: 3.6 m at 08:09; and 3.7 m at 20:49
Assume the tide heights can be modelled using a sinusoidal function.

a) Write an equation of a sinusoidal function that models these data.

b) Use the function to estimate the tide height at 09:00. Give the answer to the nearest half metre.

10. These data show the fraction of the moon that was visible on alternate days in January, 2011.

a) Graph the data, then write an equation of a sinusoidal function that models these data.

Day	Visible fraction	Day	Visible fraction
01	0.11	17	0.91
03	0.01	19	0.99
05	0.01	21	0.97
07	0.08	23	0.85
09	0.21	25	0.65
11	0.38	27	0.43
13	0.57	29	0.23
15	0.76	31	0.08

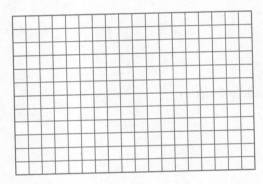

b) Use the table to identify the days when the maximum and minimum fractions of the moon were seen. Where are these points on the graph?

11. These data show the average hours of daylight for Vancouver, BC.

Date	Average daylight (h and min)
January 1	8:17
February 1	9:25
March 1	11:00
April 1	12:53
May 1	14:36
June 1	15:57
July 1	16:10
August 1	15:08
September 1	13:28
October 1	11:40
November 1	9:52
December 1	8:29

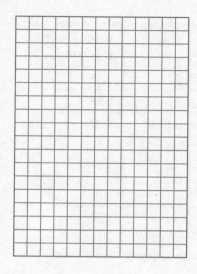

a) Graph the data, then write an equation of a sinusoidal function that models these data.

b) Use technology to graph the function. Use the graph and the equation.

    i) Estimate the average amount of daylight on April 15th.

    ii) On which dates are there 10 h of daylight?

Multiple-Choice Questions

1. Which function below best describes this graph?

    A. $y = 8 \sin \frac{1}{5}(x - 10) - 6$

    B. $y = 8 \sin \frac{1}{5}(x + 10) - 6$

    C. $y = 8 \sin \frac{\pi}{5}(x + 10) - 6$

    D. $y = 8 \sin \frac{\pi}{5}(x - 10) - 6$

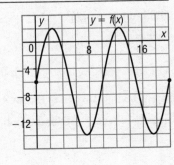

2. Which coordinates represent a maximum point of the function
$y = 2 \cos \dfrac{2\pi}{3}(x - 1) + 6$?

    A. $(1, 8)$ **B.** $(2.5, 8)$ **C.** $(0, 8)$ **D.** $(-0.5, 4)$

Study Note

Suppose you are given data that approximate a sinusoidal function. How do you determine a sine or cosine function that models the data?

STUDY GUIDE

Concept Summary

Big Ideas	Applying the Big Ideas
• The trigonometric ratio for an angle $\theta < 0°$ or $\theta > 360°$ is the value of that ratio for the related angle in standard position.	This means that: • The coordinates of a point on the terminal arm of an angle can be used to determine the sine, cosine, tangent, secant, cosecant, and cotangent ratios for any positive or negative angle. • If the value of a trigonometric ratio for an angle is known, the values of the other 5 trigonometric ratios for that angle and any coterminal angle can be determined. • If the value of a trigonometric ratio for an angle is known, it can be used to determine all possible measures for that angle in a given domain.
• The radian measure of an angle is a real number.	• The radian measure of a central angle in a circle can be used to determine the length of the arc that subtends the angle. • Any angle in radian measure can be written in degree measure, and vice versa. • The definitions of trigonometric ratios can be extended to define trigonometric functions of real numbers.
• A sine or cosine function can be used to model periodic behaviour.	• Transformations can be applied to the graphs of sine and cosine functions to model phenomena that repeat over a given interval and oscillate between a maximum and a minimum value.

Chapter Study Notes

• How can you relate the radian measure of an angle to its degree measure?

• How can you construct a function to model data that appear to be sinusoidal?

Skills Summary

Skill	Description	Example
Determine the values of the six trigonometric ratios for any positive or negative angle. **(6.1, 6.3)**	If the terminal arm of an angle θ in standard position intersects a circle, radius r, at P(x, y), then $\cos\theta = \frac{x}{r}$, $\sin\theta = \frac{y}{r}$, $\tan\theta = \frac{y}{x}$, $\sec\theta = \frac{r}{x}$, $\csc\theta = \frac{r}{y}$, and $\cot\theta = \frac{x}{y}$ If θ is a multiple of $\frac{\pi}{6}$ (30°) or $\frac{\pi}{4}$ (45°), the exact values of the trigonometric ratios can be determined. Otherwise, use a calculator to approximate the values of the primary trigonometric ratios and to determine their reciprocals.	To determine the value of $\csc\left(-\frac{5\pi}{6}\right)$: The angle $-\frac{5\pi}{6}$ is in Quadrant 3 and its reference angle is $\frac{\pi}{6}$. $\csc\left(-\frac{5\pi}{6}\right) = \dfrac{1}{\sin\left(-\frac{5\pi}{6}\right)}$ $= -\dfrac{1}{\sin\frac{\pi}{6}}$ $= -\dfrac{1}{\frac{1}{2}}$, or -2
Determine the length of an arc that subtends an angle at the centre of a circle. **(6.2, 6.3)**	The length of an arc that subtends a central angle of θ degrees in a circle with radius r is proportional to the circumference: $\dfrac{\text{arc length}}{2\pi r} = \dfrac{\theta}{360°}$ When θ is in radians: arc length $= r\theta$	To determine the length of an arc that subtends an angle of $\frac{\pi}{5}$ at the centre of a circle with radius 7 cm: Arc length $= 7\left(\frac{\pi}{5}\right)$, or $\frac{7\pi}{5}$ Arc length is $\frac{7\pi}{5}$ cm, or approximately 4.4 cm.
Relate the radian and degree measures of an angle. **(6.3)**	An angle of 2π is equal to 360°, so an angle of θ radians is equal to: $\theta\left(\frac{360°}{2\pi}\right)$, or $\theta\left(\frac{180°}{\pi}\right)$ Conversely, an angle of θ degrees is equal to: $\theta\left(\frac{2\pi}{360}\right)$ radians, or $\theta\left(\frac{\pi}{180}\right)$ radians	To determine the radian measure of an angle of 310°: Radian measure: $310\left(\frac{\pi}{180}\right) = \frac{31\pi}{18}$ An angle of 310° is $\frac{31\pi}{18}$ radians.
Use transformations to graph a trigonometric function. **(6.5, 6.6)**	Relate the constants in the equation of a function to vertical and horizontal stretches or compressions, reflections in the axes, and translations of the graph of the sine or cosine function.	To graph $y = 2\sin 3\left(x - \frac{\pi}{3}\right) - 1$, apply these transformations to the graph of $y = \sin x$: a vertical stretch by a factor of 2, which changes the amplitude to 2; a horizontal compression by a factor of $\frac{1}{3}$, which changes the period to $\frac{2\pi}{3}$; a phase shift of $\frac{\pi}{3}$, which moves the graph $\frac{\pi}{3}$ units right; a vertical translation of -1, which moves the graph 1 unit down.

6.1

1. Determine the value of each trigonometric ratio. Use exact values where possible; otherwise write the value to the nearest thousandth.

   a) $\tan(-45°)$

   b) $\cos 600°$

   c) $\sec(-210°)$

   d) $\sin 765°$

   e) $\cot 21°$

   f) $\csc 318°$

2. To the nearest degree, determine all possible values of θ for which $\cos \theta = 0.76$, when $-360° \leq \theta \leq 360°$.

6.2

3. As a fraction of π, determine the length of the arc that subtends a central angle of $225°$ in a circle with radius 3 units.

6.3

4. a) Convert each angle to degrees. Give the answer to the nearest degree where necessary.

   i) $\dfrac{5\pi}{3}$

   ii) $-\dfrac{10\pi}{7}$

   iii) 4

b) Convert each angle to radians.

    i) 150°   **ii)** −240°   **iii)** 485°

5. In a circle with radius 5 cm, an arc of length 6 cm subtends a central angle. What is the measure of this angle in radians, and to the nearest degree?

6. A race car is travelling around a circular track at an average speed of 120 km/h. The track has a diameter of 1 km. Visualize a line segment joining the race car to the centre of the track. Through what angle, in radians, will the segment have rotated in 10 s?

7. Determine the value of each trigonometric ratio. Use exact values where possible; otherwise write the value to the nearest thousandth.

    a) $\sin \dfrac{\pi}{3}$ **b)** $\cos \dfrac{5\pi}{6}$ **c)** $\sec \left(-\dfrac{\pi}{2}\right)$

    d) $\tan \dfrac{15\pi}{4}$ **e)** $\csc 5$ **f)** $\cot (-22.8)$

8. P(3, −1) is a terminal point of angle θ in standard position.

  a) Determine the exact values of all the trigonometric ratios for θ.

  b) To the nearest tenth of a radian, determine possible values of θ in the domain $-2\pi \leq \theta \leq 2\pi$.

6.4

9. Use graphing technology to graph each function below for $-2\pi \leq x \leq 2\pi$, then list these characteristics of the graph: amplitude, period, zeros, domain, range, and the equations of the asymptotes.

  a) $y = \sin x$

  b) $y = \cos x$

  c) $y = \tan x$

10. On the same grid, sketch graphs of the functions in each pair for $0 \leq x \leq 2\pi$, then describe your strategy.

a) $y = \sin x$ and $y = \sin\left(x - \dfrac{\pi}{4}\right)$

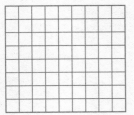

b) $y = \cos x$ and $y = \dfrac{3}{2}\cos x$

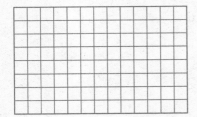

11. a) Graph $y = \frac{1}{2} \sin 3\left(x + \frac{\pi}{6}\right) + 2$ for $-2\pi \leq x \leq 2\pi$.

Explain your strategy.

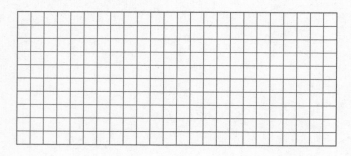

b) List the characteristics of the graph you drew.

12. An equation of the function graphed below has the form
$y = a \cos b(x - c) + d$. Identify the values of a, b, c, and d in the
equation, then write an equation for the function.

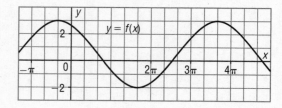

13. A water wheel has diameter 10 m and completes 4 revolutions each minute. The axle of the wheel is 8 m above a river.

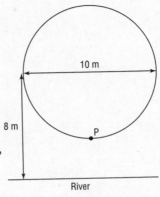

10 m

8 m

P

River

a) The wheel is at rest at time $t = 0$ s, with point P at the lowest point on the wheel. Determine a function that models the height of P above the river, h metres, at any time t seconds. Explain how the characteristics of the graph relate to the given information.

b) Use technology to graph the function. Use this graph to determine:

    i) the height of P after 35 s

ii) the times, to the nearest tenth of a second, in the first 15 s of motion that P is 11 m above the river

ANSWERS

1. a) -1 **b)** $-\dfrac{1}{2}$ **c)** $-\dfrac{2}{\sqrt{3}}$ **d)** $\dfrac{1}{\sqrt{2}}$ **e)** approximately 2.605

f) approximately -1.494 **2.** approximately: $\pm41°, \pm319°$ **3.** $\dfrac{15}{4}\pi$ **4. a) i)** $300°$

ii) approximately $-257°$ **iii)** approximately $229°$ **b) i)** $\dfrac{5\pi}{6}$ **ii)** $-\dfrac{4\pi}{3}$ **iii)** $\dfrac{97\pi}{36}$

5. 1.2 radians or approximately $69°$ **6.** $\dfrac{1}{3}$ radian **7. a)** $\dfrac{\sqrt{3}}{2}$ **b)** $-\dfrac{\sqrt{3}}{2}$ **c)** undefined

d) -1 **e)** approximately -1.043 **f)** approximately -0.954

8. a) $\sin\theta = -\dfrac{1}{\sqrt{10}}$; $\csc\theta = -\sqrt{10}$; $\cos\theta = \dfrac{3}{\sqrt{10}}$; $\sec\theta = \dfrac{\sqrt{10}}{3}$; $\tan\theta = -\dfrac{1}{3}$; $\cot\theta = -3$

b) approximately: $6.0, -0.3$ **9. a)** amplitude: 1; period: 2π; zeros: $0, \pm\pi, \pm2\pi$; domain: $-2\pi \le x \le 2\pi$; range: $-1 \le y \le 1$; no asymptotes

b) amplitude: 1; period: 2π; zeros: $\pm\dfrac{\pi}{2}, \pm\dfrac{3\pi}{2}$; domain: $-2\pi \le x \le 2\pi$; range: $-1 \le y \le 1$; no asymptotes

c) no amplitude; period: π; zeros: $0, \pm\pi, \pm2\pi$; domain: $x \ne \pm\dfrac{\pi}{2}, \pm\dfrac{3\pi}{2}$; range: $y \in \mathbb{R}$; asymptotes: $x = \pm\dfrac{\pi}{2}$ and $x = \pm\dfrac{3\pi}{2}$

11. b) amplitude: $\dfrac{1}{2}$; period: $\dfrac{2\pi}{3}$; no zeros; domain: $-2\pi \le x \le 2\pi$; range: $\dfrac{3}{2} \le y \le \dfrac{5}{2}$

13. b) i) 10.5 m **ii)** approximately: 5.3 s, 9.7 s

1. **Multiple Choice** Given $\cos \theta = 0.4$, which is the value of $\cos (\theta + \pi)$?

   A. 0.6   **B.** -0.6 **C.** 0.4   **D.** -0.4

2. **Multiple Choice** A sinusoidal function $f(x)$ has period 5 and passes through the point $P(5, 0)$. Which of the following values can be determined from this information?

   I. $f(0)$ II. $f(5)$ III. $f(15)$

   A. I only   **B.** II only   **C.** III only   **D.** I, II, and III

3. A pulley with radius 5 cm has its axle 300 cm above the ground. A load is on the ground. Through which positive angle will the pulley have to rotate to lift the load 100 cm? Give the answer in radians and to the nearest degree.

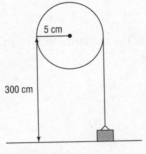

The diagram is not drawn to scale.

4. Determine the value of each trigonometric ratio. Use exact values where possible; otherwise write the values to the nearest hundredth.

   a) $\sin 505°$ **b)** $\cos \left(-\dfrac{7\pi}{6}\right)$ **c)** $\csc (-570°)$

   d) $\tan \dfrac{9\pi}{4}$ **e)** $\sec 51°$ **f)** $\cot \left(-\dfrac{11\pi}{12}\right)$

5. Given $\sin \theta = -\dfrac{3}{7}$ and $\tan \theta > 0$

    a) Determine the values of the other 5 trigonometric ratios for θ.

    b) For $0 \leq \theta < 2\pi$, determine the measure of θ in radians and in degrees, to the nearest tenth.

6. Given the function: $y = \dfrac{1}{2} \cos \left(2x + \dfrac{\pi}{2} \right) + 1$

    a) Determine these characteristics of the function:
       amplitude; period; phase shift

    b) Graph the function for $-2\pi \leq x \leq 2\pi$.

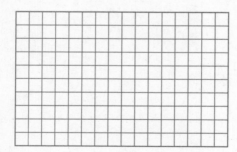

c) Determine these characteristics of the graph of
$y = \frac{1}{2} \cos\left(2x + \frac{\pi}{2}\right) + 1$: domain; range; zeros

7. The table shows the mean monthly temperatures for Winnipeg, MB, from May, 2010 to April, 2011.

Month	Mean monthly temperature (°C)
May	12.7
June	16.9
July	20.4
Aug.	19.1
Sept.	11.6
Oct.	8.2
Nov.	−3.1
Dec.	−13.8
Jan.	−18.4
Feb.	−13.8
Mar.	−8.0
Apr.	4.6

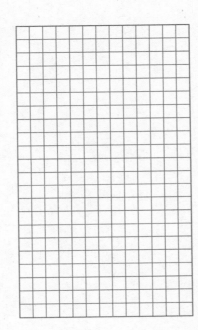

a) Graph the data, then write an equation of a sinusoidal function that models the data.

b) Use graphing technology to estimate the mean monthly temperature for April 2010 and for May 2011.

ANSWERS

1. D   **2.** D   **3.** 20 radians; approximately 1146°   **4. a)** approximately 0.57

b) $-\dfrac{\sqrt{3}}{2}$ **c)** 2   **d)** 1   **e)** approximately 1.59   **f)** approximately 3.73

5. a) $\csc \theta = -\dfrac{7}{3}$; $\cos \theta = -\dfrac{\sqrt{40}}{7}$; $\sec \theta = -\dfrac{7}{\sqrt{40}}$; $\tan \theta = \dfrac{3}{\sqrt{40}}$; $\cot \theta = \dfrac{\sqrt{40}}{3}$

b) approximately: 205.4°, 3.6 radians   **6. a)** amplitude: $\dfrac{1}{2}$; period: π; phase shift: $-\dfrac{\pi}{4}$

c) domain: $-2\pi \le x \le 2\pi$; range: $0.5 \le y \le 1.5$; no zeros

7 Trigonometric Equations and Identities

BUILDING ON

- solving trigonometric equations
- graphing trigonometric functions
- general form of coterminal angles

BIG IDEAS

- Trigonometric equations can be solved graphically or algebraically.
- The general solution of a trigonometric equation is related to the zeros of a corresponding trigonometric function.
- A trigonometric identity is a trigonometric equation that is true for all permissible values of the variable.

LEADING TO

- determining derivatives of trigonometric functions in calculus
- simplifying trigonometric expressions

NEW VOCABULARY

first-degree trigonometric equation	Pythagorean identities
second-degree trigonometric equation	sum identities
reciprocal identities	difference identities
quotient identities	double-angle identities

Solving Trigonometric Equations Graphically

FOCUS Use graphing technology to solve trigonometric equations.

Get Started

On a Ferris wheel, the height of a person above the ground, h metres, at time t seconds after getting on the ride is modelled by this function:

$$h = -15 \cos \frac{2\pi}{40}t + 16$$

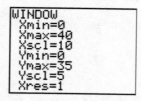
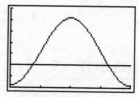

Enter the settings above on a graphing calculator.
To the nearest second, when is the person first at a height of 10 m? How do you know?

How could the coordinates of the point of intersection be determined algebraically?

Construct Understanding

Use graphing technology to solve each trigonometric equation below for x in the domain $-4\pi < x < 4\pi$.

$$\sin x = -\frac{2}{3} \qquad \tan x = 2$$

Give the solutions to the nearest hundredth.
What patterns do you see in the solutions?
Suppose the domain was not restricted.
How many solutions would there be?

Trigonometric equations can be solved over a restricted domain, such as for $0 \le x < 2\pi$; or they can be solved over the set of real numbers and their general solutions determined.

Here are two methods to solve the **first-degree trigonometric equation** $5 \sin x = 3 \cos x - 1$, for $0 \le x < 2\pi$, using graphing technology.

Method 1

Each side of the equation is entered as a separate function. The solution is the x-coordinates of the points of intersection.

Input: $Y_1 = 5 \sin(X)$ and $Y_2 = 3 \cos(X) - 1$

Press: [2nd] [TRACE] for CALC, then 5: intersect

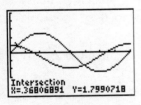

Method 2

The equation is rearranged so that 0 is on one side. The solution is the zeros of the corresponding function.

Write the equation as:

$0 = 3 \cos x - 1 - 5 \sin x$

Input: $Y_1 = 3 \cos(X) - 1 - 5 \sin(X)$

Press: [2nd] [TRACE] for CALC, then 2: zero

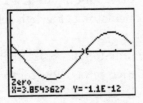

To the nearest hundredth, the solution in the domain $0 \le x < 2\pi$ is $x = 0.37$ and $x = 3.85$.

To verify a solution, begin with the graphing calculator screen that shows a solution on the graph, such as the screen above left. Press: [2nd] [MODE] for QUIT; then press: [X,T,Θ,n] [ENTER] to display the solution to many decimal places.

Always use the original equation to verify a solution.

Press: [5] [SIN] [X,T,Θ,n] [ )]; then press: [ENTER] to display 1.799071756

Press: [3] [COS] [X,T,Θ,n] [ )] [−] [1]; then press: [ENTER] to display 1.799071756

The calculator evaluates each expression for the last value of X.

The display of equal numbers verifies that the solution satisfies the equation.

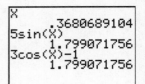

Consider the graph of $y = 3 \cos x - 1 - 5 \sin x$ for $-4\pi \le x \le 4\pi$. The zeros of this graph are the roots of the equation $3 \cos x - 1 - 5 \sin x = 0$ over the same domain. The period of the graph is 2π, so to determine roots beyond this domain add multiples of 2π to, and subtract these multiples from, the roots in the domain $0 \le x < 2\pi$. This leads to the general solution of this equation; that is, the solution over the set of real numbers:

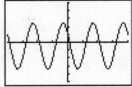

$x \doteq 0.37 + 2\pi k, k \in \mathbb{Z}$ or $x \doteq 3.85 + 2\pi k, k \in \mathbb{Z}$

The strategy for solving a first-degree trigonometric equation can be applied to solving a **second-degree trigonometric equation**; for example, $3 \sin^2 x + \sin x = 3$. Recall that $\sin^2 x$ means $(\sin x)^2$.

Example 1	Solving a Second-Degree Trigonometric Equation Graphically

a) Solve $3 \sin^2 x + \sin x = 3$ over the domain $0 \le x < 2\pi$. Give the roots to the nearest hundredth.

b) Determine the general solution of the equation.

SOLUTION

a) Write: $3 \sin^2 x + \sin x = 3$ as $3 \sin^2 x + \sin x - 3 = 0$

Enter the corresponding function $y = 3 \sin^2 x + \sin x - 3$ in a graphing calculator, below left. Set the window to: $0 \le X \le 2\pi$ and $-4 \le Y \le 4$

Graph the function. Press: [2nd] [TRACE] for CALC, then use 2: zero to determine each zero, below centre and right.

 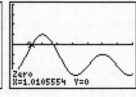 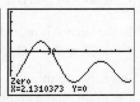

To the nearest hundredth, the zeros are: $x = 1.01$ and $x = 2.13$
To verify, after determining each zero; press: [2nd] [MODE] for QUIT;
then press: [X,T,Θ,n] [ENTER]
Press: [3] [(] [SIN] [X,T,Θ,n] [)] [)] [x²] [+] [SIN] [X,T,Θ,n] [)]; then
press: [ENTER] to display 3
Since the left side of the equation is equal to the right side, the
solution is verified.

b) Change the window on the calculator
screen to $0 \leq X \leq 4\pi$ to identify the
period of the corresponding function.
This period is 2π, so the general solution
is approximately: $x = 1.01 + 2\pi k$,
$k \in \mathbb{Z}$ or $x = 2.13 + 2\pi k, k \in \mathbb{Z}$

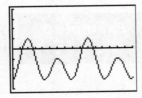

Example 2   Solving a First-Degree Equation with a Double Angle

Check Your Understanding

a) Solve $\cos 2x = 0$ over the domain $0 \leq x < 2\pi$. Give the roots to
the nearest hundredth.

b) Determine the general solution of the equation.

2. a) Solve $\sin 3x = 0$ over the
domain $0 \leq x < 2\pi$. Give
the roots to the nearest
hundredth.

b) State the general solution
of the equation.

SOLUTION

a) Enter the corresponding function
$y = \cos 2x$ into a graphing calculator.
Set the window to: $0 \leq X \leq 2\pi$ and
$-2 \leq Y \leq 2$
Graph the function. Press: [2nd] [TRACE]
for CALC, then use 2: zero to determine
each approximate zero:

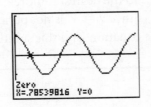

X = 0.78539816   X = 2.3561945
X = 3.9269908   X = 5.4977871
To the nearest hundredth, the roots are: $x = 0.79$, $x = 2.36$,
$x = 3.93$, and $x = 5.50$
Use the graphing calculator to verify.

b) The period of $y = \cos 2x$ is π, so integral multiples of π are added
to each of the 2 roots in the first cycle to obtain the general
solution. The general solution is approximately:
$x = 0.79 + \pi k, k \in \mathbb{Z}$ or $x = 2.36 + \pi k, k \in \mathbb{Z}$

THINK FURTHER

In *Example 2*, what are the exact roots of the equation $\cos 2x = 0$ for $0 \le x < 2\pi$?

Example 3	Solving a Trigonometric Equation Involving Different Types of Functions

Check Your Understanding

3. Solve $\cos x = x^2$ over the set of real numbers. Give the roots to the nearest hundredth.

Solve $\sin x = x^3$ over the set of real numbers. Give the roots to the nearest hundredth.

SOLUTION

Enter the corresponding functions $y = \sin x$ and $y = x^3$ into a graphing calculator.
Set the window to: $-2\pi \le X \le 2\pi$ and $-2 \le Y \le 2$

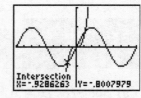

Graph the functions. Press: 2nd TRACE for CALC, then use 5: intersect to determine the approximate x-coordinate of each point of intersection:

$X = -0.9286263 \qquad X = 0 \qquad X = 0.9286263$

To the nearest hundredth, the roots are: $x = -0.93, x = 0, x = 0.93$
Since $y = x^3$ is not periodic, these roots are the only roots of the equation, and this solution is over the set of real numbers.

Discuss the Ideas

1. Can a trigonometric equation have no solution? Justify your answer.

2. How does knowing the period of a trigonometric function help to determine a general solution of a corresponding trigonometric equation?

DO NOT COPY. ©P

3. When does a trigonometric equation not have infinitely many roots?

Exercises

Use graphing technology to solve each equation. Where necessary, round the roots to the nearest hundredth.

A

4. Use a graphing calculator and enter the settings shown below to solve the equation $3 \cos x = 1.5$. State the restricted domain indicated by the WINDOW screen, then determine the roots of the equation over this domain.

 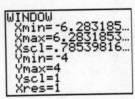 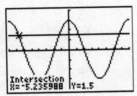

5. Solve each equation for $0 \le x < 2\pi$.

   a) $\sin x = \dfrac{2}{5}$ **b)** $\cos x = -\dfrac{1}{3}$

6. Solve the equation $\sin x = -\dfrac{4}{7}$ over the domain $0 \leq x < 2\pi$. Assume x is an angle in standard position. In which quadrants do the terminal arms of the angles lie? How do you know?

7. Solve each equation for $-2\pi \leq x < 0$.

    a) $\tan x - 3 = \cos x + 2$ **b)** $2 = 4 \sin x - 3 \cos x$

8. Use a graphing calculator and enter the settings below to solve a trigonometric equation. State the restricted domain indicated by the WINDOW screen, then determine the roots of the equation over this domain.

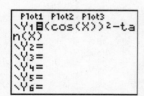 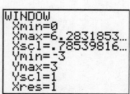 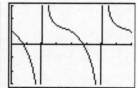

9. Solve each equation for $0 \leq x < 2\pi$, then write the general solution.

    a) $5 \sin^2 x - \sin x = 2$ **b)** $3 \tan x - 1 = \tan^2 x$

10. Solve each equation for $0 \leq x < 2\pi$, then write the general solution.

  a) $\cos 3x = \frac{1}{2}$

  b) $1 - 4 \tan 3x = -7$

11. The first two positive roots of the equation $\sin 5x = \frac{1}{3}$ are $x \doteq 0.07$ and $x \doteq 0.56$. Determine the general solution of this equation. Explain how this solution is determined.

12. Solve each equation over the given domain, then write the general solution.

  a) $\cos \pi x = 0$ for $-3 \leq x \leq 3$

  b) $-1 = 2 \sin 3\pi x$ for $-1 \leq x \leq 1$

13. Solve each equation over the set of real numbers.

    a) $3 \cos x = x^2 + 1$ **b)** $x^3 - 2 = 2 \sin x$

14. a) Solve $\dfrac{\cos x}{1 - \sin x} = \dfrac{1 + \sin x}{\cos x}$ over the set of real numbers by

    graphing the two functions $y = \dfrac{\cos x}{1 - \sin x}$ and $y = \dfrac{1 + \sin x}{\cos x}$.

    What do you notice about the solution?

    b) The equation in part a is called an *identity*. Why is that an appropriate name?

C

15. Solve each equation over the set of real numbers.

    a) $\sec x = \sqrt{4 - x^2}$ **b)** $\sin x + 2 = 2x$

16. a) Solve each equation, and explain the results.

    i) $\dfrac{\sin x}{x} = 1$ **ii)** $\sin x = x$

    b) Why are the solutions in part a different?

17. a) Solve each equation, and explain the results.

    i) $\dfrac{\cos x}{x} = 1$ **ii)** $\cos x = x$

   b) Why are the solutions in part a the same?

Multiple-Choice Questions

1. Use these two screens. Which equation below could be solved using the graph?

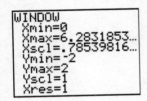
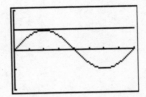

   A. $\cos x = 1$ **B.** $\sin x = 1$

   C. $\cos x = -1$ **D.** $\sin x = -1$

2. The first two positive roots of the equation $\cos 4x = \dfrac{1}{2}$ are approximately 0.26 and 1.31. Which expression represents the general solution, where $k \in \mathbb{Z}$?

   A. $x \doteq 0.26 + 2\pi k$ or $x \doteq 1.31 + 2\pi k$

   B. $x \doteq 0.26 + 4\pi k$ or $x \doteq 1.31 + 4\pi k$

   C. $x \doteq 0.26 + \dfrac{\pi}{2}k$ or $x \doteq 1.31 + \dfrac{\pi}{2}k$

   D. $x \doteq 0.26 + \dfrac{\pi}{4}k$ or $x \doteq 1.31 + \dfrac{\pi}{4}k$

Study Note

How does the general solution of a trigonometric equation relate to the zeros of a corresponding trigonometric function?

ANSWERS

Check Your Understanding

1. a) $x \doteq 1.76, x \doteq 4.53$ **b)** $x \doteq 1.76 + 2\pi k, k \in \mathbb{Z}$ or $x \doteq 4.53 + 2\pi k, k \in \mathbb{Z}$

2. a) $x = 0, x \doteq 1.05, x \doteq 2.09, x \doteq 3.14, x \doteq 4.19, x \doteq 5.24$

b) $x = \frac{2\pi k}{3}, k \in \mathbb{Z}$ or $x \doteq 1.05 + \frac{2\pi k}{3}, k \in \mathbb{Z}$ **3.** $x \doteq -0.82, x \doteq 0.82$

Exercises

4. $x \doteq \pm 5.24, x \doteq \pm 1.05$ **5. a)** $x \doteq 0.41, x \doteq 2.73$ **b)** $x \doteq 1.91$ and $x \doteq 4.37$

6. $x \doteq 3.75, x \doteq 5.67$ **7. a)** $x \doteq -4.90, x \doteq -1.78$

b) $x \doteq -5.23, x \doteq -2.91$ **8.** $x \doteq 0.60, x \doteq 3.74$ **9. a)** $x \doteq 0.83, x \doteq 2.31,$
$x \doteq 3.71, x \doteq 5.71; x \doteq 0.83 + 2\pi k, k \in \mathbb{Z}$ or $x \doteq 2.31 + 2\pi k, k \in \mathbb{Z}$ or
$x \doteq 3.71 + 2\pi k, k \in \mathbb{Z}$ or $x \doteq 5.71 + 2\pi k, k \in \mathbb{Z}$ **b)** $x \doteq 0.36, x \doteq 1.21,$
$x \doteq 3.51, x \doteq 4.35; x \doteq 0.36 + \pi k, k \in \mathbb{Z}$ or $x \doteq 1.21 + \pi k, k \in \mathbb{Z}$

10. a) $x \doteq 0.35, x \doteq 1.75, x \doteq 2.44, x \doteq 3.84, x \doteq 4.54, x \doteq 5.93; x \doteq 0.35 + \frac{2\pi k}{3},$
$k \in \mathbb{Z}$ or $x \doteq 1.75 + \frac{2\pi k}{3}, k \in \mathbb{Z}$ **b)** $x \doteq 0.37, x \doteq 1.42, x \doteq 2.46, x \doteq 3.51,$
$x \doteq 4.56, x \doteq 5.61; x \doteq 0.37 + \frac{\pi k}{3}, k \in \mathbb{Z}$ **11.** $x \doteq 0.07 + \frac{2\pi k}{5}, k \in \mathbb{Z}$ or
$x \doteq 0.56 + \frac{2\pi k}{5}, k \in \mathbb{Z}$ **12. a)** $x = \pm 2.5, x = \pm 1.5, x = \pm 0.5; x = 0.5 + k, k \in \mathbb{Z}$

b) $x \doteq -0.94, x \doteq -0.72, x \doteq -0.28, x \doteq -0.06, x \doteq 0.39, x \doteq 0.61;$
$x \doteq -0.72 + \frac{2k}{3}, k \in \mathbb{Z}$ or $x \doteq -0.94 + \frac{2k}{3}, k \in \mathbb{Z}$ **13. a)** $x \doteq \pm 0.91$ **b)** $x \doteq 1.59$

15. a) $x \doteq \pm 0.96$ **b)** $x \doteq 1.50$ **16. a) i)** no real solution **ii)** $x = 0$
17. a) i) $x \doteq 0.74$ **ii)** $x \doteq 0.74$

Multiple Choice

1. B **2.** C

FOCUS Use an algebraic method to solve first- and second-degree trigonometric equations.

Get Started

Solve the equation: $\sin \theta = -\frac{1}{2}$ for $0° \leq \theta < 360°$

Construct Understanding

Without graphing, solve the equation $4 \cos x + 3 = 7 \cos x + 2$ for $0 \leq x < 2\pi$.

Check the solution graphically.

To solve a first-degree trigonometric equation, isolate the trigonometric function to reduce the equation to the form $\sin x = a$, $\cos x = a$, or $\tan x = a$, where a is a constant. Some of these equations have exact numerical solutions. In these cases, the solution is a multiple of $\frac{\pi}{6}$ or $\frac{\pi}{4}$.

Consider solving this equation for $0 \leq x < 2\pi$:
$2 \cos x + 1 = 0$ Isolate $\cos x$.

$$2 \cos x = -1$$
$$\cos x = -\frac{1}{2}$$

Use the completed table in Chapter 6, page 476, to identify the exact angle.

The cosine of an angle is negative when its terminal arm lies in Quadrant 2 or 3.

The reference angle is: $\cos^{-1}\left(\frac{1}{2}\right) = \frac{\pi}{3}$

In Quadrant 2, x is: $\pi - \frac{\pi}{3} = \frac{2\pi}{3}$

In Quadrant 3, x is: $\pi + \frac{\pi}{3} = \frac{4\pi}{3}$

So, the roots are: $x = \frac{2\pi}{3}$ and $x = \frac{4\pi}{3}$

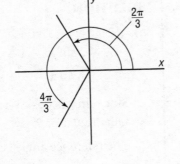

The graph of $y = 2 \cos x + 1$ has period 2π.

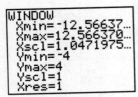 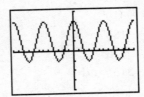

So, the general solution of the equation $2 \cos x + 1 = 0$ is:

$x = \frac{2\pi}{3} + 2\pi k$ or $x = \frac{4\pi}{3} + 2\pi k$, where $k \in \mathbb{Z}$

THINK FURTHER

What are the roots of $2 \cos x + 1 = 0$ over the domain $-2\pi \leq x < 0$?

1. a) Use algebra to solve the equation $7 + 2\sin x = 4\sin x + 5$ for $-360° < x \le 0°$, then write the general solution.

b) Use algebra to determine the general solution of the equation $\cos 3x = -1$ over the set of real numbers, then list the roots in the domain $-2\pi \le x < 0$.

a) Use algebra to solve the equation $\sqrt{2}\sin x - 3 = -2$ for $-360° < x \le 0°$, then write the general solution.

b) Use algebra to determine the general solution of the equation $\cos 3x = -\dfrac{1}{2}$ over the set of real numbers, then list the roots in the domain $-\pi \le x < \pi$.

SOLUTION

a) $\sqrt{2}\sin x - 3 = -2$ ⠀⠀⠀ Solve for $\sin x$.

$$\sqrt{2}\sin x = 1$$

$$\sin x = \frac{1}{\sqrt{2}}$$

Since $\sin x$ is positive, the terminal arm of angle x lies in Quadrant 1 or 2.

The reference angle is: $\sin^{-1}\left(\dfrac{1}{\sqrt{2}}\right) = 45°$

In Quadrant 1, $x = -360° + 45°$

⠀⠀⠀⠀⠀⠀⠀ $x = -315°$

In Quadrant 2, $x = -180° - 45°$

⠀⠀⠀⠀⠀⠀⠀ $x = -225°$

The roots are: $x = -315°$ and $x = -225°$

The period of $\sin x$ is $360°$, so the general solution is:

$x = -315° + k360°, k \in \mathbb{Z}$

or $x = -225° + k360°, k \in \mathbb{Z}$

b) $\cos 3x = -\dfrac{1}{2}$

Since $\cos 3x$ is negative, the terminal arm of angle $3x$ lies in Quadrant 2 or 3.

The reference angle for angle $3x$ is: $\cos^{-1}\left(\dfrac{1}{2}\right) = \dfrac{\pi}{3}$

In Quadrant 2:
A solution is:

$$3x = \pi - \frac{\pi}{3}$$

$$3x = \frac{2\pi}{3}$$

$$x = \frac{2\pi}{9}$$

In Quadrant 3:
A solution is:

$$3x = \pi + \frac{\pi}{3}$$

$$3x = \frac{4\pi}{3}$$

$$x = \frac{4\pi}{9}$$

For angle $3x$ For angle x

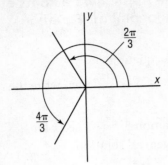 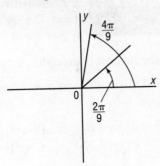

The period of $\cos 3x$ is $\dfrac{2\pi}{3}$, so the general solution is:

$x = \dfrac{2\pi}{9} + \dfrac{2\pi}{3}k,\, k \in \mathbb{Z}$ or $x = \dfrac{4\pi}{9} + \dfrac{2\pi}{3}k,\, k \in \mathbb{Z}$

Substitute integer values for k to obtain all other roots between $-\pi$ and π.

When $k = 1$:

$x = \dfrac{2\pi}{9} + \dfrac{2\pi}{3}$ or $x = \dfrac{4\pi}{9} + \dfrac{2\pi}{3}$

$x = \dfrac{8\pi}{9}$ $x = \dfrac{10\pi}{9}$, not in the domain

When $k = -1$:

$x = \dfrac{2\pi}{9} - \dfrac{2\pi}{3}$ or $x = \dfrac{4\pi}{9} - \dfrac{2\pi}{3}$

$x = -\dfrac{4\pi}{9}$ $x = -\dfrac{2\pi}{9}$

When $k = -2$:

$x = \dfrac{2\pi}{9} - \dfrac{4\pi}{3}$ or $x = \dfrac{4\pi}{9} - \dfrac{4\pi}{3}$

$x = -\dfrac{10\pi}{9}$, not in $x = -\dfrac{8\pi}{9}$

the domain

The roots are: $x = \pm\dfrac{2\pi}{9}$, $x = \pm\dfrac{4\pi}{9}$, and $x = \pm\dfrac{8\pi}{9}$

In *Example 1*, each root can be verified by substituting it into the original equation.

Check Your Understanding

2. a) To the nearest hundredth, solve the equation $\cos x - 6 = 4 \cos x - 4$ for $-\frac{\pi}{2} \le x < \frac{3\pi}{2}$, then write the general solution.

b) To the nearest degree, solve the equation $\sqrt{2} \csc x = -5$ for $-180° \le x < 180°$, then write the general solution.

a) To the nearest hundredth, solve the equation

$5 - 3 \tan x = 2 \tan x + 1$ for $-\pi \le x < \frac{3\pi}{2}$, then write the general solution.

b) To the nearest degree, solve the equation $3 = \sqrt{3} \sec x$ for $-90° \le x < 270°$, then write the general solution.

SOLUTION

a) $5 - 3 \tan x = 2 \tan x + 1$ Solve for $\tan x$.

$$4 = 5 \tan x$$

$$\tan x = \frac{4}{5}$$

Since $\tan x$ is positive, the terminal arm of angle x lies in Quadrant 1 or 3.

The reference angle is: $\tan^{-1}\left(\frac{4}{5}\right) = 0.6747\ldots$

For $0 \le x < \frac{3\pi}{2}$:

In Quadrant 1, $x = 0.6747\ldots$

In Quadrant 3, $x = \pi + 0.6747\ldots$

$$x = 3.8163\ldots$$

For $-\pi \le x < 0$:

In Quadrant 3, $x = -\pi + 0.6747\ldots$

$$x = -2.4668\ldots$$

To the nearest hundredth, the roots are:

$x = 0.67$, $x = 3.82$, and $x = -2.47$

The period of $\tan x$ is π, so the general solution is approximately:

$x = 0.67 + \pi k, k \in \mathbb{Z}$

b) $3 = \sqrt{3} \sec x$ Solve for $\cos x$.

$$\sec x = \frac{3}{\sqrt{3}}, \text{ or } \sqrt{3}$$

$$\cos x = \frac{1}{\sqrt{3}}$$

Since $\cos x$ is positive, the terminal arm of angle x lies in Quadrant 1 or 4.

The reference angle is: $\cos^{-1}\left(\frac{1}{\sqrt{3}}\right) = 54.7356\ldots°$

For $0 \le x < 270°$, in Quadrant 1, $x \doteq 55°$

For $-90° \le x < 0°$, in Quadrant 4, $x \doteq -55°$

To the nearest degree, the roots are: $x = 55°$ and $x = -55°$

The period of $\cos x$ is $360°$, so the general solution is approximately: $x = \pm 55° + k360°, k \in \mathbb{Z}$

Recall the strategy for solving a quadratic equation such as:

$$5x^2 = 1 - 4x \qquad \text{Move all the terms to one side.}$$
$$5x^2 + 4x - 1 = 0 \qquad \text{Factor.}$$
$$(5x - 1)(x + 1) = 0 \qquad \text{Equate each factor to 0, then solve for } x.$$

$$\text{Either } 5x - 1 = 0 \quad \text{ or } \quad x + 1 = 0$$
$$5x = 1 \qquad\qquad\qquad x = -1$$
$$x = \frac{1}{5}$$

The algebraic strategies for solving a quadratic equation can be applied to solve a second-degree trigonometric equation. Consider solving the equation $5 \cos^2 x = 1 - 4 \cos x$ over the domain $0 \le x < 2\pi$.

$$5 \cos^2 x = 1 - 4 \cos x \qquad \text{Move all the terms to one side.}$$
$$5 \cos^2 x + 4 \cos x - 1 = 0 \qquad \text{Factor the expression, treating } \cos x \text{ as the variable.}$$

$$(5 \cos x - 1)(\cos x + 1) = 0 \qquad \text{Equate each factor to 0, then solve for } \cos x.$$

$$\text{Either } 5 \cos x - 1 = 0 \quad \text{ or } \quad \cos x + 1 = 0$$
$$5 \cos x = 1 \qquad\qquad\qquad \cos x = -1$$
$$\cos x = \frac{1}{5}$$

$\cos x$ is positive when the terminal arm of angle x lies in Quadrant 1 or 4.

The terminal arm of angle x lies on the negative x-axis, so: $x = \pi$

In Quadrant 1, $x = \cos^{-1}\left(\dfrac{1}{5}\right)$

$$x = 1.3694\ldots$$

In Quadrant 4, $x = 2\pi - 1.3694\ldots$

$$x = 4.9137\ldots$$

The roots are: $x \doteq 1.37$, $x = \pi$, and $x \doteq 4.91$

The roots can be verified graphically.

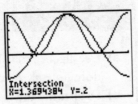

The roots can also be verified by substituting in the original equation.

Example 3 — Solving a Second-Degree Trigonometric Equation by Using Square Roots

Check Your Understanding

3. Use algebra to solve the equation $2\cos^2 x = 1$ over the domain $0° \le x \le 360°$.

Use algebra to solve the equation $4\sin^2 x = 3$ over the domain $-360° \le x \le 0°$.

SOLUTION

$4\sin^2 x = 3$ Solve for $\sin x$.

$\sin^2 x = \dfrac{3}{4}$

$\sin x = \pm\sqrt{\dfrac{3}{4}}$, or $\pm\dfrac{\sqrt{3}}{2}$

Since $\sin x$ is positive or negative, there is a solution in every quadrant.

The reference angle is: $\sin^{-1}\left(\dfrac{\sqrt{3}}{2}\right) = 60°$

In Quadrant 1, $x = -360° + 60°$, or $-300°$
In Quadrant 2, $x = -180° - 60°$, or $-240°$
In Quadrant 3, $x = -180° + 60°$, or $-120°$
In Quadrant 4, $x = -60°$
Verify by substituting each root in the equation: $4\sin^2 x = 3$
The roots are: $x = -60°$, $x = -120°$, $x = -240°$, and $x = -300°$

When a second-degree equation cannot be solved by factoring or using square roots, the quadratic formula is used.

Example 4 — Solving a Trigonometric Equation Using the Quadratic Formula

Check Your Understanding

4. a) Use algebra to solve the equation $\cos x = 1 - 3\cos^2 x$ over the domain $-\pi \le x \le \pi$.

   b) Determine the general solution.
Give the answers to the nearest hundredth.

a) Use algebra to solve the equation $4\tan^2 x = 2\tan x + 1$ over the domain $-\pi \le x \le \pi$.

b) Determine the general solution.

Give the answers to the nearest hundredth.

SOLUTION

a) $4\tan^2 x = 2\tan x + 1$ Move all the terms to one side.
$4\tan^2 x - 2\tan x - 1 = 0$ This does not factor.

Use the quadratic formula: $\tan x = \dfrac{-b \pm \sqrt{b^2 - 4ac}}{2a}$

Substitute: $a = 4$, $b = -2$, $c = -1$

$\tan x = \dfrac{2 \pm \sqrt{(-2)^2 - 4(4)(-1)}}{2(4)}$

$\tan x = \dfrac{2 \pm \sqrt{20}}{8}$, or $\dfrac{1 \pm \sqrt{5}}{4}$

Either $\tan x = \dfrac{1 + \sqrt{5}}{4}$ or $\tan x = \dfrac{1 - \sqrt{5}}{4}$

$\tan x$ is positive when the terminal arm of angle x lies in Quadrant 1 or 3.
The reference angle is:

$\tan^{-1}\!\left(\dfrac{1 + \sqrt{5}}{4}\right) = 0.6802\ldots$

In Quadrant 1, $x = 0.6802\ldots$
In Quadrant 3,
$x = -\pi + 0.6802\ldots$
$x = -2.4613\ldots$

$\tan x$ is negative when the terminal arm of angle x lies in Quadrant 2 or 4.
The reference angle is:

$\tan^{-1}\!\left(\dfrac{\sqrt{5} - 1}{4}\right) = 0.2997\ldots$

In Quadrant 2,
$x = \pi - 0.2997\ldots$
$x = 2.8418\ldots$
In Quadrant 4, $x = -0.2997\ldots$

Verify by substituting each root in the given equation.
To the nearest hundredth, the roots are: $x = -2.46$, $x = -0.30$, $x = 0.68$, and $x = 2.84$

b) The period of $\tan x$ is π, so the general solution is approximately:
$x = 0.68 + \pi k,\, k \in \mathbb{Z}$ or $x = 2.84 + \pi k,\, k \in \mathbb{Z}$

THINK FURTHER

In *Example 4*, when tan x is negative, why is the reference angle $\tan^{-1}\!\left(\dfrac{\sqrt{5} - 1}{4}\right)$?

The solution of the equation in *Example 4* can be verified by graphing.
On a graphing calculator, input $y = 4 \tan^2 x$ and $y = 2 \tan x + 1$, then determine the approximate x-coordinates of the points of intersection:

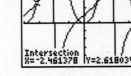

X = −2.461378
X = −0.2997086
X = 0.68021498
X = 2.8418841

These values match the values determined algebraically, so the solution is verified.

Discuss the Ideas

1. For equations of the form $\sin x = c$, $\cos x = c$, and $\tan x = c$, where c is a constant, what restrictions are there on the value of c for the equations to have real solutions?

2. How do you recognize when an exact solution to a trigonometric equation exists?

3. A second-degree trigonometric equation in terms of $\sin x$, $\cos x$, or $\tan x$ is solved over the domain $0 \leq x < 2\pi$. How many roots could the equation have?

Exercises

A

Use algebra to solve each equation. Give exact values when possible; otherwise write the roots to the nearest degree or the nearest hundredth of a radian. Verify the solutions.

4. Solve each equation over the domain $0 \leq x < 2\pi$.

    a) $\sin x = \dfrac{\sqrt{3}}{2}$

    b) $\tan x = \dfrac{1}{\sqrt{3}}$

5. Verify that each given value of x is a root of the equation.

a) $\tan^2 x - 3 = 0$;
$x = \dfrac{\pi}{3}$

b) $8 \sin^2 x + 6 \sin x + 1 = 0$;
$x = \dfrac{7\pi}{6}$

B

6. Solve each equation over the domain $0 \leq x < 2\pi$, then state the general solution.

a) $3 \cos x - 2 = 0$

b) $2 \tan x + \sqrt{5} = 0$

7. Solve each equation for $-\pi \leq x \leq \pi$.

a) $3 \tan x - 3 = 5 \tan x - 1$ **b)** $5(1 + 2 \sin x) = 2 \sin x + 1$

8. a) Solve each equation for $-180° \leq x \leq 90°$.

  i) $2 \csc x = 6$ **ii)** $-6 = 3 \cot x$

b) Solve each equation for $-90° \leq x \leq 180°$.

  i) $4 \sec x = -5$ **ii)** $-\frac{1}{2} = \frac{1}{3} \csc x$

9. For each equation, determine the general solution over the set of real numbers, then list the roots over the domain $-\pi \leq x < 0$.

   a) $\cos 3x - 1 = 5 \cos 3x + 2$ b) $3 \sin 4x = 3 - 2 \sin 4x$

10. Two students determined the general solution of the equation $3 \sin x + 5 = 5(\sin x + 1)$. Joseph said the solution is $x = 2\pi k$ or $x = \pi + 2\pi k$, where k is an integer. Yeoun Sun said the solution is $x = \pi k$, where k is an integer. Who is correct? Explain.

11. Solve each equation over the domain $-\pi \leq x \leq \frac{\pi}{2}$.

    a) $4\cos^2x - 3 = 0$ **b)** $2\tan^2x = 3$

12. Use factoring to solve each equation over the domain $-90° \leq x < 270°$.

    a) $2\cos x \sin x - \cos x = 0$ **b)** $3\tan x + \tan^2x = 2\tan x$

13. A student wrote the solution below to solve the equation $2\sin^2x + \sin x = 1$ over the domain $0 \leq x < 2\pi$. Identify any errors, then write a correct solution.

$2\sin^2x + \sin x = 1$

$(\sin x)(2\sin x + 1) = 1$

$\sin x = 1 \quad$ or $\quad 2\sin x + 1 = 1$

$\qquad x = \dfrac{\pi}{2} \qquad\qquad\qquad \sin x = 0$

$\qquad\qquad\qquad\qquad x = 0 \text{ or } x = \pi$

14. Solve each equation over the domain $-2\pi \le x \le 2\pi$, then determine the general solution.

a) $2\cos^2 x - \cos x - 1 = 0$ **b)** $5\sin^2 x + 3\sin x = 2$

15. Solve each equation over the domain $0 \leq x < 2\pi$.

    a) $4 \tan^2 x = 2 - 5 \tan x$ **b)** $4 \sin x + 3 = 2 \sin^2 x$

16. Write a second-degree trigonometric equation that has roots $\frac{\pi}{6}, \frac{\pi}{2}, \frac{5\pi}{6}$ over the domain $0 \leq x < 2\pi$.

17. Determine the number of roots each equation has over the domain $0 \leq x < 2\pi$, where $1 < a < b$.

 a) $(a \cos x - b)(b \sin x + a) = 0$ **b)** $(b \sin^2 x - 1)(a \tan x + b) = 0$

Multiple-Choice Questions

1. What are the roots of the equation $5 \cos x - 2 = 4 \cos x - 3$ over the domain $-\pi \leq x \leq \pi$?

 A. $0, \pi$ **B.** π **C.** $-\pi, \pi$ **D.** $-\pi, 0, \pi$

2. How many roots does the equation $2 \cos^2 bx = 1$ have over the domain $0 \leq x < 2\pi$, where b is a positive integer?

 A. 2   **B.** 4   **C.** $2b$ **D.** $4b$

Study Note

Solve these equations: $4x^2 = 2x$ and $4 \sin^2 x = 2 \sin x$ for $0 \leq x < 2\pi$
How are the strategies the same? How are they different?

ANSWERS

Check Your Understanding

1. a) $x = -270°$; $x = -270° + k360°, k \in \mathbb{Z}$

b) $x = \dfrac{\pi}{3} + \dfrac{2\pi}{3}k, k \in \mathbb{Z}$; $x = -\dfrac{\pi}{3}, x = -\pi, x = -\dfrac{5\pi}{3}$

2. a) $x \doteq 2.30, x \doteq 3.98$; $x \doteq 3.98 + 2\pi k, k \in \mathbb{Z}$ or $x \doteq 2.30 + 2\pi k, k \in \mathbb{Z}$

b) $x \doteq -16°, x \doteq -164°$; $x \doteq -16° + k360°, k \in \mathbb{Z}$ or $x \doteq -164° + k360°, k \in \mathbb{Z}$

3. $x = 45°, x = 135°, x = 225°, x = 315°$ **4. a)** $x \doteq \pm 1.12, x \doteq \pm 2.45$

b) $x \doteq \pm 1.12 + 2\pi k, k \in \mathbb{Z}$ or $x \doteq \pm 2.45 + 2\pi k, k \in \mathbb{Z}$

Exercises

4. a) $x = \dfrac{\pi}{3}, x = \dfrac{2\pi}{3}$ **b)** $x = \dfrac{\pi}{6}, x = \dfrac{7\pi}{6}$ **6. a)** $x \doteq 0.84, x \doteq 5.44$; $x \doteq 0.84 + 2\pi k,$

$k \in \mathbb{Z}$ or $x \doteq 5.44 + 2\pi k, k \in \mathbb{Z}$ **b)** $x \doteq 2.30, x \doteq 5.44$; $x \doteq 2.30 + \pi k, k \in \mathbb{Z}$ or

$x \doteq 5.44 + \pi k, k \in \mathbb{Z}$ **7. a)** $x = \dfrac{3\pi}{4}, x = -\dfrac{\pi}{4}$ **b)** $x = -\dfrac{\pi}{6}, x = -\dfrac{5\pi}{6}$

8. a) i) $x \doteq 19°$ **ii)** $x \doteq -27°$ **b) i)** $x \doteq 143°$ **ii)** $x \doteq -42°$

9. a) $x \doteq 0.81 + \dfrac{2\pi}{3}k, k \in \mathbb{Z}$, or $x \doteq 1.29 + \dfrac{2\pi}{3}k, k \in \mathbb{Z}$; $x \doteq -1.29, x \doteq -0.81,$

$x \doteq -2.90$ **b)** $x \doteq 0.16 + \dfrac{\pi}{2}k, k \in \mathbb{Z}$, or $x \doteq 0.62 + \dfrac{\pi}{2}k, k \in \mathbb{Z}$; $x \doteq -1.41,$

$x \doteq -2.98, x \doteq -0.95, x \doteq -2.52$ **11. a)** $x = \pm\dfrac{\pi}{6}, x = -\dfrac{5\pi}{6}$ **b)** $x \doteq \pm 0.89,$

$x \doteq -2.26$ **12. a)** $x = 30°, x = \pm 90°, x = 150°$ **b)** $x = 0°, x = 180°, x = 135°,$

$x = -45°$ **14. a)** $x = 0, x = \pm\dfrac{2\pi}{3}, x = \pm\dfrac{4\pi}{3}, x = \pm 2\pi$; $x = \dfrac{2\pi}{3}k, k \in \mathbb{Z}$

b) $x \doteq -5.87, x \doteq -3.55, x = -\dfrac{\pi}{2}, x \doteq 0.41, x \doteq 2.73, x = \dfrac{3\pi}{2}$; $x \doteq 0.41 + 2\pi k,$

$k \in \mathbb{Z}$ or $x \doteq 2.73 + 2\pi k, k \in \mathbb{Z}$ or $x = \dfrac{3\pi}{2} + 2\pi k, k \in \mathbb{Z}$ **15. a)** $x \doteq 0.31, x \doteq 2.14,$

$x \doteq 3.45, x \doteq 5.28$ **b)** $x \doteq 3.76, x \doteq 5.66$ **17. a)** 2 roots   **b)** 6 roots

Multiple Choice

1. C   **2.** D

✔ CHECKPOINT

Self-Assess

Can you. . .	Try *Checkpoint* question	For review, see
determine, using technology, the approximate solution of a trigonometric equation in a restricted domain?	2	Page 574 in Lesson 7.1 (Example 1)
determine, using technology, the general solution of a trigonometric equation?	3	Page 574 in Lesson 7.1 (Example 1)
verify, without technology, that a given value is a solution of a trigonometric equation?	4, 6	Page 593 in Lesson 7.2 (Question 5)
determine, algebraically, the solution of a first-degree trigonometric equation, stating the solution in exact form?	5	Page 586 in Lesson 7.2 (Example 1)
determine, algebraically, the solution of a second-degree trigonometric equation?	7	Page 589 in Lesson 7.2

Assess Your Understanding

7.1

1. **Multiple Choice** How many roots does the equation $\sin 6x = \frac{1}{3}$ have over the domain $0 \leq x < 2\pi$?

   A. 2   **B.** 4   **C.** 6   **D.** 12

2. Use graphing technology to solve each equation over the given domain. Give the roots to the nearest hundredth.

   a) $1 + 2 \sin x = 1 - 3 \cos x; 0 \leq x \leq 2\pi$

   b) $2 = \cos x + 2 \cos^2 x; -2\pi \leq x \leq 2\pi$

3. Use graphing technology to determine the general solution of each equation over the set of real numbers. Give the answers to the nearest hundredth.

a) $4 \tan x - 5 = 0$

b) $6 \cos^2 x + \cos x = 1$

7.2

4. Multiple Choice Which number is a root of the equation $3 \sin x + 1 = 5 \sin x - 1$ over the domain $0 \le x < 2\pi$?

A. 0 B. π C. $\dfrac{\pi}{2}$ D. $\dfrac{3\pi}{2}$

5. Use algebra to solve the equation $\sqrt{2} \cos 2x + 1 = 0$ over the domain $-\pi < x < \pi$, then write the general solution of the equation.

6. Verify that $\frac{\pi}{6}$ and $\frac{5\pi}{6}$ are two roots of the equation $4\cos^2 x - 3 = 0$.

7. Use algebra to solve the equation $10\sin^2 x + 11\sin x = -3$ over the domain $90° \leq x \leq 360°$. Give the roots to the nearest degree.

ANSWERS

1. D   2. a) $x \doteq 2.16, x \doteq 5.30$ b) $x \doteq \pm 0.67, x \doteq \pm 5.61$

3. a) $x \doteq 0.90 + \pi k, k \in \mathbb{Z}$ b) $x \doteq 1.23 + 2\pi k, k \in \mathbb{Z}$ or $x \doteq 2.09 + 2\pi k, k \in \mathbb{Z}$ or
$x \doteq 4.19 + 2\pi k, k \in \mathbb{Z}$ or $x \doteq 5.05 + 2\pi k, k \in \mathbb{Z}$ 4. C

5. $x = \pm\frac{3\pi}{8}, x = \pm\frac{5\pi}{8}; x = \frac{3\pi}{8} + \pi k, k \in \mathbb{Z}$ or $x = \frac{5\pi}{8} + \pi k, k \in \mathbb{Z}$

7. $x = 210°, x \doteq 217°, x \doteq 323°, x = 330°$

Get Started

Simplify each expression, where $a, b, c, d \neq 0$

$$\frac{a}{b} + \frac{b}{c}$$
$$\frac{a^2 - ab}{b^2 - a^2}$$

$$\frac{\dfrac{a}{b}}{\dfrac{c}{d}}$$
$$\frac{\dfrac{a}{c} + \dfrac{1}{b}}{b + \dfrac{c}{a}}$$

Construct Understanding

Use these values: $\theta = 0, \theta = \dfrac{\pi}{4}, \theta = \dfrac{\pi}{3}, \theta = \dfrac{\pi}{2}$

For which values of θ is each equation below true?

Is either equation true for all values of θ for which the trigonometric ratios are defined? Justify your response.

$\tan \theta \cos \theta = \sin \theta$ $\tan \theta \sin \theta = \cos \theta$

A **trigonometric identity** is a statement that relates trigonometric ratios, and is true for all values of the variable for which the trigonometric ratios are defined.

The equation $\tan \theta \cos \theta = \sin \theta$ is an identity because it is true for all values of θ except $\theta = \frac{\pi}{2} + \pi k$, $k \in \mathbb{Z}$, where $\tan \theta$ is not defined.

In Lesson 6.1, six trigonometric functions were defined in terms of an angle θ in standard position in a unit circle and a terminal point $P(x, y)$ on the unit circle.

$\sin \theta = y$ $\qquad\qquad$ $\cos \theta = x$ $\qquad\qquad$ $\tan \theta = \frac{y}{x}, x \neq 0$

$\csc \theta = \frac{1}{y}, y \neq 0$ $\qquad$ $\sec \theta = \frac{1}{x}, x \neq 0$ $\qquad$ $\cot \theta = \frac{x}{y}, y \neq 0$

The following identities are developed from the definitions above.

Reciprocal Identities

$\csc \theta = \dfrac{1}{\sin \theta}$, $\qquad\qquad$ $\sec \theta = \dfrac{1}{\cos \theta}$, $\qquad\qquad$ $\cot \theta = \dfrac{1}{\tan \theta}$,

$\sin \theta \neq 0$ $\qquad\qquad$ $\cos \theta \neq 0$ $\qquad\qquad$ $\sin \theta \neq 0$ and $\cos \theta \neq 0$

Quotient Identities

$\tan \theta = \dfrac{\sin \theta}{\cos \theta}$, $\cos \theta \neq 0$ $\qquad\qquad$ $\cot \theta = \dfrac{\cos \theta}{\sin \theta}$, $\sin \theta \neq 0$

The reciprocal identities can be rearranged and written in other forms:

$\csc \theta = \dfrac{1}{\sin \theta}$, $\sin \theta \neq 0$ $\qquad\qquad\qquad$ $\sec \theta = \dfrac{1}{\cos \theta}$, $\cos \theta \neq 0$

or, $\csc \theta \sin \theta = 1$ $\qquad\qquad\qquad\qquad$ or, $\sec \theta \cos \theta = 1$

$\cot \theta = \dfrac{1}{\tan \theta}$, $\sin \theta \neq 0$ and $\cos \theta \neq 0$

or, $\cot \theta \tan \theta = 1$

The restrictions on page 606 indicate that the expressions on both sides of an identity are equal for all values of the variable for which each expression is defined. This is true for all identities, so it is not necessary to write the non-permissible values of an identity because they can be identified by determining where each side of the identity is undefined.

A trigonometric identity can be verified algebraically by substituting a value for the variable. A verification shows that an identity is true for specific values of the variable; it does not prove that the identity is true for all values of the variable for which each trigonometric ratio is defined.

To prove an identity is valid, it must be shown that one side of the identity is equal to the other side, or that both sides are equal to the same expression.

When proving an identity, it is often helpful to start by writing all the trigonometric ratios in the identity in terms of the sine and cosine ratios to identify what can be simplified.

Example 1   Verifying then Proving an Identity

For each identity below:
   i) Verify the identity for $\theta = \frac{\pi}{4}$.
   ii) Prove the identity.
a) $\sin \theta \sec \theta \cot \theta = 1$ **b)** $\dfrac{\sin \theta + \cos \theta}{\sin \theta} = 1 + \cot \theta$

Check Your Understanding

1. For each identity below:
  i) Verify the identity for $\theta = 30°$.
  ii) Prove the identity.
  a) $(\sec \theta)(1 + \cos \theta)$
     $= 1 + \sec \theta$
  b) $1 - \tan \theta = \dfrac{\cot \theta - 1}{\cot \theta}$

SOLUTION

a) i) $\sin \theta \sec \theta \cot \theta = 1$ Substitute: $\theta = \frac{\pi}{4}$

   L.S. $= \sin \frac{\pi}{4} \sec \frac{\pi}{4} \cot \frac{\pi}{4}$ R.S. $= 1$

       $= \left(\dfrac{1}{\sqrt{2}}\right)(\sqrt{2})(1)$

       $= 1$

The left side is equal to the right side, so $\theta = \frac{\pi}{4}$ is verified.

ii) Simplify the left side.

   L.S. $= \sin \theta \sec \theta \cot \theta$ Substitute: $\sec \theta = \dfrac{1}{\cos \theta}$, $\cot \theta = \dfrac{\cos \theta}{\sin \theta}$

       $= \cancel{\sin \theta}^{1} \cdot \dfrac{1}{\cancel{\cos \theta}^{1}} \cdot \dfrac{\cancel{\cos \theta}^{1}}{\cancel{\sin \theta}^{1}}$

       $= 1$

       $=$ R.S.

The left side is equal to the right side, so the identity is proved.

b) **i)** $\dfrac{\sin \theta + \cos \theta}{\sin \theta} = 1 + \cot \theta$ Substitute: $\theta = \dfrac{\pi}{4}$

$$\text{L.S.} = \frac{\sin \dfrac{\pi}{4} + \cos \dfrac{\pi}{4}}{\sin \dfrac{\pi}{4}} \qquad \text{R.S.} = 1 + \cot \frac{\pi}{4}$$
$$= 1 + 1$$
$$= 2$$

$$= \frac{\dfrac{1}{\sqrt{2}} + \dfrac{1}{\sqrt{2}}}{\dfrac{1}{\sqrt{2}}}$$

$$= \frac{\dfrac{2}{\sqrt{2}}}{\dfrac{1}{\sqrt{2}}}$$

$$= 2$$

The left side is equal to the right side, so $\theta = \dfrac{\pi}{4}$ is verified.

ii) Simplify the right side.

$$\text{R.S.} = 1 + \cot \theta \qquad \text{Substitute: } \cot \theta = \frac{\cos \theta}{\sin \theta}$$
$$= 1 + \frac{\cos \theta}{\sin \theta}$$
$$= \frac{\sin \theta + \cos \theta}{\sin \theta}$$
$$= \text{L.S.}$$

The left side is equal to the right side, so the identity is proved.

THINK FURTHER

In *Example 1a*, why did it make sense to start with the left side?

In *Example 1b*, the identity can also be proved by beginning with the left side of the identity:

$$\text{L.S.} = \frac{\sin \theta + \cos \theta}{\sin \theta}$$
$$= \frac{\sin \theta}{\sin \theta} + \frac{\cos \theta}{\sin \theta}$$
$$= 1 + \cot \theta$$
$$= \text{R.S.}$$

An identity can be verified graphically by graphing the functions that correspond to each side of the identity. For *Example 1b*, graph $y = \dfrac{\sin \theta + \cos \theta}{\sin \theta}$ and $y = 1 + \cot \theta$; notice that $\cot \theta$ is entered as $\dfrac{1}{\tan \theta}$.

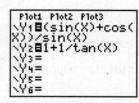
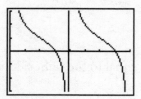

The graphs coincide, so the identity is verified.

When both sides of an identity are complicated, it may be easier to prove the identity by showing that both sides simplify to the same expression. This is illustrated in *Example 2b*.

Example 2	Identifying Restrictions then Proving an Identity

For each identity below:
  i) Determine the non-permissible values of θ.
  ii) Prove the identity.

a) $\cos^2\theta = \dfrac{\cot\theta \sin\theta}{\sec\theta}$

b) $\dfrac{\sin\theta + \tan\theta}{1 + \cos\theta} = \sin\theta \sec\theta$

Check Your Understanding

2. For each identity below:
  i) Determine the non-permissible values of θ.
  ii) Prove the identity.
  a) $\dfrac{\cot\theta}{\csc\theta} = \cos\theta$
  b) $\cos\theta = \dfrac{1 + \cos\theta}{1 + \sec\theta}$

SOLUTION

a) i) $\cos^2\theta = \dfrac{\cot\theta \sin\theta}{\sec\theta}$

$\sec\theta = \dfrac{1}{\cos\theta}$, $\cot\theta = \dfrac{\cos\theta}{\sin\theta}$, and $\sec\theta$ is a denominator that is never 0, so the non-permissible values occur when:

$\cos\theta = 0$ or $\sin\theta = 0$

$\theta = \dfrac{\pi}{2} + \pi k, k \in \mathbb{Z}$ $\theta = \pi k, k \in \mathbb{Z}$

These non-permissible values can be combined and written as:
$\theta = \dfrac{\pi}{2}k, k \in \mathbb{Z}$

ii) Simplify the right side.

R.S. $= \dfrac{\cot\theta \sin\theta}{\sec\theta}$ Substitute: $\cot\theta = \dfrac{\cos\theta}{\sin\theta}$, $\sec\theta = \dfrac{1}{\cos\theta}$

$= \dfrac{\dfrac{\cos\theta}{\cancel{\sin\theta}} \cdot \cancel{\sin\theta}}{\dfrac{1}{\cos\theta}}$

$= \cos\theta \left(\dfrac{\cos\theta}{1}\right)$

$= \cos^2\theta$

$=$ L.S.

The left side is equal to the right side, so the identity is proved.

b) i) $\dfrac{\sin\theta + \tan\theta}{1 + \cos\theta} = \sin\theta \sec\theta$

$\tan\theta = \dfrac{\sin\theta}{\cos\theta}$, $\sec\theta = \dfrac{1}{\cos\theta}$, and $1 + \cos\theta$ is a denominator, so the non-permissible values occur when:

$\cos\theta = 0$ or $1 + \cos\theta = 0$

$\theta = \dfrac{\pi}{2} + \pi k, k \in \mathbb{Z}$ $\cos\theta = -1$

$\theta = \pi + 2\pi k, k \in \mathbb{Z}$

ii) Simplify the left side. Simplify the right side.

$$\text{L.S.} = \frac{\sin\theta + \tan\theta}{1 + \cos\theta}$$ $$\text{R.S.} = \sin\theta\sec\theta$$

Substitute: $\tan\theta = \dfrac{\sin\theta}{\cos\theta}$ $= \sin\theta\left(\dfrac{1}{\cos\theta}\right)$

$$\text{L.S.} = \frac{\sin\theta + \dfrac{\sin\theta}{\cos\theta}}{1 + \cos\theta}$$ $$= \frac{\sin\theta}{\cos\theta}$$

$$= \frac{\cos\theta\sin\theta + \sin\theta}{\cos\theta(1 + \cos\theta)}$$

$$= \frac{\sin\theta\,\cancel{(\cos\theta + 1)}^{\,1}}{\cos\theta\,\cancel{(1 + \cos\theta)}^{\,1}}$$

$$= \frac{\sin\theta}{\cos\theta}$$

The left and right sides simplify to the same expression, so the identity is proved.

Example 3	**Using Identities in the Solution of an Equation**

Check Your Understanding

3. Use algebra to solve each equation over the domain $0 \le x < 2\pi$.

a) $2\sin x = 3 + 2\csc x$

b) $\sin x = \cos x$

Use algebra to solve each equation over the domain $0 \le x < 2\pi$. Give the roots to the nearest hundredth where necessary.

a) $3\cos x + 1 = 2\sec x$ **b)** $\sin x + \sqrt{3}\cos x = 0$

SOLUTION

a) $3\cos x + 1 = 2\sec x$ Substitute: $\sec x = \dfrac{1}{\cos x}$

$3\cos x + 1 = 2\left(\dfrac{1}{\cos x}\right)$ Multiply each side by $\cos x$.

$3\cos^2 x + \cos x = 2$ Solve for x.

$3\cos^2 x + \cos x - 2 = 0$

$(3\cos x - 2)(\cos x + 1) = 0$

$3\cos x - 2 = 0$ or $\cos x + 1 = 0$

$\cos x = \dfrac{2}{3}$ $\cos x = -1$

$x \doteq 0.84$ or $x \doteq 5.44$ $x = \pi$

The roots are: $x \doteq 0.84$, $x \doteq 5.44$, and $x = \pi$

Verify the roots by substitution.

b) $\sin x + \sqrt{3}\cos x = 0$ Assume $\cos x \ne 0$, then divide by $\cos x$.

$\dfrac{\sin x}{\cos x} + \dfrac{\sqrt{3}\cos x}{\cos x} = 0$

$\tan x + \sqrt{3} = 0$

$\tan x = -\sqrt{3}$

$x = \dfrac{2\pi}{3}$ or $x = \dfrac{5\pi}{3}$

For $\cos x = 0, x = \dfrac{\pi}{2}$ or $x = \dfrac{3\pi}{2}$

Verify by substitution that neither value of x is a root of the given equation.

The roots are: $x = \dfrac{2\pi}{3}$ and $x = \dfrac{5\pi}{3}$

Verify the roots by substitution.

Here are some strategies to use to prove an identity:

- Start by simplifying the side of the identity that is more complex.
- Write the expressions in terms of $\sin x$ and $\cos x$.

Discuss the Ideas

1. What is the difference between a trigonometric identity and a trigonometric equation? Suppose you are given a trigonometric equation. What strategy can you use to check whether it might be an identity?

2. Can you conclude that an equation is an identity when it is shown to be valid for a given value of the variable? Explain.

Exercises

A

3. Write each expression in terms of a single trigonometric function.

a) $\dfrac{\cos \theta}{\sin \theta}$

b) $\dfrac{\sin^2\theta}{\cos^2\theta}$

c) $\sin^2\theta \sec \theta \cos \theta \csc \theta$

d) $\dfrac{\sin^2\theta}{\tan^2\theta}$

4. Determine the non-permissible values of θ.

a) $\sec \theta$

b) $\tan \theta$

c) $\dfrac{\csc \theta}{\cos \theta}$

d) $\dfrac{\sec \theta}{\sin \theta}$

5. Verify each identity for the given value of θ.

a) $\tan \theta \csc \theta \sec \theta = \sec^2\theta; \theta = 150°$

b) $\dfrac{\tan\theta\csc^2\theta}{\sec^2\theta} = \cot\theta;\ \theta = \dfrac{4\pi}{3}$

6. Prove each identity in question 5.

7. For each identity:

    i) Verify the identity using graphing technology.

    ii) Prove the identity.

    a) $1 - \sin\theta = (\sin\theta)(\csc\theta - 1)$ **b)** $-\cot\theta = \dfrac{1 - \cot\theta}{1 - \tan\theta}$

8. For each identity:

    i) Verify the identity for $\theta = 45°$.

    ii) Prove the identity.

    a) $\dfrac{\cot\theta}{\cos\theta} - \csc\theta = 0$ **b)** $\tan^2\theta\cos^2\theta + \sin^2\theta = \dfrac{2}{\csc^2\theta}$

9. For each identity:

    i) Verify the identity for $\theta = \dfrac{7\pi}{6}$.

    ii) Prove the identity.

a) $\csc \theta = \dfrac{\csc \theta - 1}{1 - \sin \theta}$

b) $\dfrac{\cos \theta - \cot \theta}{1 - \sin \theta} = -\cot \theta$

10. Use algebra to solve each equation over the domain $0 \leq x < 2\pi$. Give the roots to the nearest hundredth where necessary.

a) $\tan x = \cot x$

b) $\cos x + \sqrt{3} \sin x = 0$

c) $2 \cos x = 7 - 3 \sec x$

d) $\sin^2 x = \sin x \cos x$

11. Identify any errors in this proof, then write a correct algebraic proof.

To prove: $\dfrac{\sin \theta}{1 - \sin \theta} = \dfrac{1}{\csc \theta - 1}$

$\text{L.S.} = \dfrac{\sin \theta}{1 - \sin \theta}$

$= \dfrac{\sin \theta}{1} - \dfrac{\sin \theta}{\sin \theta}$

$= \sin \theta - 1$

$= \dfrac{1}{\csc \theta} - 1$

$= \dfrac{1}{\csc \theta - 1}$

$= \text{R.S.}$

12. Identify which equation below is an identity. Justify your answer. Prove the identity. Solve the other equation over the domain $-\pi \le x \le \pi$. Give the roots to the nearest hundredth.

a) $\dfrac{2 \sin^2 x + 1}{\sin x} = 2 \csc^2 x - 1$ b) $\dfrac{\sin^2 x + 1}{\sin x} = \dfrac{1 + \csc^2 x}{\csc x}$

C

13. Here are two identities that involve the cotangent ratio:

$\cot \theta = \dfrac{1}{\tan \theta}$ and $\cot \theta = \dfrac{\cos \theta}{\sin \theta}$

a) Show how you can derive one identity from the other.

b) Determine the non-permissible values of θ for each identity. Explain why these values are different. How could you illustrate this using graphing technology?

Multiple-Choice Questions

1. Which expression is the simplest form of $\sec \theta \tan \theta \cos \theta \csc \theta$?

   A. $\sec \theta$ **B.** $\csc \theta$ **C.** $\dfrac{\cos \theta}{\sin^2 \theta}$ **D.** $\dfrac{\sin \theta}{\cos^2 \theta}$

2. What are the restrictions on the expression $\dfrac{\sin \theta + 1}{\tan \theta}$?

   A. $\cos \theta \neq 0$

   B. $\cos \theta \neq 0, \sin \theta \neq 0$

   C. $\cos \theta \neq 0, \sin \theta \neq 0, \sin \theta \neq 1$

   D. $\cos \theta \neq 0, \sin \theta \neq 1$

Study Note

Write a trigonometric identity in terms of θ that is different from any in this lesson. Identify the non-permissible values of θ. Verify your identity graphically.

©P   DO NOT COPY.

7.4   The Pythagorean Identities

FOCUS Prove then apply the three Pythagorean identities.

Get Started

In the unit circle at the right, explain why $\sin^2\theta + \cos^2\theta = 1$. This equation is an identity. Why do you think it is called the Pythagorean identity?

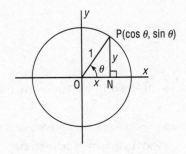

Construct Understanding

Prove algebraically that each equation below is an identity. Determine any non-permissible values of θ.

$$\tan^2\theta + 1 = \sec^2\theta \qquad 1 + \cot^2\theta = \csc^2\theta$$

The following identities are the Pythagorean identities.

> **Pythagorean Identities**
>
> $\sin^2\theta + \cos^2\theta = 1$
>
> $\tan^2\theta + 1 = \sec^2\theta$
>
> $1 + \cot^2\theta = \csc^2\theta$

These identities can be rearranged to form equivalent identities.

$\sin^2\theta + \cos^2\theta = 1$ can be written as:
$\sin^2\theta = 1 - \cos^2\theta$ or $\cos^2\theta = 1 - \sin^2\theta$

$\tan^2\theta + 1 = \sec^2\theta$ can be written as:
$\tan^2\theta = \sec^2\theta - 1$ or $\sec^2\theta - \tan^2\theta = 1$

$1 + \cot^2\theta = \csc^2\theta$ can be written as:
$\cot^2\theta = \csc^2\theta - 1$ or $\csc^2\theta - \cot^2\theta = 1$

The Pythagorean identities can be used to prove other identities or to simplify an equation before solving it.

| Example 1 | Using the Pythagorean Identities to Prove Other Identities |

Check Your Understanding

Prove each identity.

a) $\csc\theta\cos^2\theta + \sin\theta = \csc\theta$ **b)** $\sin^4\theta - \cos^4\theta = \sin^2\theta - \cos^2\theta$

1. Prove each identity.

   a) $\cot\theta + \tan\theta = \csc\theta\sec\theta$

   b) $\cot^3\theta = \cot\theta\csc^2\theta - \cot\theta$

SOLUTION

a) $\csc\theta\cos^2\theta + \sin\theta = \csc\theta$

$\text{L.S.} = \csc\theta\cos^2\theta + \sin\theta$ Replace $\csc\theta$ with $\dfrac{1}{\sin\theta}$.

$= \dfrac{1}{\sin\theta}(\cos^2\theta) + \sin\theta$

$= \dfrac{\cos^2\theta}{\sin\theta} + \sin\theta$ Use a common denominator.

$= \dfrac{\cos^2\theta + \sin^2\theta}{\sin\theta}$ Replace $\cos^2\theta + \sin^2\theta$ with 1.

$= \dfrac{1}{\sin\theta}$

$= \csc\theta$

$= \text{R.S.}$

The left side is equal to the right side, so the identity is proved.

b) $\sin^4\theta - \cos^4\theta = \sin^2\theta - \cos^2\theta$

$\text{L.S.} = \sin^4\theta - \cos^4\theta$ Factor using a difference of squares.

$= (\sin^2\theta - \cos^2\theta)(\sin^2\theta + \cos^2\theta)$ Replace $\sin^2\theta + \cos^2\theta$ with 1.

$= \sin^2\theta - \cos^2\theta$

$= \text{R.S.}$

The left side is equal to the right side, so the identity is proved.

Example 1 illustrates these strategies to help to prove an identity:

- writing terms with a common denominator
- factoring using the difference of squares

Recall how to rationalize a binomial denominator, such as $\dfrac{2}{1 + \sqrt{3}}$, by

multiplying the numerator and denominator by the conjugate $1 - \sqrt{3}$:

$\left(\dfrac{2}{1 + \sqrt{3}}\right)\left(\dfrac{1 - \sqrt{3}}{1 - \sqrt{3}}\right) = \dfrac{2 - 2\sqrt{3}}{-2}$

$= \dfrac{-2(\sqrt{3} - 1)}{-2}$

$= \sqrt{3} - 1$

This strategy may also be used in the proofs for some trigonometric identities that involve factors such as $1 \pm \sin\theta$ or $1 \pm \cos\theta$.

THINK FURTHER

How could you prove the identity in *Example 1b*, by beginning with the right side?

Example 2   **Proving Identities Involving Fractions**

2. Prove each identity.

a) $\dfrac{1 - \cos\theta}{\sin\theta} = \dfrac{\sin\theta}{1 + \cos\theta}$

b) $\dfrac{1}{1 - \cos\theta} + \dfrac{1}{1 + \cos\theta}$
$= 2\csc^2\theta$

Prove each identity.

a) $\dfrac{\cos\theta\sin\theta}{1 + \sin\theta} = \dfrac{1 - \sin\theta}{\cot\theta}$ b) $2\sec\theta = \dfrac{\cos\theta}{1 - \sin\theta} + \dfrac{\cos\theta}{1 + \sin\theta}$

SOLUTION

a) $\dfrac{\cos\theta\sin\theta}{1 + \sin\theta} = \dfrac{1 - \sin\theta}{\cot\theta}$

L.S. $= \dfrac{\cos\theta\sin\theta}{1 + \sin\theta}$ Multiply numerator and denominator by the conjugate of the denominator.

$= \left(\dfrac{\cos\theta\sin\theta}{1 + \sin\theta}\right)\left(\dfrac{1 - \sin\theta}{1 - \sin\theta}\right)$

$= \dfrac{\cos\theta\sin\theta(1 - \sin\theta)}{1 - \sin^2\theta}$

$= \dfrac{\cancel{\cos\theta}^{\,1}\sin\theta(1 - \sin\theta)}{\cos^{\cancel{2}}\theta}$ Replace $\dfrac{\sin\theta}{\cos\theta}$ with $\tan\theta$.

$= \tan\theta(1 - \sin\theta)$ Replace $\tan\theta$ with $\dfrac{1}{\cot\theta}$.

$= \dfrac{1 - \sin\theta}{\cot\theta}$

$=$ R.S.

The left side is equal to the right side, so the identity is proved.

b) $2\sec\theta = \dfrac{\cos\theta}{1 - \sin\theta} + \dfrac{\cos\theta}{1 + \sin\theta}$

R.S. $= \dfrac{\cos\theta}{1 - \sin\theta} + \dfrac{\cos\theta}{1 + \sin\theta}$ Write the fractions with a common denominator.

$= \dfrac{\cos\theta(1 + \sin\theta) + \cos\theta(1 - \sin\theta)}{(1 - \sin\theta)(1 + \sin\theta)}$ Expand.

$= \dfrac{\cos\theta + \cos\theta\sin\theta + \cos\theta - \cos\theta\sin\theta}{1 - \sin^2\theta}$ Replace $1 - \sin^2\theta$ with $\cos^2\theta$.

$= \dfrac{2\cancel{\cos\theta}}{\cos^{\cancel{2}}\theta}$

$= \dfrac{2}{\cos\theta}$

$= 2\sec\theta$

$=$ L.S.

The left side is equal to the right side, so the identity is proved.

Use algebra to solve the equation $2\cos^2 x - 3\sin x = 0$ over the domain $\frac{\pi}{2} \leq x < 2\pi$.

SOLUTION

$$2\cos^2 x - 3\sin x = 0 \qquad \text{Replace } \cos^2 x \text{ with } 1 - \sin^2 x.$$
$$2(1 - \sin^2 x) - 3\sin x = 0$$
$$2 - 2\sin^2 x - 3\sin x = 0$$
$$2\sin^2 x + 3\sin x - 2 = 0 \qquad \text{Factor.}$$
$$(2\sin x - 1)(\sin x + 2) = 0$$

Either $2\sin x - 1 = 0$ or $\sin x + 2 = 0$

$$\sin x = \frac{1}{2} \qquad\qquad \sin x = -2$$

Since -2 is outside the range of $\sin x$, there is no solution.

$$x = \frac{5\pi}{6}$$

So, the root is: $x = \frac{5\pi}{6}$

Verify the root by substitution.

3. Use algebra to solve the equation
$$3 - 3\cos x - 2\sin^2 x = 0$$
over the domain $0 \leq x < \frac{3\pi}{2}$.

Discuss the Ideas

1. When can you use a conjugate to help prove an identity?

2. The Pythagorean identity $\sin^2 \theta + \cos^2 \theta = 1$ was shown to be true for an angle θ in Quadrant 1 in Grade 11. How do you know that this identity and the other two Pythagorean identities are true for all values of θ for which the trigonometric ratios are defined?

Exercises

3. For each expression below:

    i) Determine any non-permissible values of θ.

    ii) Write the expression as a single term.

a) $1 - \cos^2\theta$ **b)** $\cos^2\theta - 1$

c) $\sec^2\theta - 1$ **d)** $1 - \sec^2\theta$

e) $\csc^2\theta - \cot^2\theta$ **f)** $\sin^2\theta + \cos^2\theta + 1$

4. a) Verify the identity $\tan^2\theta + 1 = \sec^2\theta$ for $\theta = \dfrac{2\pi}{3}$.

b) Verify the identity $1 + \cot^2\theta = \csc^2\theta$ using graphing technology.

c) Verify the identity $\sin^2\theta + \cos^2\theta = 1$ for $\theta = 300°$.

B

5. For each expression below:

    i) Determine any non-permissible values of θ.

    ii) Write the expression as a single term.

a) $\dfrac{\sqrt{1 - \sin^2\theta}}{\sqrt{1 + \tan^2\theta}}$

b) $\dfrac{1 - \sin^2\theta + \cos^2\theta}{\cos\theta}$

c) $\dfrac{\cos\theta}{1 + \sin\theta} + \dfrac{\cos\theta}{1 - \sin\theta}$

d) $\dfrac{\csc\theta}{\cot\theta + \tan\theta}$

6. For each identity:

    i) Verify the identity using graphing technology.

    ii) Prove the identity.

  a) $1 - \cos^2\theta = \cos^2\theta \tan^2\theta$ **b)** $\sin^2\theta + \cos^2\theta + \tan^2\theta = \sec^2\theta$

7. For each identity:

    i) Verify the identity for $\theta = 240°$.   **ii)** Prove the identity.

  a) $\cot^2\theta \sec\theta + \dfrac{1}{\cos\theta} = \csc^2\theta \sec\theta$ **b)** $\dfrac{\tan\theta}{\cos\theta - \sec\theta} = -\csc\theta$

8. Is either of these statements true? Justify your answer.

   a) Since $\tan \theta = \dfrac{\sin \theta}{\cos \theta}$, then $\tan^2\theta = \dfrac{\sin^2\theta}{\cos^2\theta}$

   b) Since $\sin^2\theta + \cos^2\theta = 1$, then $\sin \theta + \cos \theta = 1$

9. For each identity:

   i) Determine the non-permissible values of θ.

   ii) Prove the identity.

   a) $\dfrac{1}{\csc \theta + \cot \theta} = \csc \theta - \cot \theta$ **b)** $\sin \theta + \dfrac{\cos \theta}{\tan \theta} = \dfrac{1}{\cos \theta \tan \theta}$

10. Use algebra to solve each equation over the domain $-90° \leq x \leq 270°$. Give the roots to the nearest degree.

a) $4 - 4\cos^2 x = \sin x$ b) $\cos x + 1 = 2\sin^2 x$

11. Identify whether each equation is an identity. Justify your answer. Prove each identity. Use algebra to solve each equation that is not an identity over the domain $-\pi \leq x \leq \pi$. Give the roots to the nearest hundredth.

a) $\cos^2 x = (\sin x)(\csc x + \sin x)$

b) $(\cos x)(\sec x - \cos x) = \cos^2 x$

12. a) Prove this identity: $\dfrac{\cot \theta}{\csc \theta + 1} = \dfrac{\csc \theta - 1}{\cot \theta}$

b) Predict a similar identity involving $\tan \theta$ and $\sec \theta$.
Prove this identity.

13. Determine a single trigonometric function for m such that the equation $\dfrac{2 - \sin^2\theta}{\cos\theta} = m + \cos\theta$ is an identity. Verify your answer by proving the identity.

Multiple-Choice Questions

1. Which expression is equivalent to $\cos^2\theta + \sin^2\theta \cot^2\theta$?

    A. $\cos^4\theta$ **B.** $2\cos^2\theta$ **C.** $\cot^2\theta$ **D.** $1 + \cot^2\theta$

2. Which expression is equivalent to $\tan\theta + \cot\theta$?

    A. 1 **B.** $\cos\theta\sin\theta$ **C.** $\csc\theta\sec\theta$ **D.** $\sin\theta + \cos\theta$

Study Note

Write the three Pythagorean identities. Show how the identities that involve $\tan \theta$ and $\cot \theta$ can be determined from the identity that involves $\sin \theta$ and $\cos \theta$.

Check Your Understanding

3. $x = 0, x = \dfrac{\pi}{3}$

Exercises

3. a) ii) $\sin^2\theta$ b) ii) $-\sin^2\theta$ c) i) $\theta \neq \dfrac{\pi}{2} + \pi k, k \in \mathbb{Z}$ ii) $\tan^2\theta$

d) i) $\theta \neq \dfrac{\pi}{2} + \pi k, k \in \mathbb{Z}$ ii) $-\tan^2\theta$ e) i) $\theta \neq \pi k, k \in \mathbb{Z}$

ii) 1   f) ii) 2   5. a) i) $\theta \neq \dfrac{\pi}{2} + \pi k, k \in \mathbb{Z}$ ii) $\cos^2\theta$ b) i) $\theta \neq \dfrac{\pi}{2} + \pi k, k \in \mathbb{Z}$

ii) $2\cos \theta$ c) i) $\theta \neq \dfrac{\pi}{2} + \pi k, k \in \mathbb{Z}$ ii) $2\sec \theta$ d) i) $\theta \neq \dfrac{\pi}{2} + \pi k, k \in \mathbb{Z}$ and

$\theta \neq \pi k, k \in \mathbb{Z}$ ii) $\cos \theta$ 8. a) true   b) false   9. a) i) $\theta \neq \pi k, k \in \mathbb{Z}$

b) i) $\theta \neq \dfrac{\pi}{2} + \pi k, k \in \mathbb{Z}$ and $\theta \neq \pi k, k \in \mathbb{Z}$ 10. a) $x = 0°, x = 180°, x \doteq 14°,$

$x \doteq 166°$ b) $x = 60°, x = -60°, x = 180°$ 11. a) no solution

b) $x \doteq 0.79, x \doteq 2.36, x \doteq -2.36, x \doteq -0.79$

Multiple Choice

1. B   2. C

Get Started

In the following statements, a and b are real numbers. Determine some values of a and b for which each statement is true. Identify any identities. Justify your answers.

$3(a + b) = 3a + 3b$

$\log (a + b) = \log a + \log b$

$(a + b)^2 = a^2 + b^2$

$\sin (a + b) = \sin a + \sin b$

Construct Understanding

Verify that each statement is true:

$\sin (30° + 60°) = \sin 30° \cos 60° + \cos 30° \sin 60°$

$\cos (30° + 60°) = \cos 30° \cos 60° - \sin 30° \sin 60°$

Determine similar statements for $\sin (30° - 60°)$ and $\cos (30° - 60°)$.

The statements that were verified above can be generalized to form the **sum and difference identities**.

Sum and Difference Identities for Sine and Cosine

$\sin(\alpha + \beta) = \sin\alpha\cos\beta + \cos\alpha\sin\beta$

$\cos(\alpha + \beta) = \cos\alpha\cos\beta - \sin\alpha\sin\beta$

$\sin(\alpha - \beta) = \sin\alpha\cos\beta - \cos\alpha\sin\beta$

$\cos(\alpha - \beta) = \cos\alpha\cos\beta + \sin\alpha\sin\beta$

The sum or difference identities can be used to determine the exact values of some sine and cosine ratios. For example, to determine the exact value of sin 75°, write 75° as 45° + 30°, then use:

$\sin(\alpha + \beta) = \sin\alpha\cos\beta + \cos\alpha\sin\beta$ Substitute: $\alpha = 45°, \beta = 30°$

$\sin(45° + 30°) = \sin 45°\cos 30° + \cos 45°\sin 30°$

$$\sin 75° = \left(\frac{1}{\sqrt{2}}\right)\left(\frac{\sqrt{3}}{2}\right) + \left(\frac{1}{\sqrt{2}}\right)\left(\frac{1}{2}\right)$$

$$= \frac{\sqrt{3}}{2\sqrt{2}} + \frac{1}{2\sqrt{2}}$$

$$= \frac{\sqrt{3} + 1}{2\sqrt{2}}$$

THINK FURTHER

How else could you use a sum or difference identity to determine sin 75°?

Example 1 **Applying the Sum and Difference Identities**

Given angle α in standard position with its terminal arm in Quadrant 2 and $\cos \alpha = -\frac{5}{13}$, and angle β in standard position with its terminal arm in Quadrant 1 and $\sin \beta = \frac{3}{5}$, determine the exact value of $\cos (\alpha - \beta)$.

SOLUTION

Use the identity: $\cos (\alpha - \beta) = \cos \alpha \cos \beta + \sin \alpha \sin \beta$
To determine the values of $\cos \beta$ and $\sin \alpha$, sketch each angle in standard position.

For angle α

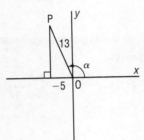

For angle β

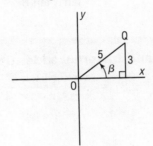

Use: $x^2 + y^2 = r^2$
Substitute: $x = -5, r = 13$
$(-5)^2 + y^2 = 13^2$
$\quad\quad y^2 = 144$
$\quad\quad\; y = \pm 12$
Since the terminal arm of angle α lies in Quadrant 2, y is positive.
So, $\sin \alpha = \frac{12}{13}$

Use: $x^2 + y^2 = r^2$
Substitute: $y = 3, r = 5$
$x^2 + 3^2 = 5^2$
$\quad\; x^2 = 16$
$\quad\;\; x = \pm 4$
Since the terminal arm of angle β lies in Quadrant 1, x is positive.
So, $\cos \beta = \frac{4}{5}$

Substitute the values of the trigonometric ratios in the identity:
$\cos (\alpha - \beta) = \cos \alpha \cos \beta + \sin \alpha \sin \beta$
$\cos (\alpha - \beta) = \left(-\frac{5}{13}\right)\left(\frac{4}{5}\right) + \left(\frac{12}{13}\right)\left(\frac{3}{5}\right)$
$\cos (\alpha - \beta) = -\frac{20}{65} + \frac{36}{65}$
$\cos (\alpha - \beta) = \frac{16}{65}$

1. Given angle α in standard position with its terminal arm in Quadrant 3 and $\cos \alpha = -\frac{3}{5}$, and angle β in standard position with its terminal arm in Quadrant 2 and $\sin \beta = \frac{1}{3}$, determine the exact value of $\sin (\alpha + \beta)$.

There are sum and difference identities for the tangent ratio.

$$\tan(\alpha + \beta) = \frac{\sin(\alpha + \beta)}{\cos(\alpha + \beta)}$$ Expand.

$$= \frac{\sin\alpha\cos\beta + \cos\alpha\sin\beta}{\cos\alpha\cos\beta - \sin\alpha\sin\beta}$$ Divide numerator and denominator by $\cos\alpha\cos\beta$.

$$= \frac{\dfrac{\sin\alpha\cos\beta}{\cos\alpha\cos\beta} + \dfrac{\cos\alpha\sin\beta}{\cos\alpha\cos\beta}}{\dfrac{\cos\alpha\cos\beta}{\cos\alpha\cos\beta} - \dfrac{\sin\alpha\sin\beta}{\cos\alpha\cos\beta}}$$ Simplify.

$$= \frac{\dfrac{\sin\alpha}{\cos\alpha} + \dfrac{\sin\beta}{\cos\beta}}{1 - \dfrac{\sin\alpha\sin\beta}{\cos\alpha\cos\beta}}$$ Use the tangent identity.

$$= \frac{\tan\alpha + \tan\beta}{1 - \tan\alpha\tan\beta}$$

Sum and Difference Identities for Tangent

$$\tan(\alpha + \beta) = \frac{\tan\alpha + \tan\beta}{1 - \tan\alpha\tan\beta} \qquad \tan(\alpha - \beta) = \frac{\tan\alpha - \tan\beta}{1 + \tan\alpha\tan\beta}$$

Example 2 **Using Sum and Difference Identities to Simplify and Evaluate**

Write each expression in simplest form, then evaluate where possible.

a) $\sin 3\theta \sin\theta - \cos 3\theta \cos\theta$ **b)** $\dfrac{\tan\dfrac{\pi}{2} - \tan\dfrac{\pi}{3}}{1 + \tan\dfrac{\pi}{2}\tan\dfrac{\pi}{3}}$

SOLUTION

a) $\sin 3\theta \sin\theta - \cos 3\theta \cos\theta = -(\cos 3\theta \cos\theta - \sin 3\theta \sin\theta)$

Use the sum identity for cosine with $\alpha = 3\theta$ and $\beta = \theta$.

$\sin 3\theta \sin\theta - \cos 3\theta \cos\theta = -\cos(3\theta + \theta)$

$\qquad\qquad\qquad\qquad\qquad = -\cos 4\theta$

This simplest form cannot be evaluated because the angle contains a variable.

2. Write each expression in simplest form, then evaluate where possible.

a) $\sin 8x \cos 3x - \cos 8x \sin 3x$

b) $\dfrac{\tan\dfrac{\pi}{6} + \tan\dfrac{\pi}{12}}{1 - \tan\dfrac{\pi}{6}\tan\dfrac{\pi}{12}}$

b)
$$\dfrac{\tan \dfrac{\pi}{2} - \tan \dfrac{\pi}{3}}{1 + \tan \dfrac{\pi}{2}\,\tan \dfrac{\pi}{3}}$$

Use the difference identity for tangent with $\alpha = \dfrac{\pi}{2}$ and $\beta = \dfrac{\pi}{3}$.

$$\dfrac{\tan \dfrac{\pi}{2} - \tan \dfrac{\pi}{3}}{1 + \tan \dfrac{\pi}{2}\,\tan \dfrac{\pi}{3}} = \tan\left(\dfrac{\pi}{2} - \dfrac{\pi}{3}\right)$$

$$= \tan \dfrac{\pi}{6}$$

$$= \dfrac{1}{\sqrt{3}}$$

Example 3	Using a Difference Identity to Prove an Identity

Check Your Understanding

3. Prove this identity:
$\sin(\pi - x) = \sin x$

Prove this identity: $\cos\left(\dfrac{\pi}{2} - x\right) = \sin x$

SOLUTION

Use the difference identity, $\cos(\alpha - \beta) = \cos \alpha \cos \beta + \sin \alpha \sin \beta$.

Substitute: $\alpha = \dfrac{\pi}{2}, \beta = x$

$$\text{L.S.} = \cos\left(\dfrac{\pi}{2} - x\right)$$

$$= \cos \dfrac{\pi}{2} \cos x + \sin \dfrac{\pi}{2} \sin x$$

$$= (0)\cos x + (1)\sin x$$

$$= \sin x$$

$$= \text{R.S.}$$

Since the left side is equal to the right side, the identity is proved.

THINK FURTHER

What geometric strategy could you use to verify the identity in *Example 3*, when x is an acute angle?

Example 4

4. Solve the equation
$\cos 4x \cos x + \sin 4x \sin x = 1$
over the domain $0 \leq x < 2\pi$.

Solve the equation $\sin 5x \cos 3x - \cos 5x \sin 3x = 1$ over the domain $0 \leq x < 2\pi$.

SOLUTION

$$\sin 5x \cos 3x - \cos 5x \sin 3x = 1$$
$$\sin (5x - 3x) = 1$$
$$\sin 2x = 1$$

The given domain for angle x is $0 \leq x < 2\pi$,
so the domain for angle $2x$ is $0 \leq 2x < 4\pi$.

$$2x = \frac{\pi}{2} \qquad \text{or} \qquad 2x = \frac{5\pi}{2}$$
$$x = \frac{\pi}{4} \qquad\qquad\qquad x = \frac{5\pi}{4}$$

The roots are: $x = \frac{\pi}{4}$ and $x = \frac{5\pi}{4}$

Discuss the Ideas

1. How do you know whether you can use a sum or difference identity to determine the exact value of a trigonometric ratio of a given angle?

2. What strategies do you have for remembering the sum and difference formulas?

Exercises

3. Verify each identity for the given values of α and β.

a) $\sin(\alpha + \beta) = \sin \alpha \cos \beta + \cos \alpha \sin \beta$;
for $\alpha = 90°$ and $\beta = 30°$

b) $\cos(\alpha - \beta) = \cos \alpha \cos \beta + \sin \alpha \sin \beta$; for $\alpha = \dfrac{\pi}{2}$ and $\beta = \dfrac{\pi}{4}$

c) $\tan(\alpha + \beta) = \dfrac{\tan \alpha + \tan \beta}{1 - \tan \alpha \tan \beta}$; for $\alpha = \dfrac{2\pi}{3}$ and $\beta = \dfrac{\pi}{3}$

4. Simplify each expression.

    a) $\cos 8\theta \cos 2\theta + \sin 8\theta \sin 2\theta$ **b)** $\cos \theta \sin 4\theta - \sin \theta \cos 4\theta$

    c) $\dfrac{\tan 7x - \tan 3x}{1 + \tan 7x \tan 3x}$ **d)** $\sin 5x \sin 3x - \cos 5x \cos 3x$

B

5. Simplify each expression, then determine its exact value.

    a) $\cos 75° \cos 15° - \sin 75° \sin 15°$ **b)** $\sin \pi \cos \dfrac{\pi}{4} + \cos \pi \sin \dfrac{\pi}{4}$

    c) $\cos \dfrac{\pi}{3} \sin \dfrac{\pi}{6} - \sin \dfrac{\pi}{3} \cos \dfrac{\pi}{6}$ **d)** $\dfrac{\tan \pi + \tan \dfrac{\pi}{3}}{1 - \tan \pi \tan \dfrac{\pi}{3}}$

6. a) Expand $\sin \left(\dfrac{\pi}{2} + \dfrac{\pi}{2} \right)$ to verify that $\sin \pi = 0$.

    b) Expand $\cos \left(\dfrac{\pi}{2} + \dfrac{\pi}{2} \right)$ to verify that $\cos \pi = -1$.

c) Expand $\cos\left(\dfrac{\pi}{2} - \dfrac{\pi}{3}\right)$ to verify that $\cos\dfrac{\pi}{6} = \dfrac{\sqrt{3}}{2}$.

d) Expand $\tan\left(\dfrac{\pi}{6} + \dfrac{\pi}{6}\right)$ to verify that $\tan\dfrac{\pi}{3} = \sqrt{3}$.

7. Determine each exact value.

a) $\cos 75°$

b) $\sin 15°$

c) $\tan\dfrac{\pi}{12}$

d) $\tan\dfrac{5\pi}{12}$

8. a) Given $\sin \beta = -\frac{1}{3}$ and $\cos \alpha = \frac{2}{5}$, where angle β is in standard position with its terminal arm in Quadrant 3 and angle α is in standard position with its terminal arm in Quadrant 4; determine each exact value.

    i) $\sin (\alpha - \beta)$ **ii)** $\cos (\alpha - \beta)$

   iii) $\tan (\alpha + \beta)$ **iv)** $\tan (\alpha - \beta)$

b) What other strategy could you use to determine $\tan (\alpha - \beta)$?

9. Prove each identity.

a) $\cos \theta = \sin \left(\dfrac{\pi}{2} + \theta \right)$

b) $-\tan \theta = \tan (\pi - \theta)$

10. For each identity below:

    i) Use the diagram at the right to explain why each identity is true.

    ii) Prove the identity.

a) $\cos (-\theta) = \cos \theta$

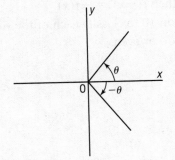

b) $\sin (-\theta) = -\sin \theta$

c) $\tan(-\theta) = -\tan\theta$

11. If $f(x)$ is an even function, then $f(-x) = f(x)$

If $f(x)$ is an odd function, then $f(-x) = -f(x)$

Use the identities in question 10 to classify each of the sine, cosine, and tangent functions as odd or even.

12. Solve this equation over the domain $-90° < x < 270°$:

$$\frac{\tan 4x - \tan 3x}{1 + \tan 4x \tan 3x} = \sqrt{3}$$

13. Given $\tan\alpha = \frac{4}{3}$ and $\tan\beta = -\frac{5}{12}$, where angle α is in standard position in Quadrant 1 and angle β is in standard position with its terminal arm in Quadrant 2, determine the exact value of $\cos(\alpha - \beta)$.

14. Prove each identity.

a) $\sin\left(\dfrac{\pi}{4} + \theta\right) + \sin\left(\dfrac{\pi}{4} - \theta\right) = \sqrt{2}\cos\theta$

b) $\cos\left(\dfrac{\pi}{6} + \theta\right) - \cos\left(\dfrac{\pi}{6} - \theta\right) = -\sin\theta$

c) $\tan(\alpha - \beta) = \dfrac{\tan\alpha - \tan\beta}{1 + \tan\alpha\tan\beta}$

15. Solve each equation over the domain $-\dfrac{3\pi}{2} \le x < \dfrac{\pi}{2}$.

a) $\sin 7x \cos 5x - \cos 7x \sin 5x = -1$

b) $\cos 2x \cos x - \sin 2x \sin x = 0$

16. Here are two solutions for solving the equation $\sin(\pi + x) = \dfrac{1}{\sqrt{2}}$

over the set of real numbers. Are both solutions correct? Explain.

Solution 1

$\sin(\pi + x) = \dfrac{1}{\sqrt{2}}$

Either $\pi + x = \dfrac{\pi}{4} + 2\pi k,\, k \in \mathbb{Z}$

$x = -\dfrac{3\pi}{4} + 2\pi k,\, k \in \mathbb{Z}$

Or $\pi + x = \dfrac{3\pi}{4} + 2\pi k,\, k \in \mathbb{Z}$

$x = -\dfrac{\pi}{4} + 2\pi k,\, k \in \mathbb{Z}$

Solution 2

$\sin(\pi + x) = \dfrac{1}{\sqrt{2}}$

$\sin \pi \cos x + \cos \pi \sin x = \dfrac{1}{\sqrt{2}}$

$(0)\cos x + (-1)\sin x = \dfrac{1}{\sqrt{2}}$

$-\sin x = \dfrac{1}{\sqrt{2}}$

$\sin x = -\dfrac{1}{\sqrt{2}}$

$x = \dfrac{5\pi}{4} + 2\pi k,\, k \in \mathbb{Z}$

or $x = \dfrac{7\pi}{4} + 2\pi k,\, k \in \mathbb{Z}$

17. Determine the general solution of each equation over the set of real numbers.

a) $\cos(\pi + x) = \frac{1}{2}$

b) $\tan(\pi + x) = -1$

C

18. Use algebra to determine the amplitude and the period of the graph of $y = \sin\left(\frac{\pi}{4} + x\right) + \sin\left(\frac{\pi}{4} - x\right)$. Describe your strategy. Use graphing technology to check.

Multiple-Choice Questions

1. Which expression is equivalent to $\cos(x - 90°)$?

A. $-\cos x$ B. $-\sin x$ C. $\sin x$ D. $\cos x - \cos 90°$

2. Which expression is equal to $-\cos 8x$?

A. $\sin 6x \sin 2x - \cos 6x \cos 2x$ B. $\sin 8x$

C. $\cos 6x \cos 2x - \sin 6x \sin 2x$ D. $\sin 6x \cos 2x + \cos 6x \sin 2x$

Study Note

Choose an angle in radians whose exact trigonometric ratios can be determined using the sum or difference identities. Use these identities to determine the sine, cosine, and tangent of the angle you chose.

7.6 Double-Angle Identities

FOCUS Prove identities using the double-angle identities.

Get Started

In the following statements, x is a real number.
Which statements are true? Justify your answers.

$$\log 2x = 2 \log x \qquad 2 \log x = \log x^2 \qquad \sin 2x = 2 \sin x$$

Construct Understanding

Write an identity for each trigonometric ratio below in terms of θ.
What strategies did you use?
Verify each identity for a value of θ.

$\sin 2\theta \qquad\qquad \cos 2\theta \qquad\qquad \tan 2\theta$

Here is one identity for $\cos 2\theta$: $\cos 2\theta = \cos^2\theta - \sin^2\theta$

There are two other identities for $\cos 2\theta$ that can be derived using the Pythagorean identity.

$\cos 2\theta = \cos^2\theta - \sin^2\theta$

$\cos 2\theta = \cos^2\theta - (1 - \cos^2\theta)$

$\cos 2\theta = \cos^2\theta - 1 + \cos^2\theta$

$\cos 2\theta = 2\cos^2\theta - 1$

$\cos 2\theta = \cos^2\theta - \sin^2\theta$

$\cos 2\theta = (1 - \sin^2\theta) - \sin^2\theta$

$\cos 2\theta = 1 - \sin^2\theta - \sin^2\theta$

$\cos 2\theta = 1 - 2\sin^2\theta$

The **double-angle identities** are summarized below.

Example 1   Applying the Double-Angle Identities

Check Your Understanding

1. Given angle θ is in standard position with its terminal arm in Quadrant 4 and $\cos \theta = \frac{2}{5}$, determine the exact value of each trigonometric ratio.

a) $\sin 2\theta$ **b)** $\cos 2\theta$

Given angle θ is in standard position with its terminal arm in Quadrant 3 and $\sin \theta = -\frac{1}{3}$, determine the exact value of each trigonometric ratio.

a) $\sin 2\theta$ **b)** $\tan 2\theta$

SOLUTION

Suppose point P(x, y) lies on the terminal arm of angle θ.

Since the terminal arm of θ lies in Quadrant 3, $\cos \theta$ is negative.

From $\sin \theta = -\frac{1}{3}$, set $y = -1$ and $r = 3$

Sketch a diagram.

Use mental math and the Pythagorean Theorem to determine the x-coordinate of P, which is $-\sqrt{8}$, or $-2\sqrt{2}$.

So, $\cos \theta = -\dfrac{2\sqrt{2}}{3}$ and $\tan \theta = \dfrac{1}{2\sqrt{2}}$

a) $\sin 2\theta$

Substitute $\sin \theta = -\frac{1}{3}$ and $\cos \theta = -\dfrac{2\sqrt{2}}{3}$ in:

$\sin 2\theta = 2 \sin \theta \cos \theta$

$ = 2\left(-\dfrac{1}{3}\right)\left(-\dfrac{2\sqrt{2}}{3}\right)$

$ = \dfrac{4\sqrt{2}}{9}$

b) $\tan 2\theta$

Substitute $\tan \theta = \dfrac{1}{2\sqrt{2}}$ in:

$$\tan 2\theta = \dfrac{2 \tan \theta}{1 - \tan^2\theta}$$

$$= \dfrac{2\left(\dfrac{1}{2\sqrt{2}}\right)}{1 - \left(\dfrac{1}{2\sqrt{2}}\right)^2}$$

$$= \dfrac{\dfrac{1}{\sqrt{2}}}{\dfrac{7}{8}}, \text{ or } \dfrac{4\sqrt{2}}{7}$$

THINK FURTHER

In *Example 1b*, what other strategy could have been used to determine $\tan 2\theta$? Show that this strategy results in the same answer.

Example 2	Using Double-Angle Identities to Simplify and Evaluate

Write each expression as a single trigonometric ratio, then evaluate where possible.

a) $\sin \dfrac{\pi}{3} \cos \dfrac{\pi}{3}$

b) $6 \cos^2\theta - 3$

SOLUTION

a) $\sin \dfrac{\pi}{3} \cos \dfrac{\pi}{3}$

Use: $2 \sin \theta \cos \theta = \sin 2\theta$

Then, $\sin \theta \cos \theta = \dfrac{1}{2} \sin 2\theta$

So, $\sin \dfrac{\pi}{3} \cos \dfrac{\pi}{3} = \dfrac{1}{2}\left(\sin 2\left(\dfrac{\pi}{3}\right)\right)$

$$= \dfrac{1}{2}\left(\sin \dfrac{2\pi}{3}\right)$$

$$= \dfrac{1}{2}\left(\dfrac{\sqrt{3}}{2}\right)$$

$$= \dfrac{\sqrt{3}}{4}$$

b) $6 \cos^2\theta - 3$

Use: $2 \cos^2\theta - 1 = \cos 2\theta$

Then, $6 \cos^2\theta - 3 = 3(2 \cos^2\theta - 1)$

$$= 3 \cos 2\theta$$

Check Your Understanding

2. Write each expression as a single trigonometric ratio, then evaluate where possible.

a) $\cos^2\left(\dfrac{\pi}{4}\right) - \sin^2\left(\dfrac{\pi}{4}\right)$

b) $\dfrac{2 \tan \dfrac{\pi}{6}}{\tan^2\left(\dfrac{\pi}{6}\right) - 1}$

Example 3   **Using Double-Angle Identities to Prove Other Identities**

3. Prove each identity.

a) $\cot \theta = \dfrac{\cos 2\theta + 1}{\sin 2\theta}$

b) $\cot \theta \csc 2\theta = \dfrac{1}{2 \sin^2 \theta}$

Prove each identity.

a) $\dfrac{1 - \cos 2\theta}{\sin 2\theta} = \tan \theta$ b) $\csc 2\theta + 1 = \dfrac{(\sin \theta + \cos \theta)^2}{\sin 2\theta}$

SOLUTION

a) $\dfrac{1 - \cos 2\theta}{\sin 2\theta} = \tan \theta$

L.S. $= \dfrac{1 - \cos 2\theta}{\sin 2\theta}$ Use identities for $\sin 2\theta$ and $\cos 2\theta$.

$= \dfrac{1 - (1 - 2\sin^2\theta)}{2 \sin \theta \cos \theta}$

$= \dfrac{\cancel{2} \sin^2\theta}{\cancel{2} \cancel{\sin \theta} \cos \theta}$

$= \dfrac{\sin \theta}{\cos \theta}$

$= \tan \theta$

$=$ R.S.

Since the left side is equal to the right side, the identity is proved.

b) $\csc 2\theta + 1 = \dfrac{(\sin \theta + \cos \theta)^2}{\sin 2\theta}$

R.S. $= \dfrac{(\sin \theta + \cos \theta)^2}{\sin 2\theta}$ Expand the numerator.

$= \dfrac{\sin^2\theta + 2 \sin \theta \cos \theta + \cos^2\theta}{\sin 2\theta}$ Use the Pythagorean identity and the identity for $\sin 2\theta$.

$= \dfrac{1 + \sin 2\theta}{\sin 2\theta}$

$= \dfrac{1}{\sin 2\theta} + \dfrac{\sin 2\theta}{\sin 2\theta}$

$= \csc 2\theta + 1$

$=$ L.S.

Since the left side is equal to the right side, the identity is proved.

Example 4 | Using Double-Angle Identities to Solve an Equation

Solve the equation $\cos 2x = 1 - 2 \sin x$ over the domain $0 \leq x < 2\pi$.

4. Solve the equation

$$\frac{1}{2} \sin 2x - \cos^2 x = 0$$

over the domain $0 \leq x < 2\pi$.

SOLUTION

$\cos 2x = 1 - 2 \sin x$ Use the identity for $\cos 2x$ that involves $\sin x$.

$\quad 1 - 2 \sin^2 x = 1 - 2 \sin x$

$\quad 2 \sin^2 x - 2 \sin x = 0$ Factor.

$\quad 2 \sin x (\sin x - 1) = 0$

$\quad 2 \sin x = 0 \quad$ or $\quad \sin x - 1 = 0$

$\quad \sin x = 0 \qquad\qquad \sin x = 1$

$\quad x = 0 \text{ or } x = \pi \qquad x = \dfrac{\pi}{2}$

Verify the solution.

The roots are: $x = 0$, $x = \pi$, and $x = \dfrac{\pi}{2}$

Discuss the Ideas

1. What is a double-angle identity? How is it different from double a trigonometric ratio?

2. Why are there three double-angle identities for $\cos 2\theta$ but only one identity for $\sin 2\theta$?

3. What are two identities for $\tan 2\theta$? Give an example of when it would be better to use each identity.

Exercises

4. Write each expression as a single trigonometric ratio.

  a) $\sin(\theta + \theta)$

  b) $\sin\theta + \sin\theta$

  c) $\sin\theta \sin\theta$

  d) $\cos^2\theta \cos\theta$

  e) $3\sin\theta \sin\theta$

  f) $3\sin\theta + \sin\theta$

5. Determine the exact value of each expression.

  a) $2\sin 45° \cos 45°$

  b) $\cos^2\left(\dfrac{\pi}{6}\right)\sin^2\left(\dfrac{\pi}{6}\right)$

  c) $2\cos^2\left(\dfrac{\pi}{8}\right) - 1$

  d) $\dfrac{2\tan 210°}{1 - \tan^2(210°)}$

6. Simplify each expression.

  a) $-\cos^2\theta - \sin^2\theta$

  b) $1 - \sin^2\theta$

  c) $2\cos^2\theta - 2$

  d) $4\cos^2\theta - 2$

7. Verify each identity for the given value of θ.

   a) $\sin 2\theta = 2 \sin \theta \cos \theta$; $\theta = 30°$ **b)** $\cos 2\theta = \cos^2\theta - \sin^2\theta$; $\theta = \dfrac{5\pi}{4}$

8. For the identity $\tan 2\theta = \dfrac{2 \tan \theta}{1 - \tan^2\theta}$, determine the non-permissible values of θ over the set of real numbers, then verify the identity for $\theta = \dfrac{2\pi}{3}$.

9. Given angle θ is in standard position with its terminal arm in Quadrant 2 and $\tan \theta = -\frac{2}{5}$, determine the exact value of each trigonometric ratio.

a) $\sin 2\theta$

b) $\cos 2\theta$

c) $\tan 2\theta$

10. Prove each identity.

a) $2 \cot \theta \sin^2\theta = \sin 2\theta$

b) $1 + \sin 2\theta = (\sin \theta + \cos \theta)^2$

c) $2 \cot \theta = \dfrac{\sin 2\theta}{1 - \cos^2\theta}$

d) $\tan 2\theta \cos 2\theta = 2 \sin \theta \cos \theta$

11. Prove each identity.

a) $\dfrac{\cos 2\theta - 2\cos^2\theta}{2\cos\theta} = \dfrac{-\sin 2\theta \sec^2\theta}{4\sin\theta}$ b) $\dfrac{\sin 2\theta}{\cos 2\theta - 1} = -\cot\theta$

c) $\dfrac{2\cos^2\theta}{\sin 2\theta} = \dfrac{1 + \cos\theta}{\tan\theta + \sin\theta}$ d) $\dfrac{\sin 2\theta}{2 + 2\cos 2\theta} = \dfrac{\sec^2\theta - 1}{2\tan\theta}$

12. Solve each equation over the domain $-180° \leq x < 180°$.

    a) $\cos 2x = 2 \cos x - 1$ **b)** $\sin x = \cos 2x$

13. Solve each equation over the domain $-2\pi < x < 2\pi$.

    a) $\sqrt{2} \sin 2x - 2 \sin x = 0$ **b)** $3 \sin^2 x + \cos 2x - 2 = 0$

14. For this solution of the equation $\sin 2x = \cos x$ over the domain $0 \leq x < 2\pi$, identify the error then write a correct solution.

$$\sin 2x = \cos x$$
$$2 \sin x \cos x = \cos x$$
$$\frac{2 \sin x \cancel{\cos x}^{1}}{\cancel{\cos x}^{1}} = \frac{\cancel{\cos x}^{1}}{\cancel{\cos x}^{1}}$$
$$2 \sin x = 1$$
$$\sin x = \frac{1}{2}$$
$$x = \frac{\pi}{6} \text{ or } x = \frac{5\pi}{6}$$

15. Use algebra to solve the equation $\cos 2x = 2 \cos x$ over the set of real numbers. Give the answer to the nearest hundredth.

16. A student said that the identity $\sin 2\theta = 2 \sin \theta \cos \theta$ could be extended so that $\sin 4\theta = 4 \sin \theta \cos \theta$ and $\sin 6\theta = 6 \sin \theta \cos \theta$.

    a) Is the student correct? If your answer is yes, explain why. If your answer is no, write correct identities for $\sin 4\theta$ and $\sin 6\theta$.

    b) Write an identity for $\sin b\theta$, where b is a positive even number.

C

17. Prove each identity.

    a) $-\sec 2x = \dfrac{\tan x + \cot x}{\tan x - \cot x}$
      b) $\cot 2x = \dfrac{\cot x - \tan x}{2}$

18. For each equation, determine the solution over the set of real numbers.

a) $4 \sin 3x \cos 3x = 1$

b) $4 \cos^2 5x - 2 + \sqrt{3} = 0$

Multiple-Choice Questions

1. The terminal arm of angle θ in standard position intersects the unit circle at the point $P(m, n)$. Which expression represents $\sin 2\theta$?

A. $2m$ **B.** $2n$ **C.** $2mn$ **D.** $\frac{2m}{n}$

2. Which expression is equal to $10 \sin 4x \cos 4x$?

A. $\sin 4x$ **B.** $\sin 8x$ **C.** $5 \sin 4x$ **D.** $5 \sin 8x$

Study Note

The statement of the Pythagorean identity is similar to the statement of a certain double-angle identity. Write these identities and explain how you remember them. List other forms of these identities.

ANSWERS

Check Your Understanding

1. a) $-\dfrac{4\sqrt{21}}{25}$ b) $-\dfrac{17}{25}$ 2. a) $\cos\dfrac{\pi}{2} = 0$ b) $-\tan\dfrac{\pi}{3} = -\sqrt{3}$

4. $x = \dfrac{\pi}{4}, x = \dfrac{\pi}{2}, x = \dfrac{5\pi}{4}, x = \dfrac{3\pi}{2}$

Exercises

4. a) $\sin 2\theta$ b) $2\sin\theta$ c) $\sin^2\theta$ d) $\cos^3\theta$ e) $3\sin^2\theta$ f) $4\sin\theta$

5. a) 1 b) $\dfrac{3}{16}$ c) $\dfrac{1}{\sqrt{2}}$ d) $\sqrt{3}$ 6. a) -1 b) $\cos^2\theta$ c) $-2\sin^2\theta$ d) $2\cos 2\theta$

8. $\theta \neq \dfrac{\pi}{4} + \dfrac{\pi}{2}k, k \in \mathbb{Z}$ or $\theta \neq \dfrac{\pi}{2} + \pi k, k \in \mathbb{Z}$ or $\theta \neq \dfrac{\pi}{4}(2k + 1), k \in \mathbb{Z}$

9. a) $-\dfrac{20}{29}$ b) $\dfrac{21}{29}$ c) $-\dfrac{20}{21}$ 12. a) $x = 0°, x = \pm 90°$ b) $x = 30°, x = 150°, x = -90°$

13. a) $x = 0, x = \pm\dfrac{\pi}{4}, x = \pm\pi, x = \pm\dfrac{7\pi}{4}$ b) $x = \pm\dfrac{\pi}{2}, x = \pm\dfrac{3\pi}{2}$

15. a) $x \doteq 1.95 + 2\pi k, k \in \mathbb{Z}$ or $x \doteq 4.34 + 2\pi k, k \in \mathbb{Z}$

18. a) $x = \dfrac{\pi}{36} + \dfrac{\pi}{3}k, k \in \mathbb{Z}$, or $x = \dfrac{5\pi}{36} + \dfrac{\pi}{3}k, k \in \mathbb{Z}$

b) $x = \dfrac{\pi}{12} + \dfrac{\pi}{5}k, k \in \mathbb{Z}$, or $x = \dfrac{7\pi}{60} + \dfrac{\pi}{5}k, k \in \mathbb{Z}$

Multiple Choice

1. C   2. D

666 | Chapter 7: Trigonometric Equations and Identities

DO NOT COPY.   ©P

STUDY GUIDE

Concept Summary

Big Ideas	Applying the Big Ideas
• Trigonometric equations can be solved graphically or algebraically.	This means that • For a graphical solution, the roots of the equation are equal to the zeros of a corresponding function. • For an algebraic solution, the roots may be determined by writing the trigonometric equation in terms of a single trigonometric ratio and simplifying the equation, then solving for the possible values of the trigonometric ratio, and finally determining the corresponding angles.
• The general solution of a trigonometric equation is related to the zeros of the corresponding trigonometric function.	• Since a trigonometric function is periodic, the general solution is determined by adding and subtracting multiples of the period to all the roots in one period.
• A trigonometric identity is a trigonometric equation that is true for all permissible values of the variable.	• Trigonometric identities can be verified numerically or graphically. • A verification of a trigonometric identity is not a proof. A trigonometric identity may be proved algebraically.

Chapter Study Notes

• What strategies could you use to identify whether a trigonometric equation is an identity?

• What strategies do you use to prove an identity?

Skills Summary

Skill	Description	Example
Use graphing technology to solve a trigonometric equation. **(7.1)**	Determine the zeros of a corresponding function.	Solve $4 \sin 3x = 6 + 5 \cos 3x$ over the domain $0 \leq x < 2\pi$. Give the roots to the nearest hundredth, then write the general solution. Graph: $y = 4 \sin 3x - 6 - 5 \cos 3x$ There are 6 roots in the given domain. $x \doteq 0.70,\ 0.94,\ 2.80,\ 3.04,\ 4.89,$ or 5.13 Each root repeats at intervals of $\frac{2\pi}{3}$, so the general solution is: $x \doteq 0.70 + \frac{2\pi}{3}k,\ k \in \mathbb{Z}$ or $x \doteq 0.94 + \frac{2\pi}{3}k,\ k \in \mathbb{Z}$
Use algebra to solve a trigonometric equation. **(7.2)**	One strategy is to rearrange the terms so one side is 0, then factor the other side. Use inverse trigonometric ratios to determine the reference angle, then use the given domain to determine the solution. If a second-degree trigonometric equation does not factor, use the quadratic formula to solve the equation.	Solve $2 \cos^2 x = -\sqrt{3} \cos x$ over the domain $-180° \leq x \leq 180°$. $2 \cos^2 x + \sqrt{3} \cos x = 0$ $(\cos x)(2 \cos x + \sqrt{3}) = 0$ Either $\cos x = 0$ $x = -90°$ or $x = 90°$ Or $2 \cos x + \sqrt{3} = 0$ $\cos x = -\dfrac{\sqrt{3}}{2}$ $x = 150°$ or $x = -150°$
Determine the non-permissible values of the variable in a trigonometric identity. **(7.3, 7.4, 7.5, 7.6)**	Equate any denominators to 0. The roots of each equation formed this way are the non-permissible values of the variable. Determine the values of the angles for which any trigonometric ratios in the equation are undefined; these are also non-permissible values of the variable.	Determine the non-permissible values of θ for the identity: $\dfrac{\cos \theta \sin \theta}{1 + \sin \theta} = \dfrac{1 - \sin \theta}{\cot \theta}$ For non-permissible values: $1 + \sin \theta = 0 \qquad \cot \theta = 0$ $\sin \theta = -1 \qquad \theta = \dfrac{\pi}{2} + \pi k,\ k \in \mathbb{Z}$ $\theta = \dfrac{3\pi}{2} + 2\pi k,\ k \in \mathbb{Z}$ Since $\cot \theta = \dfrac{\cos \theta}{\sin \theta}$, consider: $\sin \theta = 0$ $\theta = \pi k,\ k \in \mathbb{Z}$ The non-permissible values are: $\dfrac{\pi}{2}k,\ k \in \mathbb{Z}$

Prove a trigonometric identity. **(7.3, 7.4, 7.5, 7.6)**	Rewrite one side of the identity to match the other side. Identities that can be used to prove other identities are: reciprocal identities; quotient identities; Pythagorean identity; sum or difference identities; double-angle identities; and any identity that has already been proved.	Prove the identity: $$\frac{\cos\theta\sin\theta}{1+\sin\theta}=\frac{1-\sin\theta}{\cot\theta}$$ $$\begin{aligned}\text{L.S.}&=\frac{\cos\theta\sin\theta}{1+\sin\theta}\\&=\frac{\cos\theta\sin\theta}{1+\sin\theta}\cdot\frac{1-\sin\theta}{1-\sin\theta}\\&=\frac{(\cos\theta\sin\theta)(1-\sin\theta)}{1-\sin^2\theta}\\&=\frac{(\cos\theta\sin\theta)(1-\sin\theta)}{\cos^2\theta}\\&=\frac{(\sin\theta)(1-\sin\theta)}{\cos\theta}\\&=\frac{1-\sin\theta}{\cot\theta}\\&=\text{R.S.}\end{aligned}$$ Since the left side is equal to the right side, the identity is proved.
Use identities to solve trigonometric equations. **(7.3, 7.4, 7.5, 7.6)**	The identities that are used in proofs can be used to simplify a trigonometric equation before solving it. All solutions should be verified.	Solve $\cos x-2\sin^2 x=1$ over the domain $-2\pi\le x\le 2\pi$. $$\begin{aligned}\cos x-2\sin^2 x&=1\\\cos x-2(1-\cos^2 x)-1&=0\\2\cos^2 x+\cos x-3&=0\\(2\cos x+3)(\cos x-1)&=0\end{aligned}$$ Either $2\cos x+3=0$ $$\cos x=-\frac{3}{2};\text{ no solution}$$ Or $\cos x-1=0$ $$\cos x=1$$ $x=-2\pi, x=0,\text{ or }x=2\pi$
Use the sum, difference, or double-angle identities to determine the exact value of a trigonometric ratio. **(7.5, 7.6)**	Express the angle as a sum or difference of angles that are multiples of $\frac{\pi}{6}$ (30°) or $\frac{\pi}{4}$ (45°).	Determine the exact value of $\cos 165°$. $$\begin{aligned}&\cos 165°\\&=\cos(120°+45°)\\&=\cos 120°\cos 45°-\sin 120°\sin 45°\\&=\left(-\frac{1}{2}\right)\left(\frac{1}{\sqrt{2}}\right)-\left(\frac{\sqrt{3}}{2}\right)\left(\frac{1}{\sqrt{2}}\right)\\&=\frac{-1-\sqrt{3}}{2\sqrt{2}}\end{aligned}$$

7.1

1. Use graphing technology to solve each equation over the given domain. Give the roots to the nearest hundredth, then determine the general solution.

   a) $5 \cos 2x + 1 = 3 \sin x$; for $0 \le x < 2\pi$

   b) $3 \sin^2 x + 2 = \tan x$; for $-2\pi < x < 2\pi$

   c) $2 \cos^2 x = 2x$; over the set of real numbers

2. The first two positive roots of the equation $\sin 3x = \frac{2}{5}$ are $x \doteq 0.14$ and $x \doteq 0.91$. Determine the general solution of this equation.

3. Verify that each given value of x is a root of the equation.

   a) $\sin x + \sin^2 x = 0; x = 270°$ **b)** $3 \tan x - 1 = 2 \tan^2 x; x = \dfrac{5\pi}{4}$

4. Use algebra to solve each equation over the given domain, and write the general solution. Write the answers to the nearest degree or the nearest hundredth of a radian.

   a) $1 + 5 \cos 2x = 0;$

       for $-90° \leq x \leq 180°$

   b) $10 = 5 - 3 \csc x;$

       for $-\dfrac{3\pi}{2} < x < \dfrac{\pi}{2}$

5. Use algebra to solve the equation $3 - 6 \sin^2 x = -\sin x$ over the domain $0 \leq x < 2\pi$. Give the roots to the nearest hundredth.

6. Determine the general solution of the equation $1 - 3 \cos x + 2 \cos^2 x = 0$ over the set of real numbers.

7. For each identity:

   i) Determine the non-permissible values of θ.

   ii) Prove the identity.

a) $\dfrac{1 + \tan\theta}{1 + \cot\theta} = \dfrac{1 - \tan\theta}{\cot\theta - 1}$

b) $\dfrac{\csc^2\theta + 1}{\cot^2\theta + \cos^2\theta} = \tan\theta \sec\theta \csc\theta$

8. Use algebra to solve each equation over the given domain. Give the
roots to the nearest degree.

a) $3 \tan x = 1 + 4 \cot x$;
   for $-180° < x < 180°$

b) $5 = \csc x - 6 \sin x$;
   for $-90° \leq x < 270°$

9. For each identity:
  i) Verify the identity for $\theta = \dfrac{11\pi}{6}$.
  ii) Prove the identity.

a) $\dfrac{1 - \cos\theta}{\sin^2\theta} = \dfrac{1}{1 + \cos\theta}$
b) $\dfrac{1}{1 + \sin\theta} = \sec^2\theta - \dfrac{\tan\theta}{\cos\theta}$

10. Use algebra to solve each equation over the domain $-2\pi < x < 2\pi$. Give the roots to the nearest hundredth where necessary.

a) $2 \sec^2 x - 2 = 3 + \tan x$ **b)** $4 \sin x \cos x = 2 - 2\cos^2 x$

11. Prove each identity.

    a) $\sin \theta = \cos \left(\dfrac{3\pi}{2} + \theta \right)$ **b)** $-\cos \theta = \sin \left(\dfrac{3\pi}{2} - \theta \right)$

12. Solve this equation over the domain $-90° < x < 90°$:

$$\sin x \cos 2x + \cos x \sin 2x = \dfrac{1}{\sqrt{2}}$$

13. Determine the exact value of $\tan 105°$.

14. Prove each identity.

a) $\dfrac{\cot^2\theta - 1}{\csc^2\theta} = \cos 2\theta$

b) $\sin 2\theta = \dfrac{2\tan\theta}{1 + \tan^2\theta}$

15. Solve each equation over the domain $-2\pi < x < 2\pi$.

a) $\sin 2x + \sqrt{3}\cos x = 0$

b) $\cos 2x + 5\cos x = 4\cos^2 x - 4$

ANSWERS

1. a) $x \doteq 0.69, x \doteq 2.45, x \doteq 4.36, x \doteq 5.06; x \doteq 0.69 + 2\pi k, k \in \mathbb{Z}$ or
$x \doteq 2.45 + 2\pi k, k \in \mathbb{Z}$ or $x \doteq 4.36 + 2\pi k, k \in \mathbb{Z}$ or $x \doteq 5.06 + 2\pi k, k \in \mathbb{Z}$

b) $x \doteq -4.91, x \doteq -1.77, x \doteq 1.37, x \doteq 4.51; x \doteq 1.37 + \pi k, k \in \mathbb{Z}$

c) $x \doteq 0.64$ **2.** $x \doteq 0.14 + \dfrac{2\pi}{3}k, k \in \mathbb{Z}$ or $x \doteq 0.91 + \dfrac{2\pi}{3}k, k \in \mathbb{Z}$

4. a) $x \doteq \pm 51°, x \doteq 129°; x \doteq 51° + k180°, k \in \mathbb{Z}$ or $x \doteq 129° + k180°, k \in \mathbb{Z}$

b) $x \doteq -2.50, x \doteq -0.64; x \doteq -2.50 + 2\pi k, k \in \mathbb{Z}$ or $x \doteq -0.64 + 2\pi k, k \in \mathbb{Z}$

5. $x \doteq 0.92, x \doteq 2.22, x \doteq 3.82, x \doteq 5.60$ **6.** $x = 2\pi k, k \in \mathbb{Z}$ or $x = \dfrac{\pi}{3} + 2\pi k, k \in \mathbb{Z}$

or $x = \dfrac{5\pi}{3} + 2\pi k, k \in \mathbb{Z}$ **7. a) i)** $\theta \neq \dfrac{\pi}{4}k, k \in \mathbb{Z}$ **b) i)** $\theta \neq \dfrac{\pi}{2}k, k \in \mathbb{Z}$

8. a) $x \doteq -127°, x \doteq -45°, x \doteq 53°, x = 135°$ **b)** $x = -90°, x \doteq 10°, x \doteq 170°$

10. a) $x \doteq -5.30, x = -\dfrac{5\pi}{4}, x \doteq -2.16, x = -\dfrac{\pi}{4}, x \doteq 0.98, x = \dfrac{3\pi}{4}, x \doteq 4.12,$

$x = \dfrac{7\pi}{4}$ **b)** $x = 0, x = \pm\pi, x \doteq -5.18, x \doteq -2.03, x \doteq 1.11, x \doteq 4.25$

12. $x = 15°, x = 45°, x = -75°$ **13.** $\dfrac{\sqrt{3} + 1}{1 - \sqrt{3}}$

15. a) $x = \pm\dfrac{\pi}{2}, x = \pm\dfrac{3\pi}{2}, x = -\dfrac{2\pi}{3}, x = -\dfrac{\pi}{3}, x = \dfrac{4\pi}{3}, x = \dfrac{5\pi}{3}$

b) $x = \pm\dfrac{2\pi}{3}, x = \pm\dfrac{4\pi}{3}$

1. **Multiple Choice** What are the roots of the equation
   $2 \sin x \cos x = 2 \sin^2 x$ over the domain $0 \le x < 2\pi$?

   A. $x = \dfrac{\pi}{4}, x = \dfrac{5\pi}{4}$

   B. $x = \dfrac{3\pi}{4}, x = \dfrac{7\pi}{4}$

   C. $x = \dfrac{\pi}{4}, x = \dfrac{5\pi}{4}, x = 0, x = \pi$

   D. $x = \dfrac{3\pi}{4}, x = \dfrac{7\pi}{4}, x = 0, x = \pi$

2. **Multiple Choice** What is the simplest form of
   $\cos 5x \sin 2x - \sin 5x \cos 2x$?

   A. $-\sin 3x$ B. $\sin 3x$ C. $-\sin 7x$ D. $\sin 7x$

3. Use graphing technology to determine the general solution of the
   equation $\cot x = \sin x + 1$. Give the answers to the nearest
   hundredth.

4. Solve the equation $\sin x + 1 = 2 \cos^2 x$ over the domain
   $-\dfrac{3\pi}{2} \le x < \dfrac{\pi}{2}$. Give the exact roots.

5. Determine the general solution of the equation $\sin 4x = \dfrac{1}{\sqrt{2}}$ over the set of real numbers.

6. For the identity $\dfrac{\cos \theta + \cot \theta}{1 + \sin \theta} = \cot \theta$

a) Determine the non-permissible values of θ.

b) Verify the identity graphically. Sketch or print the graph and explain how it verifies the identity.

c) Verify the identity for $\theta = \dfrac{\pi}{3}$. Explain why this verification does not prove the identity.

d) Prove the identity.

7. Given angle α in standard position with its terminal arm in Quadrant 3 and $\sin \alpha = -\frac{2}{3}$, and angle β in standard position with its terminal arm in Quadrant 4 and $\cos \beta = \frac{3}{7}$, determine each exact value.

a) $\cos(\alpha - \beta)$ **b)** $\tan 2\alpha$

8. Prove this identity: $\dfrac{2 - 2\cos 2\theta}{2\sin 2\theta} = \dfrac{\sec^2 \theta - 1}{\tan \theta}$

ANSWERS

1. C   2. A   **3.** $x \doteq 0.57 + 2\pi k, k \in \mathbb{Z}$ or $x \doteq 4.71 + 2\pi k, k \in \mathbb{Z}$

4. $x = -\dfrac{7\pi}{6}, x = -\dfrac{\pi}{2}, x = \dfrac{\pi}{6}$ **5.** $x = \dfrac{\pi}{16} + \dfrac{\pi}{2}k, k \in \mathbb{Z}$ or $x = \dfrac{3\pi}{16} + \dfrac{\pi}{2}k, k \in \mathbb{Z}$

6. a) $\theta \neq \pi k, k \in \mathbb{Z}$ and $\theta \neq \dfrac{\pi}{2} + \pi k, k \in \mathbb{Z}$ **7. a)** $\dfrac{-3\sqrt{5} + 2\sqrt{40}}{21}$ **b)** $4\sqrt{5}$

8 Permutations and Combinations

BUILDING ON

■ listing outcomes of probability experiments

■ solving equations

BIG IDEAS

■ Counting strategies can be used to determine the number of ways to choose objects from a set or to arrange a set of objects.

■ A permutation is an arrangement of a set of objects where order matters. A combination is a selection from a set of objects where order does not matter.

■ Combinations can be used to expand a power of a binomial and to generate the terms in Pascal's triangle.

LEADING TO

■ applying the properties of permutations and combinations to solve problems in probability

NEW VOCABULARY

fundamental counting principle	combination
permutation	Pascal's triangle
factorial notation	binomial theorem

8.1 The Fundamental Counting Principle

FOCUS Derive and apply the fundamental counting principle to solve problems.

Get Started

A coin is tossed and the pointer on this spinner is spun.

- List all the possible outcomes.

- What is the probability of each outcome?

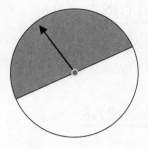

Construct Understanding

How many ways can any or all of the 3 valves on a trumpet be completely pushed down?

List all possibilities systematically.

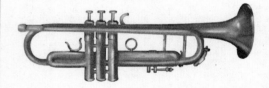

When it is necessary to list and count the number of possible choices or arrangements, graphic organizers can be useful.

Example 1 **Using a Graphic Organizer to Determine the Number of Choices**

Check Your Understanding

A room has two lamps. Each lamp has 4 settings: off, low, medium, high. How many ways are there to set both lamps?

1. A fan has 3 settings: off, low, high. How many ways are there to set 3 fans?

SOLUTION

Use a tree diagram.
Use letters to represent the possible settings.

O = Off   L = Low   M = Medium   H = High

1st Lamp

2nd Lamp   O L M H   O L M H   O L M H   O L M H

The tree diagram has 16 branches.
So, there are 16 ways to set both lamps.

THINK FURTHER

In *Example 1*, assume all lamp settings are equally likely. What is the probability that both lamps are on a high setting?

Example 1 illustrates the **fundamental counting principle**.
There are 4 ways to set the first lamp. For each of these ways, there are 4 ways to set the second lamp. So, the total number of ways is the product: $4 \cdot 4 = 16$
So, there are 16 ways to set both lamps.

The Fundamental Counting Principle

If there are n_1 different objects in one set and n_2 different objects in a second set, then the number of ways of choosing one object from each set is $n_1 \cdot n_2$.

This can be extended for k sets:

If there are n_1 different objects in one set, n_2 different objects in a second set, and so on, for k sets, then the number of ways of choosing one object from each set is $n_1 \cdot n_2 \cdot n_3 \cdot \ldots \cdot n_k$.

Example 2 — Using the Counting Principle to Determine the Number of Choices

From 2010, Alberta assigns license plates with 7 characters (ABC-1234), replacing the old 6-character plates (ABC-123). All 26 letters (A to Z) and 10 digits (0 to 9) may be used more than once.
a) How many license plates were possible with the old plate?
b) How many license plates are possible with the new plate?

SOLUTION

Use the fundamental counting principle.
a) For each letter, there are 26 choices.
For each digit there are 10 choices.
So, the number of possible plates is this product:

$$\underset{\substack{\uparrow \\ 1^{st} \\ letter}}{26} \cdot \underset{\substack{\uparrow \\ 2^{nd} \\ letter}}{26} \cdot \underset{\substack{\uparrow \\ 3^{rd} \\ letter}}{26} \cdot \underset{\substack{\uparrow \\ 1^{st} \\ digit}}{10} \cdot \underset{\substack{\uparrow \\ 2^{nd} \\ digit}}{10} \cdot \underset{\substack{\uparrow \\ 3^{rd} \\ digit}}{10} = 17\ 576\ 000$$

So, 17 576 000 license plates were possible with the old plate.

b) Adding another digit increases the number of plates by a factor of 10:
$17\ 576\ 000 \cdot 10 = 175\ 760\ 000$
So, 175 760 000 license plates are possible with the new plate.

Check Your Understanding

2. For an online banking account, the minimum security standards require a password to have 2 letters followed by 5 digits. All letters and digits may be used more than once. How many passwords are possible?

THINK FURTHER

In *Example 2*, since the letters I, O, and Q may be mistaken for the numbers 1 and 0, suppose these letters are not used on a plate. How many new plates are possible when the letters I, O, and Q are not used?

The total number of choices may decrease if repetition is not allowed.
For example, determine how many 3-digit numbers can be formed using
the digits 7, 8, and 9. Consider the number of ways to choose each digit.

Repetition is allowed.
For each digit, there
are 3 choices.
Number of ways = 3 · 3 · 3
              = 27

Twenty-seven 3-digit numbers
can be formed.

Repetition is not allowed.
There are 3 ways to choose
the 1st digit, 2 ways to choose
the 2nd digit, and 1 way to
choose the 3rd digit.
Number of ways = 3 · 2 · 1
              = 6

Six 3-digit numbers can be formed.

Discuss the Ideas

1. What is the fundamental counting principle?

2. How do you decide whether to use a graphic organizer or the
fundamental counting principle to determine the total number of
ways to choose objects from one or more sets?

Exercises

A

3. A gift-wrapping booth has 3 sizes of boxes, 2 colours of gift wrap,
and 4 different bows. How many choices of wrapping are possible
using a box, gift wrap, and bow?

©P DO NOT COPY.

4. A school cafeteria offers a soup and sandwich combo. There are 3 kinds of soup (pea, tomato, black bean) and 4 kinds of sandwiches (egg salad, tuna, veggie, ham). Use a graphic organizer to show the number of possible combos.

5. a) How many Alberta license plates were possible in 1912? Assume there were no restrictions on the digits.

b) Suppose 0 is not permitted as the first digit. How many license plates were possible?

B

6. Use the digits 5, 6, 7, and 8.

   a) How many 4-digit numbers can be formed when repetition is allowed?

   b) How many 4-digit numbers can be formed when repetition is not allowed?

7. How many 2-digit numbers less than 60 are even? Verify your work using another strategy.

8. In the women's gold-medal hockey game at the 2010 Vancouver Olympics, Team Canada defeated Team U.S.A. 2 – 0. Each team had 21 players on its roster. Assume each of the 21 players on Team Canada shook hands with each of the 21 players on Team U.S.A. What was the total number of handshakes?

9. A mobile phone has an 8-digit code called a PIN Unlock Key (PUK). This code is used to unlock a phone when an incorrect PIN number has been used three times in succession. All digits can be used. How many PUK codes are possible?

10. How many radio call letters beginning with C and consisting of 4 letters can be assigned to radio stations in Canada when repetition is not allowed?

11. A pizza chain offers cheese pizzas with a choice of these toppings: pepperoni, onion, sausage, mushrooms, and anchovies.

    a) Explain why the pizza chain can claim to offer 32 different pizzas.

    b) Another pizza chain claims that with its choice of toppings, it can create just over 1000 pizzas. What is the minimum number of toppings it must offer?

12. There are 700 students in a high school. Explain why at least two students must have the same first initial and the same last initial.

13. Which event is more likely? Why?
    • Tossing 23 tails with 23 pennies
    • Rolling 9 sixes with 9 dice

14. A die has faces labelled 1 to 6. The number of outcomes when n dice are rolled is 279 936. How many dice were rolled? Explain your reasoning.

15. Determine the number of ways of rolling 4 or 7 with two dice labelled from 1 to 6. Explain why you cannot use the fundamental counting principle.

16. Three couples go to see a movie at Cinematheque in Winnipeg. They sit together in 6 consecutive seats and couples sit together. How many seating arrangements are possible?

1. A multiple-choice test has 10 questions. Each question has 4 choices: A, B, C, or D. How many ways can the test be answered?

   A. 14   **B.** 40   **C.** 10 000   **D.** 1 048 576

2. How many 4-digit numbers greater than 1000 can be formed with no repetition in their digits?

   A. 4536   **B.** 3024   **C.** 9000   **D.** 10 000

3. The final score in a recreational soccer game is 6 – 3. How many scores are possible at the end of the first half?

   A. 9   **B.** 10   **C.** 18   **D.** 28

Study Note

When you use the fundamental counting principle to determine the total number of possible choices, why do you multiply instead of add? Use an example to explain.

ANSWERS

Check Your Understanding
1. 27 ways   2. 67 600 000

Exercises
3. 24 choices   4. 12 combos   5. a) 10 000   b) 9000   6. a) 256   b) 24
7. 25   8. 441   9. 100 000 000   10. 13 800   11. b) 10
13. Tossing 23 tails with 23 pennies   14. 7   15. 9 ways   16. 48

Multiple Choice
1. D   2. A   3. D

FOCUS Create and apply strategies to determine the number of ways to arrange a set of different objects.

Get Started

Evaluate each expression without using a calculator.

$$\frac{4 \cdot 3 \cdot 2 \cdot 1}{3 \cdot 2 \cdot 1} \qquad \frac{6 \cdot 5 \cdot 4 \cdot 3 \cdot 2 \cdot 1}{4 \cdot 3 \cdot 2 \cdot 1} \qquad \frac{8 \cdot 7 \cdot 6 \cdot 5 \cdot 4 \cdot 3 \cdot 2 \cdot 1}{5 \cdot 4 \cdot 3 \cdot 2 \cdot 1}$$

Construct Understanding

There are 4 ferry routes from the Vancouver area to Vancouver Island.

In how many ways is it possible to travel to Vancouver Island by one ferry route and return to the Vancouver area by a different route?

How would your answer change if a 5th route was added?

A 6th route?

What patterns do you see?

An arrangement of a set of objects is called a **permutation**.
The word *permutation* comes from the Latin words *per + mutare* that together mean "by change" or "through change."
In a permutation, order matters; for example, a pin code for a debit card.

To determine the number of 7-letter permutations of KELOWNA, use the fundamental counting principle.

There are 7 ways to choose the first letter,
6 ways to choose the second letter,
5 ways to choose the third letter,
4 ways to choose the fourth letter,
3 ways to choose the fifth letter,
2 ways to choose the sixth letter,
and 1 way to choose the last letter.
$7 \cdot 6 \cdot 5 \cdot 4 \cdot 3 \cdot 2 \cdot 1 = 5040$
There are 5040 ways to arrange the letters in KELOWNA.

The expression $7 \cdot 6 \cdot 5 \cdot 4 \cdot 3 \cdot 2 \cdot 1$ can be represented as 7!
This is **factorial notation**. 7! is read as seven factorial.
The factorial sign, !, means to take the product of all natural numbers less than or equal to the given number.

For example,
$1! = 1$
$2! = 2 \cdot 1 = 2$
$3! = 3 \cdot 2 \cdot 1 = 6$
$4! = 4 \cdot 3 \cdot 2 \cdot 1 = 24$
In general, for any natural number n:

$$n! = n(n - 1)(n - 2) \cdot \ldots \cdot 3 \cdot 2 \cdot 1$$
$$0! = 1$$

$n!$ represents the number of permutations of n different objects.

To evaluate a factorial on a TI-83 Plus or
TI-84 graphing calculator:
Enter the number, press MATH ◀ to select PRB,
then press 4 ENTER.
When $n \geq 14$, $n!$ is very large and most
calculators display an approximate number.

```
14!
       8.71782912E10
```

1. A puzzle designer decides to scramble the letters in the word EDUCATION to create a jumble puzzle. How many 9-letter permutations of EDUCATION can be created?

A student has a jumble puzzle phone app. He is trying to identify a common word that has been scrambled as LOUVME. How many 6-letter permutations of LOUVME can be created?

SOLUTION

The number of permutations is: $6! = 6 \cdot 5 \cdot 4 \cdot 3 \cdot 2 \cdot 1$
$$= 720$$

There are 720 six-letter permutations of LOUVME.

Only *some* of the objects from a set may be arranged. That is, the number of permutations of a set of objects chosen from a larger set can be determined. For example, Chico has 7 songs on his iPod. He has time to listen to 3 songs on his way to school. How many arrangements of 3 different songs are possible?

There are 7 choices for the first song, 6 choices for the second song, and 5 choices for the third song. So, the number of arrangements of 3 songs is: $7 \cdot 6 \cdot 5 = 210$

This product can be represented using factorial notation.

$$7 \cdot 6 \cdot 5 = \frac{7 \cdot 6 \cdot 5 \cdot 4 \cdot 3 \cdot 2 \cdot 1}{4 \cdot 3 \cdot 2 \cdot 1}$$

$$= \frac{7!}{4!}, \text{ or } \frac{7!}{(7 - 3)!}$$

    7 is the number of songs from which he chooses.
    3 is the number of songs he listens to.

$$= 210$$

The notation $_7P_3$ represents the number of ways of choosing 3 from 7.

This relationship can be expressed in general terms.

Permutations of Different Objects

The number of permutations of *n* distinct objects taken *r* at a time is:

$$_nP_r = \frac{n!}{(n - r)!}, n \geq r$$

Suppose Chico has 3 songs on his iPod and he wants to listen to all 3 songs.

There are $3 \cdot 2 \cdot 1$, or 6 arrangements of the 3 songs.

This number of arrangements can also be determined by using the formula:

$_nP_r = \dfrac{n!}{(n-r)!}$ Substitute: $n = 3$ and $r = 3$

$_3P_3 = \dfrac{3!}{(3-3)!}$

$= \dfrac{3!}{0!}$

$= \dfrac{6}{0!}$

Compare the two results. Since $\dfrac{6}{0!}$ must equal 6, $0!$ is equal to 1.

THINK FURTHER

What are the meanings and values of $_nP_0$ and $_nP_1$?

| Example 2 | Determining the Number of Permutations of *n* Different Objects Taken *r* at a Time |

Check Your Understanding

2. Eight students are competing in a 200-m race. How many ways can the students finish first, second, and third?

How many ways can a president, vice-president, and secretary-treasurer for a high school Safe Grad committee be selected from 58 Grade 12 students?

SOLUTION

Choosing a particular student for president is different from choosing that student for vice-president or secretary-treasurer. That is, order matters. So, use the permutation formula.

$_nP_r = \dfrac{n!}{(n-r)!}$ Substitute: $n = 58$ and $r = 3$

$_{58}P_3 = \dfrac{58!}{(58-3)!}$

$= \dfrac{58!}{55!}$

$= 58 \cdot 57 \cdot 56$

$= 185\ 136$

There are 185 136 ways to select the Safe Grad committee.

THINK FURTHER

In *Example 2*, suppose students were not assigned to positions of president, vice-president, and secretary-treasurer. Would the number of ways to select the committee increase or decrease? Explain.

A graphing calculator can be used to evaluate a permutation.

To evaluate $_{58}P_3$ on a TI-83 Plus or TI-84 graphing calculator: Enter 58, press MATH ◄ to select PRB, then press 2 3 ENTER.

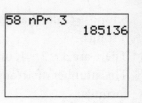

```
58 nPr 3
            185136
```

Check Your Understanding

3. Solve each equation for *n* or *r*.

   a) $_nP_2 = 56$ b) $_5P_r = 20$

Solve each equation for *n* or *r*.

a) $_nP_3 = 60$ b) $_6P_r = 30$

SOLUTION

a) $_nP_3 = 60$

Use the permutation formula.

$_nP_r = \dfrac{n!}{(n - r)!}$ Substitute: $_nP_r = 60, r = 3$

$60 = \dfrac{n!}{(n - 3)!}$

$60 = \dfrac{n(n - 1)(n - 2)\cancel{(n-3)}\cancel{(n-4)}\ldots}{\cancel{(n-3)}\cancel{(n-4)}\ldots}$

$60 = n(n - 1)(n - 2)$

Use logical reasoning to find 3 consecutive numbers whose product is 60. The perfect cube, 64, is close to 60.

$64 = 4 \cdot 4 \cdot 4$

So, try 3 consecutive numbers with 4 as the middle number:

$5 \cdot 4 \cdot 3$

$5 \cdot 4 \cdot 3 = 60$

So, $n = 5$

b) $_6P_r = 30$

Use the permutation formula.

$_nP_r = \dfrac{n!}{(n - r)!}$ Substitute: $_nP_r = 30, n = 6$

$30 = \dfrac{6!}{(6 - r)!}$

$30 = \dfrac{720}{(6 - r)!}$

$(6 - r)! = \dfrac{720}{30}$

$(6 - r)! = 24$

Since $4! = 24$, then

$6 - r = 4$

$r = 2$

DO NOT COPY. ©P

In *Example 2*, an equation involving permutations can be used to verify the solution.

Use the equation $_nP_r = \dfrac{n!}{(n-r)!}$.

Substitute $_nP_r = 185\ 136$ and $r = 3$, then solve for n.

$$185\ 136 = \frac{n!}{(n-3)!}$$

$$185\ 136 = n(n-1)(n-2)$$

Look for 3 consecutive numbers whose product is 185 136.
Use a calculator.

$$\sqrt[3]{185\ 136} \doteq 57$$

So, try 3 consecutive numbers with 57 as the middle number: $58 \cdot 57 \cdot 56$

$58 \cdot 57 \cdot 56 = 185\ 136$

So, $n = 58$

Since there were 58 Grade 12 students, the solution is correct.

Discuss the Ideas

1. In the permutation formula, $_nP_r = \dfrac{n!}{(n-r)!}$, $n \geq r$, explain why the n objects must be different.

2. In the notation $_nP_r$, why must n be greater than or equal to r?

Exercises

A

3. Evaluate each factorial.

a) 4! b) 1! c) 5! d) 0!

4. Determine each value.

a) $_7P_2$

b) $_5P_5$

c) $_8P_7$

d) $_6P_1$

5. a) Use a graphic organizer to determine the number of ways to arrange the letters in each word.

i) ELK

ii) LYNX

b) Use factorial notation to determine the number of ways to arrange the letters in each word.

i) BISON

ii) FALCON

6. a) How many 2-letter permutations are there for each word in question 5?

b) How many 3-letter permutations are there for each word in question 5?

c) Describe any patterns you notice.

7. The music teacher must arrange 5 tunes for the senior jazz band to perform at Music Night. She has 20 tunes to choose from.

a) How many arrangements are possible?

b) What other strategy could you use to determine the number of arrangements?

8. In the World Cup of soccer, 32 teams compete for the title. What is the number of ways that the winner, runners-up, third, and fourth place prizes could be awarded? Verify your answer.

9. The longest English non-technical words with no repeated letters are *dermatoglyphics*, *misconjugatedly*, and *uncopyrightable*. What is the total number of ways to arrange all the letters in each word?

10. Solve each equation for n or r.

    a) $_nP_2 = 90$ **b)** $_nP_3 = 120$

c) $_9P_r = 72$ **d)** $_7P_r = 210$

C

11. A student has 15 video games: 4 adventure games, 4 arcade games, 2 puzzle games, and 5 simulation games. How many ways can the games be positioned on a shelf if the games stay with their genre?

12. a) Seven different keys are to be placed on a key ring. How many ways can the keys be arranged?

b) How many ways can n distinct keys be arranged on a key ring? Explain.

1. How many ways can all the letters in the word ROCKIES be arranged?

   A. 5040   **B.** 49   **C.** 16 807   **D.** 117 649

2. Which expression cannot be evaluated?

   A. $_8P_5$ **B.** $_8P_0$ **C.** $_8P_8$ **D.** $_5P_8$

3. There are 8 swimmers in the finals of the 100-m butterfly. How many ways could the gold, silver, and bronze medals be awarded?

   A. 24   **B.** 336   **C.** 512   **D.** 40 320

Study Note

Explain what the notation $_4P_2$ represents. Write a problem that can be solved using $_4P_2$, then solve the problem.

ANSWERS

Check Your Understanding

1. 362 880   **2.** 336 ways   **3. a)** $n = 8$ **b)** $r = 2$

Exercises

3. a) 24 **b)** 1 **c)** 120 **d)** 1 **4. a)** 42 **b)** 120 **c)** 40 320 **d)** 6 **5. a) i)** 6
ii) 24 **b) i)** 120 **ii)** 720 **6. a)** 6; 12; 20; 30 **b)** 6; 24; 60; 120
7. a), b) 1 860 480 arrangements **8.** 863 040 ways **9.** approximately 1.31×10^{12} ways
10. a) $n = 10$ **b)** $n = 6$ **c)** $r = 2$ **d)** $r = 3$ **11.** 3 317 760 ways **12. a)** 720 ways
b) $(n - 1)!$ ways

Multiple Choice

1. A **2.** D **3.** B

8.3 Permutations Involving Identical Objects

FOCUS **Determine the number of arrangements from a set containing identical objects.**

Get Started

Determine each value.

$_3P_0$ $_3P_1$ $_3P_2$ $_3P_3$

Explain why $_3P_2$ and $_3P_3$ are equal.

Construct Understanding

Dave, Ella, and Anna listed the 4-letter permutations of the letters in their names. Which name has the greatest number of permutations? How does the number of identical letters affect the number of permutations?

In Lesson 8.2, the permutation problems involved objects that were different. Sometimes some of the objects are identical.

Consider the letters in the word DEER. If all the letters were different, the number of arrangements would be: $4! = 24$

However, each word contains 2 Es. In each word, when the Es are interchanged, the result is the same word.

DE$_1$E$_2$R   DE$_2$E$_1$R

There are 2! ways of arranging E$_1$ and E$_2$ in a word.

So, the number of arrangements becomes: $\frac{4!}{2!} = 12$

Word is used to mean an arrangement of letters.

Similarly, if all the letters in the word GEESE were different, the number of arrangements would be: $5! = 120$

However, each word contains 3 Es. In each word, when the Es are interchanged, the result is the same word.

GE$_1$E$_2$SE$_3$ GE$_1$E$_3$SE$_2$ GE$_2$E$_1$SE$_3$ GE$_2$E$_3$SE$_1$ GE$_3$E$_2$SE$_1$ GE$_3$E$_1$SE$_2$

There are 3! ways of arranging E$_1$, E$_2$, and E$_3$ in a word.

So, the number of arrangements is: $\frac{5!}{3!} = 20$

Similarly, if all the letters in the word PEEWEE were different, the number of arrangement would be: $6! = 720$

However, each word contains 4 Es. There are 4! ways of arranging E$_1$, E$_2$, E$_3$, and E$_4$ in a word. So, the number of arrangements is: $\frac{6!}{4!} = 30$

THINK FURTHER

Explain why the number of ways to arrange the letters in HOODOO is the same as the number of ways to arrange the letters in PEEWEE?

Permutations of Identical Objects

The number of permutations of *n* objects with *r* identical objects is: $\frac{n!}{r!}$

Example 1 Determining the Number of Permutations of Some Identical Objects

Check Your Understanding

There are 8 cans of soup on a shelf. Three of the cans contain tomato soup and the other 5 cans are all different. How many ways can the cans be arranged in a row?

1. There are 7 boxes of cereal on a shelf. Five of the boxes are bran cereal, one box is puffed wheat, and the other box is granola. How many ways can the boxes be arranged in a row?

SOLUTION

There are 8 cans of soup.
Three of the cans are identical.
The number of ways the cans can be arranged in a row is:
$$\frac{8!}{3!} = 8 \cdot 7 \cdot 6 \cdot 5 \cdot 4$$
$$= 6720$$
The cans can be arranged in a row in 6720 ways.

Consider a collection of 3 identical soccer balls, 2 identical baseballs, and 1 basketball. If all the sports balls were different, they could be arranged in a row in 6!, or 720 ways.

For each arrangement of the sports balls, determine the number of equivalent arrangements.

There are 3 soccer balls, so there are 3!, or 6 ways to arrange the soccer balls without a visible difference.

There are 2 baseballs, so there are 2!, or 2 ways to arrange the baseballs without a visible difference.

So, the number of ways to arrange the sports balls is: $\dfrac{6!}{3!2!1!} = 60$

When there are identical objects in a set of objects, the number of permutations in the set is less than the number of permutations with distinct objects.

Example 2 — Determining the Number of Permutations of Objects of Two Kinds

Check Your Understanding

2. Graeme walks 8 blocks from his home to the library. He always walks 4 blocks east and 4 blocks south. How many ways can Graeme walk to the library?

Abby walks 9 blocks from her home, H, to school, S. She always walks 5 blocks west and 4 blocks north. How many ways can Abby walk to school?

SOLUTION

The total number of blocks walked is 9.
There are two kinds of blocks.
Blocks walked west: 5
Blocks walked north: 4
The number of ways Abby can walk to school is:

$$\frac{9!}{5!4!} = \frac{9 \cdot 8 \cdot 7 \cdot 6}{4!}$$
$$= \frac{9 \cdot {}^2\!8 \cdot 7 \cdot {}^1\!6}{4 \cdot 3 \cdot 2 \cdot 1}$$
$$= 126$$

Abby can walk to school in 126 ways.

THINK FURTHER

How many permutations of n identical objects are there? Explain your thinking.

Permutations of Objects of Multiple Kinds

In a set of n objects with n_1 objects of one kind, n_2 objects of another kind, n_3 objects of another kind, and so on, for k kinds of objects, the number of permutations is:

$\dfrac{n!}{n_1!n_2!n_3!\ldots n_k!}$, where $n_1 + n_2 + n_3 + \ldots + n_k = n$

There are 12 pieces of trail mix in a dish. There are 5 almonds, 4 dried banana slices, and 3 papaya chunks. Corey eats the trail mix one piece at a time. In how many ways can Corey eat all the trail mix?

3. A kabob recipe requires 2 mushrooms, 2 shrimp, 2 cherry tomatoes, and 2 zucchini slices. How many ways can Amelie arrange these items on a skewer?

SOLUTION

The total number of pieces is 12.
There are three kinds of pieces: almonds, dried banana slices, and papaya chunks
Number of almonds: 5
Number of dried banana slices: 4
Number of papaya chunks: 3
The number of ways Corey can eat the trail mix is:

$$\frac{12!}{5!4!3!} = 27\ 720$$

Corey can eat the trail mix in 27 720 ways.

Discuss the Ideas

1. How is the number of permutations of a set of n distinct objects related to the number of permutations of a set of n objects with r identical objects?

2. Explain when you would use each expression to determine the number of permutations of a set of n objects:

$$n!, \frac{n!}{(n-r)!}, \frac{n!}{r!}, \text{ and } \frac{n!}{n_1!n_2!n_3! \cdots n_k!}$$

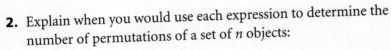

Exercises

A

3. Evaluate.

   a) $\dfrac{4!}{2!2!}$

   b) $\dfrac{9!}{3!6!}$

   c) $\dfrac{8!}{2!3!4!}$

   d) $\dfrac{10!}{2!2!5!}$

4. Which word in each pair has the greater number of permutations of all its letters?

   a) BID or BIB

   b) DEED or DIED

   c) KAYAK or KOALA

   d) RUDDER or REDDER

B

5. How many permutations are there of the 4 digits in each number?

   a) 1234

   b) 1123

c) 1113   d) 1111

6. a) How many permutations are there of all the letters in each of
     these Aboriginal words?

   i) ISKWEW   ii) TSILIKST

   iii) SUMSHASAT   iv) KINNIKINNICK

   b) How do identical letters change the number of permutations?

7. The number of permutations of all the letters in the word BRICK is
   120. How can you use this information to determine the number of
   permutations of all the letters in the word BROOK?

8. The number of permutations of all the digits in a 5-digit number is
   one. What do you know about the number? Justify your answer.

9. How many 9-digit numbers can be created from the digits 5, 5, 6, 6, 6, 7, 7, 7, 7?

10. Create a 5-digit number so that the number of permutations of all the digits is:

    a) the greatest possible   **b)** the least possible

    c) 10   **d)** 5

11. Identify a common word that satisfies each requirement.

    a) Contains 3 letters; numbers of permutations of all letters is 6.

    b) Contains 4 letters; numbers of permutations of all letters is 12.

    c) Contains 4 letters; numbers of permutations of all letters is 24.

    d) Contains 5 letters; numbers of permutations of all letters is 30.

12. a) How many ways are there to get from A to B travelling along grid lines and moving only to the right or down?

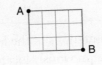

b) Why does order matter in this problem?

C

13. How many ways can all the letters in the word ABACUS be arranged so that the vowels are always together?

14. A 26-term series is written using only the integers +8 and −5. How many such series can be written with a sum of 0? Explain your reasoning.

Multiple-Choice Questions

1. What is the number of permutations of the letters in XWAYXWAY, an ancient Aboriginal village previously located in what is now Vancouver's Stanley Park?

   A. 70   **B.** 1680   **C.** 2520   **D.** 40 320

2. Which expression can be used to determine the number of permutations of the digits in the number 111 122?

   A. $6!$ **B.** $\dfrac{6!}{2!}$ **C.** $\dfrac{6!}{4!2!}$ **D.** $\dfrac{6!}{4!}$

3. A coin is tossed 12 times. What is the number of ways the coin can land with 6 heads and 6 tails?

   A. 924   **B.** 665 280   **C.** 479 001 600   **D.** 13 305 600

Study Note

Explain why there are fewer permutations of a set of objects when some of the objects are identical than when all the objects are different. Include examples in your explanation.

ANSWERS

Check Your Understanding
1. 42 ways   2. 70 ways   3. 2520 ways

Exercises
3. a) 6   b) 84   c) 140   d) 7560   4. a) BID   b) DIED   c) KOALA   d) RUDDER
5. a) 24   b) 12   c) 4   d) 1   6. a) i) 360   ii) 5040   iii) 30 240   iv) 138 600   7. 60
9. 1260   12. a) 35 ways   13. 72 ways   14. 5 311 735 series

Multiple Choice
1. C   2. C   3. A

Self-Assess

Can you . . .	Try *Checkpoint* question	For review, see
use a graphic organizer to count the number of possible choices that can be made?	1	Page 687 in Lesson 8.1 (Example 1)
use the fundamental counting principle to solve a problem?	3	Page 688 in Lesson 8.1 (Example 2)
count the number of ways objects can be arranged in a row?	4	Page 697 in Lesson 8.2
use factorial notation to determine the number of permutations of *n* different objects taken *n* at a time?	5	Page 698 in Lesson 8.2 (Example 1)
use a variety of strategies to determine the number of permutations of *n* different objects taken *r* at a time?	6	Page 699 in Lesson 8.2 (Example 2)
solve an equation that involves $_nP_r$ notation?	7	Page 700 in Lesson 8.2 (Example 3)
determine the number of permutations when two or more objects are identical?	9	Page 711 in Lesson 8.3 (Example 3)

Assess Your Understanding

8.1

1. A garage door remote has 10 code switches. Each switch can be positioned up or down to create a wireless code. How many codes are possible?

2. Multiple Choice A restaurant offers a meal combo that consists of a beverage, a main course, and a dessert. There are 5 beverages, 6 main courses, and 4 desserts. How many meal combos are available?

A. 15   **B.** 30   **C.** 20   **D.** 120

3. Morse code uses arrangements of 5 characters to represent the digits 0 through 9. Each character is either a dot or a dash. How many arrangements of 5 characters are possible?

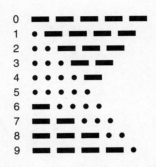

8.2

4. Multiple Choice How many 5-letter permutations of YUKON can be created?

A. 6   **B.** 24   **C.** 120   **D.** 3125

5. A family of six is to be seated in a row for a photo. The mother and father must be at either end. How many ways can the family be arranged?

6. An under-10 house-league soccer team has 11 players. Seven players are on the field at a time. How many ways can 7 starters be chosen from the members of the team?

7. Solve each equation for n or r.

    a) $_nP_2 = 42$ **b)** $_7P_r = 840$

8.3

8. Multiple Choice How many ways can 2 pennies, 3 nickels, and 5 quarters be arranged in a row?

    A. 30   **B.** 2520   **C.** 5040   **D.** 3 628 800

9. What is the number of permutations of all the letters in the name of each provincial park?

    a) VERMILION   **b)** OPAPISKAW

10. How many ways are there to get from F to G travelling along grid lines and moving only to the left or up?

ANSWERS

1. 1024   **2.** D   **3.** 32   **4.** C   **5.** 48 ways   **6.** 1 663 200 ways   **7. a)** $n = 7$
b) $r = 4$ **8.** B   **9. a)** 181 440   **b)** 90 720   **10.** 56

8.4 Combinations

Get Started

The game Mexican Train uses a set of
double-twelve domino tiles.
Each tile is rectangular with a centre line
dividing the domino face into two ends. Each end is
marked with a number of dots or "pips", ranging
from 0 to 12. How many different dominoes
are possible?
Assume a 2–1 domino is the same as a 1–2 domino.

2–1 domino

1–2 domino

Construct Understanding

Solve each problem.

A. At a restaurant, each meal comes with a choice of 4 side dishes.
A regular diner is asked to rank her 2 favourite side dishes in
order of preference. How many different rankings are possible?

B. At another restaurant, a diner can choose 2 of 4 side dishes to
accompany a meal. In how many ways can a diner choose 2 side
dishes?

How are the problems similar? How are they different?

A selection of objects where order does not matter is a **combination**. Consider the number of ways a reader can choose 3 books from 4 books. Unlike positioning books on a library shelf, order does not matter. Choosing books 1, 2, and 3 is the same as choosing books 2, 1, and 3, and so on.

Combinations of 3 books	Permutations of each combination
123	123, 132, 213, 231, 312, 321
124	124, 142, 241, 214, 412, 421
134	134, 143, 341, 314, 413, 431
234	234, 243, 342, 324, 423, 432
4 combinations	24 permutations

When order matters, there are $_4P_3$, or 24 ways to choose 3 books from 4 books. There are 3!, or 6 ways to choose the same 3 books.

So, the number of combinations is: $\dfrac{24}{3!} = 4$

In general, r objects can be chosen from n different objects in $_nP_r$ ways, and r objects can be arranged in $r!$ ways. So, the number of combinations of n different objects taken r at a time is:

$$_nC_r = \frac{_nP_r}{r!} \quad \text{Substitute: } _nP_r = \frac{n!}{(n-r)!}$$

$$= \frac{n!}{(n-r)!r!}$$

Combinations of Different Objects

The number of combinations of n distinct objects taken r at a time is:

$$_nC_r = \frac{n!}{(n-r)!r!}, \, n \geq r$$

$_nC_r$ can also be written using the notation $\binom{n}{r}$; it is read "n choose r."

Example 1 — Determining the Number of Combinations of n Different Objects Taken r at a Time

Lotto Max is a Canadian lottery where a player chooses 7 numbers from 1 to 49. To win the jackpot, all 7 numbers must match the drawn numbers. How many combinations of 7 numbers are possible?

SOLUTION

The order in which the numbers are drawn does not matter. So, use the combination formula.

$$_nC_r = \frac{n!}{(n-r)!r!} \quad \text{Substitute: } n = 49 \text{ and } r = 7$$

$$_{49}C_7 = \frac{49!}{(49-7)!7!}$$

$$= \frac{49!}{42!7!}$$

$$= \frac{49 \cdot 48 \cdot 47 \cdot 46 \cdot 45 \cdot 44 \cdot 43}{7 \cdot 6 \cdot 5 \cdot 4 \cdot 3 \cdot 2 \cdot 1}$$

$$= 85\,900\,584$$

There are 85 900 584 possible combinations of 7 numbers.

Check Your Understanding

1. In the Keno lottery, 20 numbers from 1 to 80 are chosen. How many combinations of 20 numbers are possible?

THINK FURTHER

In *Example 1*, how can you use the calculations for Lotto Max to determine the number of combinations for Lotto 6/49, where 6 numbers are chosen from 49?

A graphing calculator can be used to evaluate a combination.
To evaluate $_{49}C_7$ on a TI-83 Plus or TI-84 graphing calculator:

Enter 49, press [MATH] [◄] to select PRB, then press [3] [7] [ENTER].

```
49 nCr 7
           85900584
```

Example 2   Relating Combinations

Check Your Understanding

2. A local arena has 10 applicants interested in working in the snack bar.
   a) How many ways can 4 applicants be chosen?

   b) How many ways can 6 applicants be chosen?

A fund-raising committee is to be chosen from a group of 8 students.
a) How many ways can a committee of 5 students be chosen?
b) How many ways can a committee of 3 students be chosen?

SOLUTION

The order in which the students are chosen does not matter.
So, use the combination formula.

a) $_nC_r = \dfrac{n!}{(n-r)!r!}$ Substitute: $n = 8$ and $r = 5$

$\qquad _8C_5 = \dfrac{8!}{(8-5)!5!}$

$\qquad \quad = \dfrac{8!}{3!5!}$

$\qquad \quad = \dfrac{8 \cdot 7 \cdot 6}{3 \cdot 2 \cdot 1}$

$\qquad \quad = 56$

A committee of 5 students can be chosen in 56 ways.

b) $_nC_r = \dfrac{n!}{(n-r)!r!}$ Substitute: $n = 8$ and $r = 3$

$\qquad _8C_3 = \dfrac{8!}{(8-3)!3!}$

$\qquad \quad = \dfrac{8!}{5!3!}$

$\qquad \quad = \dfrac{8 \cdot 7 \cdot 6}{3 \cdot 2 \cdot 1}$

$\qquad \quad = 56$

A committee of 3 students can be chosen in 56 ways.

In *Example 2*, the answers to parts a and b are the same. This is because the number of ways of choosing 5 students from 8 students is the same as the number of ways of choosing 3 students (that is, not choosing 5 students) from 8 students.

This relationship can be expressed in general terms.

$$_nC_r = \frac{n!}{(n-r)!r!} \qquad \text{Replace } r \text{ with } (n-r).$$

$$_nC_{n-r} = \frac{n!}{(n-(n-r))!(n-r)!}$$

$$= \frac{n!}{(n-n+r)!(n-r)!}$$

$$= \frac{n!}{r!(n-r)!}$$

$$= {}_nC_r$$

The number of ways of choosing r objects from a set of n objects is the same as the number of ways of not choosing r objects from a set of n objects. So,

THINK FURTHER
....
Does $_nP_r = {}_nP_{n-r}$? Explain.

$$_nC_r = {}_nC_{n-r} \text{ or}$$

$$\binom{n}{r} = \binom{n}{n-r}, n \geq r$$

Example 3	Solving a Problem That Involves More than One Combination

One year, the minimum admission requirements for the University of British Columbia are a secondary school graduation diploma and successful completion of these Grades 11 and 12 courses.

- One of English 12 or English 12 First Peoples
- Three of 16 approved examinable Grade 12 courses
- English 11
- One of 3 math courses
- Civic Studies 11 or Social Studies 11
- One of 5 approved Science courses
- One of 24 approved Language courses

How many ways can a student meet the minimum admission requirements?

Check Your Understanding

3. A new store must hire 3 cashiers and 4 stock clerks. There are 7 applicants for cashier and 8 applicants for stock clerk. How many ways can the 7 employees be chosen?

SOLUTION

The minimum requirements include the successful completion of 9 specific courses.

The order in which the courses are taken does not matter.

Requirement	Number of Choices
1 Grade 12 English course	2
3 approved examinable Grade 12 courses	$_{16}C_3 = 560$
English 11	1
1 math course	3
Civic Studies 11 or Social Studies 11	2
1 Science course	5
1 Language course	24

Use the fundamental counting principle to determine the number of ways a student can meet the minimum requirements:

$2 \cdot 560 \cdot 1 \cdot 3 \cdot 2 \cdot 5 \cdot 24 = 806\ 400$

There are 806 400 ways to meet the admission requirements to U.B.C.

Discuss the Ideas

1. How do you recognize a combination problem?

2. How would you use mental math to determine $_{10}C_2$?

3. For what values of n and r is the formula $_nC_r = \dfrac{n!}{(n-r)!r!}$ defined? Justify the answer.

Exercises

4. Evaluate.

a) $\dfrac{10!}{3!7!}$

b) $\dfrac{6!}{1!5!}$

c) $\dfrac{12!}{3!9!}$

d) $\dfrac{15!}{13!2!}$

5. Determine each value.

a) $_4C_2$

b) $\dbinom{7}{5}$

c) $_{10}C_{10}$

d) $\dbinom{12}{8}$

6. How many combinations of each number of letters can be formed from the letters in the word LINE? List the combinations each time.

a) 1

b) 2

c) 3   **d)** 4

7. These are the names of lakes in western Canada. How many 4-letter combinations can be formed using the letters in each name?

   a) BISTCHO   **b)** TOEWS

   c) HOIDAS   **d)** COQUITLAM

8. **a)** How many 3-digit permutations are there of the digits in the number 67 512?

   b) How can you use your answer to part a to determine how many 3-digit combinations are possible?

9. Would you use a permutation or a combination to represent each situation? Justify your choice.

a) choosing 3 out of 4 musical notes to create a tune

b) choosing 3 out of 4 sweatshirts to take camping

c) choosing 3 out of 4 contestants to advance to the next round

d) choosing 3 out of 4 digits to create a password

10. Rafael has a list of his mom's 15 favourite songs. He will download 7 of these songs to her iPod.

a) How many ways can Rafael select 7 songs to download?

b) Suppose Rafael downloads 8 songs. Without doing any calculations, how many ways can he select 8 songs? Explain your strategy.

11. At the Soccer World Cup, 16 of the 32 teams advance beyond the second round. How many ways can 16 teams advance? Did you use a permutation or a combination to solve this problem? Explain.

12. When Tanner's team won the final game in the Genesis Hospitality High School hockey tournament in Brandon, Manitoba, each of the 6 players on the ice gave each other a high five. How many high fives were there?

13. A test has 2 parts. Students must answer 10 of 15 questions from part A and write 3 essays from a choice of 5 essay topics in part B. What is the number of possible responses to the test?

14. A jury of 6 men and 6 women is to be chosen from a jury pool of 12 men and 15 women. How many juries are possible?

15. Solve each equation for n or r.

a) $_nC_2 = 28$

b) $_nC_4 = 35$

c) $_4C_r = 6$

d) $_6C_r = 20$

16. From a standard deck of 52 playing cards, how many ways can each hand of 5 cards be dealt?

a) any 5 cards   b) 5 black cards

c) exactly 2 diamonds

17. Two players take turns writing X and O in a 3-by-3 grid until all the cells are full. How many ways are there to fill all the cells with Xs and Os?

Multiple-Choice Questions

1. Which expression is *not* equivalent to $_7C_6$?

A. $\dfrac{7!}{6!(7-6)!}$ **B.** $_7C_1$ **C.** $\dfrac{_7P_6}{6!}$ **D.** $\begin{pmatrix} 6 \\ 7 \end{pmatrix}$

2. Twelve points are located on the circumference of a circle. Lines are drawn to connect all possible pairs of points. How many lines are drawn?

A. 24   **B.** 66   **C.** 132   **D.** 144

3. How many committees of 3 men and 7 women can be selected from a group of 8 men and 10 women?

A. $_8C_3 \cdot {}_{10}C_7$ **B.** $_8P_3 \cdot {}_{10}P_7$ **C.** $_{18}C_{10}$ **D.** $_8C_3 + {}_{10}C_7$

Study Note

What is the difference between a permutation and a combination? Use an example to explain.

ANSWERS

Check Your Understanding
1. approximately 3.54×10^{18} combinations   **2. a)** 210 ways   **b)** 210 ways
3. 2450 ways

Exercises
4. a) 120   **b)** 6   **c)** 220   **d)** 105   **5. a)** 6   **b)** 21   **c)** 1   **d)** 495   **6. a)** 4: L, I, N, E
b) 6: LI, LN, LE, IN, IE, NE   **c)** 4: LIN, LIE, INE, LNE   **d)** 1: LINE   **7. a)** 35
b) 5   **c)** 15   **d)** 126   **8. a)** 60   **b)** 10   **9. a)** permutation   **b)** combination
c) combination   **d)** permutation   **10. a)** 6435 ways   **b)** 6435 ways
11. 601 080 390 ways; combination   **12.** 15   **13.** 30 030 responses
14. 4 624 620 juries   **15. a)** $n = 8$ **b)** $n = 7$ **c)** $r = 2$ **d)** $r = 3$
16. a) 2 598 960 ways   **b)** 65 780 ways   **c)** 712 842 ways   **17.** 252 ways

Multiple Choice
1. D   **2.** B   **3.** A

©P   DO NOT COPY.

8.5　Pascal's Triangle

FOCUS Understand and apply patterns and relationships in Pascal's triangle.

Get Started

Evaluate.

$_2C_0$ $_3C_1$ $_5C_2$

Construct Understanding

A. This triangle is called *Pascal's triangle*. Use the patterns in the triangle to complete rows 6 to 8. Describe characteristics of the triangle.

```
                        1                    Row 1
                     1     1                 Row 2
                  1     2     1              Row 3
               1     3     3     1           Row 4
            1     4     6     4     1        Row 5
         1    □    10    10    □    1        Row 6
      1    6    □    20    □    6    1       Row 7
      [                            ]         Row 8
```

B. How can you determine the numbers in row 9 of the triangle? Write the numbers in row 9.

C. Evaluate each combination.

$_4C_0$ $_4C_1$ $_4C_2$

$_4C_3$ $_4C_4$

How are the results related to Pascal's triangle?

Choose a value of n between 2 and 7.
Evaluate $_nC_r$ for r from 0 to your chosen n.
How are the results related to a row in Pascal's triangle?

D. Explain why the first two rows of Pascal's triangle can be written as shown. Write rows 3 to 5 using $_nC_r$ notation.

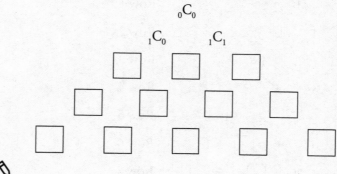

E. What is the relationship between the row number and the value of n in $_nC_r$?

What is the relationship between the rth number in row n and the value of r in $_nC_r$?

Use your results to describe the location of $_{11}C_8$ in Pascal's triangle. What is its value?

Assess Your Understanding

1. These are the numbers in row 10 of Pascal's triangle. Use these numbers to generate the numbers in row 11.

   1   9   36   84   126   126   84   36   9   1

2. Use the completed Pascal's triangle on page 735 to evaluate each expression. Use a calculator to verify your answers.

   a) $_4C_1$

   b) $_7C_2$

   c) $_6C_3$

   d) $_5C_0$

3. Use combinations to determine the numbers in row 13 of Pascal's triangle.

4. Determine the value of each number in Pascal's triangle.

   a) the second number in row 20

   b) the fourth number in row 24

ANSWERS
1. 1, 10, 45, 120, 210, 252, 210, 120, 45, 10, 1
2. a) 4   b) 21   c) 20   d) 1   3. 1, 12, 66, 220, 495, 792, 924, 792, 495, 220, 66, 12, 1
4. a) 19   b) 1771

FOCUS Use number patterns and combinations to expand binomials.

Get Started

These are the terms in a row of Pascal's triangle.
1 11 55 165 330 462 462 330 165 55 11 1
In which row are these terms? How do you know?
Write the fifth term in the row using $_nC_r$ notation.

Each number in Pascal's triangle is a term in a row.

Construct Understanding

Expand and simplify each power of the binomial $(x + y)$.
$(x + y)^0$ $(x + y)^1$ $(x + y)^2$ $(x + y)^3$ $(x + y)^4$
Describe any patterns.
Use the patterns to predict the expansion of $(x + y)^5$.
Expand to check your prediction.

Compare the expansion of the binomial
power $(x + y)^n$ with Pascal's triangle.

$(x + y)^0 = 1$

$(x + y)^1 = 1x + 1y$

$(x + y)^2 = 1x^2 + 2xy + 1y^2$

$(x + y)^3 = 1x^3 + 3x^2y + 3xy^2 + 1y^3$

$(x + y)^4 = 1x^4 + 4x^3y + 6x^2y^2$
$\qquad\qquad + 4xy^3 + 1y^4$

				1				Row 1
			1		1			Row 2
		1		2		1		Row 3
	1		3		3		1	Row 4
1		4		6		4		1 Row 5

The coefficients of the expansion of $(x + y)^n$ are the terms of row $(n + 1)$
of Pascal's triangle.

The first power of x is x^n and the exponent of the power decreases by 1 for
each subsequent term, with the last power being x^0. The first power of y is
y^0 and the exponent of the power increases by 1 for each subsequent term,
with the last power being y^n. The sum of the exponents in each term is n.

Example 1 **Using Pascal's Triangle and Patterns to Expand**

Expand, then simplify $(2a - 3)^5$.

Check Your Understanding

1. Expand, then simplify $(3b - 1)^4$.

SOLUTION

The exponent is 5, so list the terms in row 6 of Pascal's triangle.
1, 5, 10, 10, 5, 1
These are the coefficients of the terms in the expansion of the binomial:
$(x + y)^5 = 1x^5 + 5x^4y + 10x^3y^2 + 10x^2y^3 + 5xy^4 + 1y^5$
Substitute $x = 2a$ and $y = -3$, then simplify.
$(2a - 3)^5 = 1(2a)^5 + 5(2a)^4(-3) + 10(2a)^3(-3)^2 + 10(2a)^2(-3)^3$
$\qquad\qquad + 5(2a)(-3)^4 + 1(-3)^5$
$\qquad = 32a^5 + 5(16a^4)(-3) + 10(8a^3)(9) + 10(4a^2)(-27)$
$\qquad\qquad + 5(2a)(81) - 243$
$\qquad = 32a^5 - 240a^4 + 720a^3 - 1080a^2 + 810a - 243$

THINK FURTHER

In *Example 1*, how can you use the expansion of $(2a - 3)^5$ to determine the expansion of $(3a - 2)^5$?

In Lesson 8.5, the first 5 rows of Pascal's triangle were written using $_nC_r$ notation.

$_0C_0$					Row 1			1	
$_1C_0$	$_1C_1$				Row 2		1		1
$_2C_0$	$_2C_1$	$_2C_2$			Row 3	1		2		1
$_3C_0$	$_3C_1$	$_3C_2$	$_3C_3$		Row 4	1	3		3	1
$_4C_0$	$_4C_1$	$_4C_2$	$_4C_3$	$_4C_4$	Row 5	1	4	6	4	1

In general, the coefficients of the expansion of $(x + y)^n$ can be obtained from the terms in row $(n + 1)$ of Pascal's triangle:

$_nC_0, _nC_1, _nC_2, \ldots _nC_{n-1}, _nC_n$

The expansion of $(x + y)^n$ is known as the **binomial theorem**.

The binomial theorem can be written using combinations or algebraic expressions.

The Binomial Theorem (using combinations)

$$(x + y)^n = {}_nC_0x^n + {}_nC_1x^{n-1}y + {}_nC_2x^{n-2}y^2 + {}_nC_3x^{n-3}y^3 + \ldots$$
$$+ {}_nC_{n-1}xy^{n-1} + {}_nC_ny^n$$

The Binomial Theorem (using algebraic expressions)

$$(x + y)^n = x^n + nx^{n-1}y + \frac{n(n - 1)}{2!}x^{n-2}y^2 + \frac{n(n - 1)(n - 2)}{3!}x^{n-3}y^3$$
$$+ \ldots + y^n$$

Example 2   Using the Binomial Theorem to Expand

Expand and simplify $(2c^4 - 1)^3$.

SOLUTION

Expand using combinations.

$$(x + y)^n = {}_nC_0x^n + {}_nC_1x^{n-1}y + {}_nC_2x^{n-2}y^2 + {}_nC_3x^{n-3}y^3 + \cdots$$
$$+ {}_nC_{n-1}xy^{n-1} + {}_nC_ny^n$$

Substitute: $n = 3, x = 2c^4, y = -1$

$$(2c^4 - 1)^3 = {}_3C_0(2c^4)^3 + {}_3C_1(2c^4)^{3-1}(-1) + {}_3C_2(2c^4)^{3-2}(-1)^2$$
$$+ {}_3C_3(-1)^3$$
$$= {}_3C_0(2c^4)^3 + {}_3C_1(2c^4)^2(-1) + {}_3C_2(2c^4)^1(-1)^2$$
$$+ {}_3C_3(-1)^3$$
$$= 1(8c^{12}) + 3(4c^8)(-1) + 3(2c^4)(1) + 1(-1)$$
$$= 8c^{12} - 12c^8 + 6c^4 - 1$$

The binomial theorem can be used to determine the value of a specific term in an expansion, without having to complete the expansion.

To determine the kth term in the expansion of $(x + y)^n$, use the patterns in the binomial expansion.

The kth term has:

Coefficient: ${}_nC_{k-1}$

Power of y: $k - 1$

Power of x: n minus power of y, or $n - (k - 1)$

So, an expression for the kth term is: ${}_nC_{k-1}x^{n-(k-1)}y^{k-1}$

General Term in the Expansion of $(x + y)^n$

The general term, or kth term in the expansion of $(x + y)^n$ is:

$${}_nC_{k-1}x^{n-(k-1)}y^{k-1}$$

Example 3 | Determining a Specific Term in an Expansion

3. Determine the 9th term in the expansion of $(x - 2)^{10}$.

Determine the 7th term in the expansion of $(x - 3)^9$.

SOLUTION

The kth term is: $_nC_{k-1}x^{n-(k-1)}y^{k-1}$
Substitute: $k = 7$, $n = 9$, $y = -3$
$$t_7 = {_9}C_{7-1}x^{9-(7-1)}(-3)^{7-1}$$
$$= {_9}C_6x^3(-3)^6$$
$$= 84x^3(729)$$
$$= 61\ 236x^3$$
The 7th term is $61\ 236x^3$.

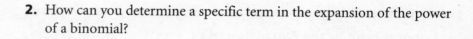

Discuss the Ideas

1. What is the relationship between the coefficients of the terms in the expansion of $(x + y)^n$ and the terms in a row of Pascal's triangle? Use an example to explain.

2. How can you determine a specific term in the expansion of the power of a binomial?

Exercises

A

3. Expand using Pascal's triangle.

a) $(x + 1)^5$

b) $(x - 1)^6$

c) $(x + y)^4$

d) $(x - y)^8$

4. Determine each missing number in the expansion of $(x + y)^7$.

$x^7 + \square x^6 y + 21x^5 y^2 + 35x^\square y^3 + \square x^3 y^4 + 21x^\square y^\square + 7xy^6 + y^\square$

5. Determine the indicated term in each expansion.

a) the last term in $(x + 1)^9$

b) the 1st term in $(x - 1)^{12}$

6. a) Multiply 4 factors of $(x - 5)$.

b) Use the binomial theorem to expand $(x - 5)^4$.

c) Compare the two methods. What conclusions can you make?

7. Expand using the binomial theorem.

a) $(x + 2)^6$

b) $(x^2 - 3)^5$

c) $(3x - 2)^4$

d) $(-2 + 2x)^4$

e) $(-4 + 3x^4)^5$

8. a) Write the terms in row 7 of Pascal's triangle.

b) Use your answer to part a to write the first 3 terms in each expansion.

i) $(x - 3)^6$

ii) $(a + 4b)^6$

iii) $(-2a + 1)^6$

iv) $(2x + 5y^2)^6$

9. Determine the coefficient of each term.

a) x^5 in $(x + 1)^8$

b) x^9 in $(x + y)^9$

c) x^2y in $(x + y)^3$

d) x^2y^3 in $(x + y)^5$

10. Explain why the coefficients of the 3rd term and the 3rd-last term in the expansion of $(x + y)^n$, $n \geq 2$, are the same.

11. Determine the indicated term in each expansion.

    a) the last term in $(3x + 2)^5$ **b)** the 1st term in $(-2x + 5)^7$

    c) the 2nd term in $(3x - 3)^4$ **d)** the 6th term in $(4x + 1)^8$

12. When will the coefficients of the terms in the expansion of $(ax + b)^n$ be the same as the terms in row $(n + 1)$ of Pascal's triangle?

13. Expand and simplify $(x + 1)^8 + (x - 1)^8$. What strategy did you use?

14. a) Show that the expansion of $(-2x + 1)^6$ is the same as the expansion of $(2x - 1)^6$.

b) Will $(-ax + b)^n$ always have the same expansion as $(ax - b)^n$? Explain.

15. Which binomial power when expanded results in $16x^4 - 32x^3 + 24x^2 - 8x + 1$? What strategy did you use to find out?

16. Expand using the binomial theorem.

a) $(0.2x - 1.2y)^5$

b) $\left(\frac{3}{8}a + \frac{1}{6}b\right)^4$

17. Determine the 3rd term in the expansion of $(x^2 + 2x + 1)^6$.

18. a) Show that $_nC_0 + {_nC_1} + {_nC_2} + \ldots + {_nC_{n-1}} + {_nC_n} = 2^n$

b) What does the relationship in part a indicate about the sum of the terms in any row of Pascal's triangle?

Multiple-Choice Questions

1. Which is the correct expansion of $(2x + 3)^3$?

   A. $8x^3 + 36x^2 + 54x + 27$ **B.** $8x^3 + 54x^2 + 36x + 27$

   C. $8x^3 + 63x^2 + 45x + 27$ **D.** $6x^3 + 36x^2 + 54x + 9$

2. Which statement is false about the expansion of $(x - 3)^5$?

   A. The last term is -243.   **B.** The 1st term is x^5.

   C. The 2nd term is $15x^4$.   **D.** The 3rd term is $90x^3$.

3. Which is the 7th term of $(-x - 1)^9$?

   A. $-9x^8$ **B.** $-36x^7$ **C.** $-84x^3$ **D.** $-126x^5$

Study Note

What are the advantages of using the binomial theorem to expand a binomial? What are some disadvantages?

ANSWERS

Check Your Understanding

1. $81b^4 - 108b^3 + 54b^2 - 12b + 1$ **2.** $64a^6 + 96a^4b + 48a^2b^2 + 8b^3$ **3.** $11\,520x^2$

Exercises

3. a) $x^5 + 5x^4 + 10x^3 + 10x^2 + 5x + 1$ **b)** $x^6 - 6x^5 + 15x^4 - 20x^3 + 15x^2 - 6x + 1$
c) $x^4 + 4x^3y + 6x^2y^2 + 4xy^3 + y^4$
d) $x^8 - 8x^7y + 28x^6y^2 - 56x^5y^3 + 70x^4y^4 - 56x^3y^5 + 28x^2y^6 - 8xy^7 + y^8$
4. 7, 4, 35, 2, 5, 7   **5. a)** 1   **b)** x^{12} **6. a), b)** $x^4 - 20x^3 + 150x^2 - 500x + 625$
7. a) $x^6 + 12x^5 + 60x^4 + 160x^3 + 240x^2 + 192x + 64$
b) $x^{10} - 15x^8 + 90x^6 - 270x^4 + 405x^2 - 243$
c) $81x^4 - 216x^3 + 216x^2 - 96x + 16$ **d)** $16 - 64x + 96x^2 - 64x^3 + 16x^4$
e) $-1024 + 3840x^4 - 5760x^8 + 4320x^{12} - 1620x^{16} + 243x^{20}$
8. a) 1, 6, 15, 20, 15, 6, 1   **b) i)** $x^6 - 18x^5 + 135x^4$ **ii)** $a^6 + 24a^5b + 240a^4b^2$
iii) $64a^6 - 192a^5 + 240a^4$ **iv)** $64x^6 + 960x^5y^2 + 6000x^4y^4$ **9. a)** 56   **b)** 1   **c)** 3
d) 10   **11. a)** 32   **b)** $-128x^7$ **c)** $-324x^3$ **d)** $3584x^3$
13. $2x^8 + 56x^6 + 140x^4 + 56x^2 + 2$ **15.** $(-2x + 1)^4$ or $(2x - 1)^4$
16. a) $0.000\,32x^5 - 0.0096x^4y + 0.1152x^3y^2 - 0.6912x^2y^3 + 2.0736xy^4 - 2.488\,32y^5$
b) $\frac{81}{4096}a^4 + \frac{9}{256}a^3b + \frac{3}{128}a^2b^2 + \frac{1}{144}ab^3 + \frac{1}{1296}b^4$ **17.** $66x^{10}$

Multiple Choice

1. A   **2.** C   **3.** C

Additional Workspace

Concept Summary

Big Ideas	Applying the Big Ideas
• Counting strategies can be used to determine the number of ways to choose objects from a set or to arrange a set of objects.	This means that: • When the number of objects is small, graphic organizers such as organized lists and tree diagrams can be used to itemize and count arrangements. • The fundamental counting principle can be used to determine the number of ways objects can be chosen or arranged.
• A permutation is an arrangement of a set of objects where order matters. A combination is a selection from a set of objects where order does not matter.	• Different rules involving factorial notation can be used to determine the number of permutations depending on whether all the objects are different or some are identical. • The number of permutations of r objects chosen from n objects is related to the number of combinations.
• Combinations can be used to expand a power of a binomial and to generate the terms in Pascal's triangle.	• The terms in one row of Pascal's triangle can be used to determine the terms in the next row. • The coefficients of the terms in the expansion of $(x + y)^n$ correspond to the terms in row $(n + 1)$ of Pascal's triangle. • The terms in each row of Pascal's triangle and the coefficients of the terms in the expansion of $(x + y)^n$ are the same when read from left to right or from right to left because $_nC_r = {_n}C_{n-r}$.

Chapter Study Notes

• How do you decide whether a situation involves a permutation or a combination? How do you decide which expression or formula to use?

• What strategies can you use to expand the power of a binomial?

Skills Summary

Skill	Description	Example
Determine the number of ways to arrange n objects with or without repetition. **(8.2)**	When all objects are different, use $n!$, where n is the number of objects. When some objects are identical, use the fundamental counting principle.	The number of ways that all the letters in the word FUN can be arranged is: $3! = 3 \cdot 2 \cdot 1$ $= 6$
Determine the number of permutations of n distinct objects taken r at a time. **(8.2)**	When order matters, use the rule $_nP_r = \dfrac{n!}{(n-r)!}$, $n \geq r$, where n and r are whole numbers.	The number of 3-digit permutations of the digits in 12 579 is: $_5P_3 = \dfrac{5!}{(5-3)!}$ $= \dfrac{5!}{2!}$ $= 5 \cdot 4 \cdot 3$ $= 60$
Determine the number of permutations of objects of multiple kinds. **(8.3)**	When order matters, use the expression $\dfrac{n!}{n_1! n_2! n_3! \ldots n_k!}$, where n is the number of objects in a set with: n_1 objects of one kind; n_2 objects of another kind; n_3 objects of another kind; and so on, for k kinds of objects.	The number of 6-letter permutations of COFFEE is: $\dfrac{6!}{2!2!} = \dfrac{6 \cdot 5 \cdot 4 \cdot 3}{2!}$ $= \dfrac{360}{2}$ $= 180$
Determine the number of combinations of n distinct objects taken r at a time. **(8.4)**	When order does not matter, use the rule $_nC_r = \dfrac{n!}{(n-r)!r!}$, $n \geq r$, where r is the number of objects chosen from n distinct objects.	The number of sets of 3 books that can be chosen from 5 books is: $_5C_3 = \dfrac{5!}{(5-3)!3!}$ $= \dfrac{5 \cdot 4}{2!}$ $= 10$
Determine the kth term of the expansion of the binomial $(x+y)^n$. **(8.6)**	Use the general term $_nC_{k-1}x^{n-(k-1)}y^{k-1}$, where n is the exponent of the binomial power and k is the term number.	The 6th term in the expansion of $(x-1)^8$ is: $_8C_{6-1}x^{8-(6-1)}(-1)^{6-1}$ $= {}_8C_5 x^3(-1)^5$ $= -56x^3$

8.1

1. A penny, a dime, and a loonie are in one bag. A nickel, a quarter, and a toonie are in another bag. Tessa removes 1 coin from each bag. Use a graphic organizer to list the total amounts she could have removed.

2. The Braille code consists of patterns of raised dots arranged in a 3 by 2 array. The pattern for the letter Z is shown. How many different patterns are possible? Explain your reasoning.

8.2

3. A hiking group consists of 12 students and 2 leaders. A leader must be at the front and back of the line. How many ways can the group hike in a line?

4. A code consists of 4 letters from the English alphabet and 3 letters from the Greek alphabet. There are 8 English letters and 6 Greek letters to choose from and repetition is not allowed. How many 7-letter codes are possible?

8.3

5. How many 12-letter permutations of GOBBLEDEGOOK can be created?

6. How many ways are there to arrange all the words in this tongue twister?
CAN YOU CAN A CAN AS A CANNER CAN CAN A CAN?

7. How many 9-letter permutations of EQUATIONS can be created if the vowels must appear together in the order A, E, I, O, and U? Explain.

8. A student volunteers at a food bank. He fills hampers with these items:

5 cans of soup chosen from 7 different soups

3 bags of pasta chosen from 4 different types of pasta

4 bags of vegetables chosen from 8 different types of vegetables

3 boxes of cereal chosen from 6 different types of cereal

How many ways can the student fill a hamper?

9. Solve each equation for n or r.

a) $_nC_3 = 84$

b) $_7C_r = 35$

10. a) These are the first 7 numbers in row 14 of Pascal's triangle:

1, 13, 78, 286, 715, 1287, 1716

Complete the row. What strategy did you use?

b) Use your results from part a to write the numbers in row 15 of the triangle.

11. Determine the value of each number in Pascal's triangle.

   a) the 4th number in row 13

   b) the 5th number in row 21

8.6

12. The 4th term in the expansion of $(x + 1)^8$ is $56x^5$. Which other term in the expansion has a coefficient of 56? Explain.

13. Expand using the binomial theorem.

   a) $(4x - 1)^5$

b) $(5x^2 + 2y)^4$

14. Determine the indicated term in each expansion.

    a) the 3rd term in $(-7x + 1)^6$ **b)** the 7th term in $(6x + 2y)^7$

15. Use the binomial theorem to evaluate $(1.2)^6$. Use a calculator to verify your result.

ANSWERS

1. 6¢, 26¢, $2.01, 15¢, 35¢, $2.10, $1.05, $1.25, $3.00   **2.** 64   **3.** 958 003 200
4. 201 600   **5.** 9 979 200   **6.** 110 880   **7.** 120   **8.** 117 600   **9. a)** $n = 9$
b) $r = 3$ or $r = 4$ **10. a)** 1716, 1287, 715, 286, 78, 13, 1
b) 1, 14, 91, 364, 1001, 2002, 3003, 3432, 3003, 2002, 1001, 364, 91, 14, 1
11. a) 220   **b)** 4845   **12.** The 6th term
13. a) $1024x^5 - 1280x^4 + 640x^3 - 160x^2 + 20x - 1$
b) $625x^8 + 1000x^6y + 600x^4y^2 + 160x^2y^3 + 16y^4$ **14. a)** $36\ 015x^4$ **b)** $2688xy^6$
15. 2.985 984

1. **Multiple Choice** A bed and breakfast has 6 rooms and 4 guests. No guests share a room. How many ways can the guests be assigned to rooms?

   A. $4!$ **B.** $_6P_4$ **C.** $_6P_2$ **D.** $_6C_4$

2. **Multiple Choice** What is the 3rd term in the expansion of $(2x - 2)^7$?

   A. $896x$ **B.** $-2688x^2$ **C.** $2688x^5$ **D.** $-896x^6$

3. A battery has a negative and a positive end. In how many different ways can 4 AAA batteries be arranged end to end? Explain.

4. **a)** Would you use a permutation or combination to solve this problem? Explain.
   In a particular week, there are 2 volleyball games, 3 floor hockey games, and 4 basketball games scheduled in Jerome's school. He has a ticket that allows him to attend 3 of the games. How many ways can Jerome attend exactly 2 floor hockey games and one other game?

   b) Solve the problem.

5. How many different ways are there to arrange all the letters in the word NANNURALUK, an Inuit word for polar bear?

6. A golfer has 13 clubs in her bag. She practises with 4 clubs from the bag. How many choices of 4 clubs can the golfer make?

7. Solve each equation.

a) $_nP_2 = 110$

b) $_nC_3 = 364$

8. These are the terms in row 5 of Pascal's triangle.

1   4   6   4   1

a) What are the terms in row 6?

b) Use the terms in row 6 to expand the binomial $(x - 1)^5$.

ANSWERS

1. B   2. C   3. 16   4. a) combination b) 18   5. 151 200   6. 715   7. a) $n = 11$
b) $n = 14$ 8. a) 1, 5, 10, 10, 5, 1 b) $x^5 - 5x^4 + 10x^3 - 10x^2 + 5x - 1$

1

1. Sketch a graph of this polynomial function:
$$g(x) = 4x^3 - 8x^2 - x + 2$$

2. Sketch the graph of $y = \dfrac{4x^2}{3x^2 + 9x + 6}$, then state its domain and range.

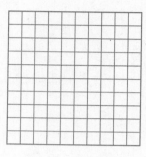

3. Restrict the domain of each function below so its inverse is a function.

a)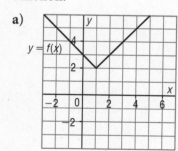

b)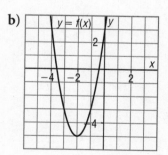

4. Here is the graph of $y = f(x)$. On the same grid, sketch the graph of $y + 2 = -\frac{1}{2}f(3(x - 4))$.

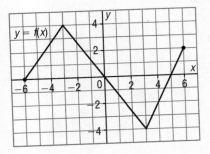

4

5. For $y = 2x^2 + 4x + 5$, determine two sets of possible functions f and g so that $y = f(g(x))$.

6. A principal of $800 is invested in a savings account that pays 7% annual interest, compounded semi-annually. To the nearest quarter of a year, how long will it take until this investment is worth $1000?

7. a) The graphs of a logarithmic function and its transformation image are shown. Corresponding points are indicated. Identify the transformations.

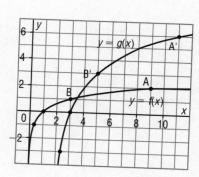

b) Given that $f(x) = \log_3 x$, what is $g(x)$? Justify your answer.

8. For each angle below:

    i) Sketch the angle in standard position.

    ii) Write an expression for the measures of all angles that are coterminal with the angle in standard position.

    iii) Determine the values of the six trigonometric ratios of the angle. Give exact answers where possible, or to the nearest thousandth.

a) $-475°$

b) $\dfrac{15\pi}{4}$

9. Given $\sin \theta = \dfrac{2}{\sqrt{13}}$, determine the exact values of the other
5 trigonometric ratios in the domain $90° \leq \theta \leq 270°$.

10. A circle has radius 5 cm. In radians and degrees, what is the measure
of the central angle subtended by an arc with length 10 cm? Give the
answers to the nearest tenth where necessary.

11. a) Sketch the graph of $y = \cos x$ for the domain $-2\pi \leq x \leq 2\pi$.

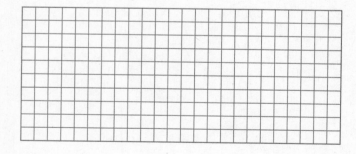

b) On the grid in part a, sketch the graph of $y = 2 \cos 2\left(x - \frac{\pi}{3}\right) + 2$. Describe your strategy.

c) For the function in part b, list the: amplitude, period, phase shift, zeros, domain, and range.

12. The pedals of an exercise bicycle are mounted on a bracket that is 30 cm above the floor. Each pedal is 18 cm from the centre of the bracket. A person pedals at 60 rotations per minute.

a) Determine a sinusoidal function that models the height of a pedal above the floor, h metres, as a function of time, t seconds.

b) During the first rotation, when is the pedal 40 cm above the floor? Give the answers to the nearest hundredth of a second.

13. Use graphing technology to solve each equation for $0 \leq x < 2\pi$, then write the general solution. Give the roots to the nearest hundredth.

a) $3 \sin 2x + 1 = 2 \cos 2x$

b) $3 \cos^2 x = 1 - 2 \cos x$

14. Use algebra to solve each equation for the domain $-180° \leq x \leq 180°$. Give the roots to the nearest degree.

a) $5 - 3 \tan x = 2 \tan x + 1$

b) $4 \sin^2 x + 5 \sin x = -1$

15. For each expression below:

    i) Determine any non-permissible values of θ.

    ii) Write the expression in simplest form.

  a) $(\sec \theta)(\sec \theta - \cos \theta)$ **b)** $\dfrac{\cos \theta + \sin \theta \tan \theta}{\tan \theta}$

16. Prove this identity: $\tan^2 x - \sin^2 x = \tan^2 x \sin^2 x$

17. Solve this equation over the domain $-90° < x < 270°$:

$$\dfrac{\tan 4x - \tan 3x}{1 + \tan 4x \tan 3x} = \sqrt{3}$$

18. Use graphing technology to verify the identity $\cos 2\theta = 2 \cos^2\theta - 1$. Sketch the graph.

19. Prove this identity: $\tan 2\theta \cos 2\theta = \dfrac{2 \tan \theta}{1 + \tan^2\theta}$

8

20. a) License plates in British Columbia have the form ABC 123 or 123 ABC. All 26 letters (A to Z) and 10 digits (0 to 9) may be used more than once. How many plates are possible?

b) Suppose a repetition of a letter or digit is not permitted. How many plates are possible?

c) Explain why the answers in parts a and b are different.

21. What is the number of permutations of all the letters in the name of each capital city?

a) WINNIPEG   **b)** REGINA

22. The pre-requisite grade 12 courses for a Bachelor of Arts program at the University of Alberta are English Language Arts 30-1; and 4 courses from a list of 10 Grade 12 courses. How many ways can a student meet the pre-requisite courses?

23. Determine the indicated term in each expansion.

    a) the first term in the expansion of $(-3x - 0.2y)^9$

    b) the third term in the expansion of $(0.5x + 2y)^7$

24. Expand using the binomial theorem: $(2x - 3y^2)^6$

ANSWERS

2. domain: $x \neq -2, x \neq -1$; range: $y \geq 0$ or $y \leq -\frac{32}{3}$ **6.** approximately 3.25 years

7. b) $g(x) = 3 \log_3 (x - 2)$ **8. a) ii)** $-475° + k360°, k \in \mathbb{Z}$
iii) $\sin(-475°) \doteq -0.906$; $\csc(-475°) \doteq -1.103$; $\cos(-475°) \doteq -0.423$;
$\sec(-475°) \doteq -2.366$; $\tan(-475°) \doteq 2.145$; $\cot(-475°) \doteq 0.466$
b) ii) $\frac{15\pi}{4} + 2\pi k, k \in \mathbb{Z}$ **iii)** $\sin \frac{15\pi}{4} = -\frac{1}{\sqrt{2}}$; $\csc \frac{15\pi}{4} = -\sqrt{2}$;
$\cos \frac{15\pi}{4} = \frac{1}{\sqrt{2}}$, $\sec \frac{15\pi}{4} = \sqrt{2}$; $\tan \frac{15\pi}{4} = -1$, $\cot \frac{15\pi}{4} = -1$

9. $\csc \theta = \frac{\sqrt{13}}{2}$; $\cos \theta = -\frac{3}{\sqrt{13}}$; $\sec \theta = -\frac{\sqrt{13}}{3}$; $\tan \theta = -\frac{2}{3}$; $\cot \theta = -\frac{3}{2}$

10. 2 radians; approximately 114.6°   **11. c)** amplitude: 2; period: π; phase shift: $\frac{\pi}{3}$;
zeros: $-\frac{7\pi}{6}, -\frac{\pi}{6}, \frac{5\pi}{6}, \frac{11\pi}{6}$; domain: $x \in \mathbb{R}$; range: $0 \leq y \leq 4$

12. b) approximately 0.34 s and 0.66 s   **13. a)** $x \doteq 0.15, x \doteq 2.01, x \doteq 3.30$,
$x \doteq 5.15$; $x \doteq 0.15 + \pi k, k \in \mathbb{Z}$ or $x \doteq 2.01 + \pi k, k \in \mathbb{Z}$ **b)** $x \doteq 1.23, x \doteq 3.14$,
$x \doteq 5.05$; $x \doteq 1.23 + 2\pi k, k \in \mathbb{Z}, x \doteq 3.14 + 2\pi k, k \in \mathbb{Z}$, or $x \doteq 5.05 + 2\pi k, k \in \mathbb{Z}$
14. a) $x \doteq 39°, x \doteq -141°$ **b)** $x \doteq -14°, x \doteq -166°, x = -90°$
15. a) i) $\theta \neq \frac{\pi}{2} + \pi k, k \in \mathbb{Z}$ **ii)** $\tan^2\theta$ **b) i)** $\theta \neq \frac{\pi}{2} + \pi k, k \in \mathbb{Z}, \theta \neq \pi k, k \in \mathbb{Z}$
ii) $\csc \theta$ **17.** $x = 60°, x = 240°$ **20. a)** 35 152 000   **b)** 22 464 000
21. a) 10 080   **b)** 720   **22.** 210   **23. a)** $-19\,683x^9$ **b)** $2.625x^5y^2$
24. $64x^6 - 576x^5y^2 + 2160x^4y^4 - 4320x^3y^6 + 4860x^2y^8 - 2196xy^{10} + 729y^{12}$

772 | Cumulative Review Chapters 1-8